MW00398800

HAZARD RECOGNITION AND CONTROL IN INSTITUTIONAL SETTINGS

A Guide for Hospitals, Universities, and Nursing Homes

George Byrns, Editor
Illinois State University

American Society of Safety Engineers
Des Plaines, Illinois

ISBN   978-1-885581-54-9

Library of Congress Cataloging-In Publication Data

American Society of Safety Engineers.
   Hazard recognition and control in institutional settings : a guide for hospitals, universities and nursing homes / George Byrns, editor.
      p. cm.
    Includes bibliographical references and index.
    ISBN 978-1-885581-54-9 (alk. paper)
 1. Industrial safety—United States. 2. Universities and colleges—United States—Safety measures. 3. Hospitals—United States—Safety measures. 4. Nursing homes—United States—Safety measures. I. Byrns, George. II. Title.

   T55.A1A42 2009
   363.1—dc22

                                                                    2008049796

Managing Editor: Michael F. Burditt, ASSE
ASSE Publication Coordinator: Jeri Ann Stucka
Text Design and Composition: Publication Services
Cover Design: Troy Courson, *Image Graphics*

Printed in the United States

15 14 13 12 11 10 09   1 2 3 4 5 6 7

Contents

Foreword

Institutions, especially healthcare facilities and universities, are complex and may offer many hazards to workers and to those served by these institutions. In the U.S., the healthcare sector is one of the fastest growing segments of our economy. Currently, there are approximately 14 million people employed in some aspect of health care. This is also a future area of employment for environmental health and safety students.

In 1973, Bond, Michaelsen, and DeRoos authored *Environmental Health and Safety in Health-Care Facilities*, which was the first textbook that focused on environmental and occupational hazards in hospitals and other healthcare operations. Despite this book, these healthcare hazards received relatively little attention until recently. The AIDS epidemic of the early to mid-1980s provided some impetus for federal regulators to take a closer look at healthcare worker protection. However, for most of the last 50 years, voluntary compliance with the Joint Commission on Accreditation of Healthcare Organizations (known as the Joint Commission or JCAHO) has been the primary motivator for environmental health and safety management in hospitals. While voluntary compliance has undoubtedly resulted in improvements, certain areas, such as ergonomics and employee exposure to hazardous chemicals, have been neglected. In addition, there are new concerns that were never considered in 1973. Hospitals and universities may be considered critical "soft targets" for potential terrorists. What better way to disrupt a community than to disable its healthcare system or harm college students? Emergency response, including respiratory protection, must now be an important element in our environmental health and safety programs. There have also been a series of new disease threats since the beginning of the AIDS epidemic. These include the hepatitis C virus, severe acute respiratory syndrome (SARS), multi-drug resistant bacteria, and now the potential for human-to-human spread of avian influenza. There have also been technological advances in diagnostic and treatment methods, such as the use of lasers and nanotechnology, which may present risks to healthcare and university workers and students. These and other emerging problems will require the services of properly trained institutional environmental health and safety professionals.

The primary reason for writing this book is to provide a textbook for environmental health and safety students who wish to learn more about controlling hazards in institutional settings. It is intended for use in an undergraduate course for junior and senior students. Introductory chemistry is a pre-requisite; ideally, students also should have taken a class in microbiology.

Many of the chapters have classroom activities that are designed to provide a sense of realism to accompany the lecture materials. Site visits to hospitals and other types of healthcare facilities may provide another effective tool in making the materials more accessible for the students. While not required, classes in epidemiology and industrial hygiene would benefit students taking this course.

This volume will focus on hospitals and universities. While this book is intended to be a college textbook, it should also be useful for environmental health and safety personnel working in these settings. One chapter is devoted specifically to unique environmental and occupational concerns in universities. It is important to remember that there are commonalities among all types of institutions. All institutions must provide a safe and healthful environmental for workers and those served by the institution. Most chapters focus on hospitals; nevertheless, all chapters address issues of particular importance for university environmental health and safety staff. For example, all universities provide health care and all must have programs in place that prevent injuries, illnesses, or environmental harm. The book is not intended to provide comprehensive coverage of all hazards one may face in an institution. Rather, the approach is to highlight the most significant threats and provide a basic framework that could be applied to analyze and control any hazard. The reason for taking this approach is that, in this rapidly evolving field, newly emerging hazards will continue to appear; however, the same basic strategies necessary to control hazards can be applied to these emerging ones.

While this is not a "how to" book, it will provide useful tools for the professional. Two of the main approaches to problem solving that will be applied throughout the book are the basic tenets of industrial hygiene (IH) and Haddon's Matrix. The basic tenets of industrial hygiene (*anticipate, recognize, evaluate,* and *control*) can be applied to each of the major environmental health and safety program areas within an institutional setting. See "Appendix: Institutional Environmental Health and Safety Matrix," which was developed by two of the authors and a group of institutional environmental health specialists with the Indian Health Service in the 1980s. The matrix was intended to describe some examples of environmental health and safety tasks in a comprehensive program. Haddon's Matrix was originally developed as a means of improving traffic safety. It provides a systematic way of sorting through solutions that may be implemented before the adverse event occurs, during the event, or after the event has occurred. The controls can also target people, equipment or supplies, and the physical or psychological environment. The point of the matrix is to determine which control will be most appropriate for a given situation.

In summary, the goal of this book is not to simply identify hazards, but to identify the most effective prevention and control strategies to protect workers and others while in an institution.

I wish to thank the American Industrial Hygiene Association's Healthcare Working Group, and especially the Hazard Evaluation and Control Technology Project Team, for their invaluable support in writing this book.

George Byrns

Preface

As the Department of the Army noted in 2007, "Hospitals are historically unsafe places to work. Therefore, hospital staff must exercise great care in protecting themselves and ensuring a safe environment for the patients as well as those who enter the hospital. The staff must be alert and identify any hazards in order to provide an environment free from unsafe acts or unsafe conditions."* In 2008 the National Institute for Occupational Safety and Health began planning national surveys of healthcare workers and management. NIOSH decided to proceed with the surveys based on "...response to needs cited by stakeholders for hazard and exposure surveillance data in the healthcare industry...".

The healthcare worker survey will collect information on "...exposures, safety and health practices, and use of exposure controls for several targeted hazards...". The management survey will collect information "...describing facility based health and safety resources, safety and health management programs, policies and practices for the same health and safety hazards covered in the worker survey."

This book is not a survey of hazards found in hospitals, universities or nursing homes. Instead the authors have provided a concise summary of best practices and proven methods to deal with the significant major hazards found in these institutions. Management approaches to environmental hazards, waste management, data gathering, hazard and risk communication, and workplace violence prevention which have proven to be effective in these types of institutions are documented. According to NIOSH, hospital workers are at a high risk for experiencing violence in the workplace.

If you are responsible for ensuring the safety of employees, patients or students, whether at the operational or administrative level, *Hazard Recognition and Control in Institutional Settings* provides a framework based on the many years of the authors' successful practice in institutional settings. Case studies and classroom activities combine to offer instructors a unique textbook in preparing safety and health students for professional practice in a growing number of healthcare facilities.

An instructor's guide and an instructor's set of PowerPoint presentations will be available from ASSE. Please contact ASSE's Technical Publications office at 847-699-2929 for more information.

---

*"Hospital/Medical Facility Safety Management." Department of the Army Pamphlet 385-80, September 4, 2007.

Contributors

Authors

Angel Boyce, MSN, RN, COHN-S/CM
Director, Occupational Health
Sandler Occupational Medicine
Associates, Inc. (SOMA)
Newark, DE
(Chapter 5)

George Byrns, Ph.D., MPH, CIH
Associate Professor of Environmental
Health
Illinois State University
Normal, IL
(Chapters 1–14)

Mary Elkins, RN, BSN, MPH, MS, CIC
Infection Control Practitioner
Northern Navajo Medical Center
Shiprock, NM
(Chapter 3)

Gregory Heck, MPH, REHS, CSP
Area Institutional Environmental Health
Officer
Phoenix Area Indian Health Service
Phoenix, AZ
(Chapter 5)

Joyce Hood, MPH, RN, COHN-S
Director, Occupational Health Services
Cook Children's Medical Center
Fort Worth, TX
(Chapter 5)

Christopher A. Janicak, Ph.D., ARM, CSP
Professor
Indiana University of Pennsylvania
Indiana, PA
(Chapters 2 and 5)

Denise Knoblauch, RN, BSN COHN-S/CM
Clinical Case Manager
OSF Saint Francis Medical Center
Peoria, IL
(Chapter 5)

David C. Regelbrugge, CIH, CSP
Director, Environmental Health &
Safety
Boelter Associates
Park Ridge, IL
(Chapter 8)

Timothy J. Ryan, Ph.D., CIH, CSP
Associate Professor & Industrial
Hygiene Program Coordinator
Ohio University
Athens, OH
(Chapter 15)

Lee Shands, MPH, CIH (Retired)
Shands Training & Consulting
Burkeville, TX
(Chapters 2, 6, 8, 9, and 13)

George Stevens, PE, MPH
Senior Facilities Consulting Engineer
Indian Health Services
Phoenix, AZ
(Chapters 5 and 7)

Reviewers

Curtis E. Cannell, CIH
St Luke's Regional Medical Center
Boise, ID

Cheryl Colton, CIH
Allina Hospitals & Clinics
Fridley, MN

Judi Gooden, RN
Kaiser Permanente Safety Manager
Santa Rosa, CA

Katherine Grubb, RN
Manager of Central Supply
BroMenn Medical Center
Normal, IL

Laurence R. Lee, III, CIH
Pacific Industrial Hygiene
Kirkland, WA

**Katherine Ciacco Palatianos, MD,
MPH**
Risk Management Consultant
U.S. Public Health Service
Rockville, MD

John D. Smart, MPH
Institutional Environmental Health
Program Manager
U.S. Public Health Service
Rockville, MD

Aubrey C. Smelley
Aberdeen Area Institutional
Environmental Health Officer
U.S. Public Health Service
Aberdeen, SD

Erica J. Stewart, CIH
Kaiser Permanente National
EH&S Chair
National Product Safety Committee
Oakland, CA

Iris Wang, MPH, HEM, CHMM
EH&S Specialist
Kaiser Permanente
Oakland, CA

Jon Wardecke, CIH
Industrial Hygienist
VA Medical Center
Milwaukee, WI

Kenneth S. Weinberg, Ph.D.
Safdoc Systems, LLC
Stoughton, MA

CHAPTER 1

Introduction
IEHS Program Basics

George Byrns

Learning Objectives

1. Describe the major categories of institutions.

2. Describe the five elements of institutional environmental health and safety.

3. Anticipate hazards in institutions.

4. Recognize hazards using surveillance and sampling approaches.

5. Evaluate hazards quantitatively and qualitatively.

6. Discuss prevention and control strategies.

7. Identify interventions using an industrial hygiene approach and a safety management approach called Haddon's Matrix.

8. Evaluate interventions for their effectiveness as control strategies.

While healthcare, educational or child care, and correctional environments have different missions and serve different clients, they share a number of common problems. By any measurement, the prudent management of institutional environments has become increasingly more complex. Institutions, especially hospitals and daycare facilities, face increasing risks from existing and evolving disease threats (DiBenedetto 1995; Spurgeon et al. 1997; Harrington 1990; Newman and Kachuba 1991; Shortridge-McCauley 1995; Weaver 1997; Foley 2004). Healthcare institutions must provide for the welfare of patients, staff, visitors, and the ongoing operation of the physical facilities. Other factors include health and safety risks imposed by emerging technology, and increasing demands placed upon staff and operations by state and federal legislation.

Occupants in educational settings may be under assault from overcrowding, communicable disease outbreaks, injuries, and exposure to hazardous materials such as lead-based paint. Correctional institutions experience similar disease threats, and the hazard is compounded by the additional burdens of social stress and the constraints of maintaining a balance between security and safety.

These sets of physical, chemical, and biological hazards, all of which are complicated by budget constraints, expanding regulation and the demand for more services, pose a challenging, dynamic problem that requires a specialized approach for resolution. Of the three classes of institutions—healthcare, childcare/educational, and correctional—the healthcare setting is the most complex and will be the primary focus of this book.

The traditional approach to environmental control in an institution is often fragmented. It is no small dilemma for those responsible for preventing and controlling environmental hazards that managing these problems has often been divided among different departments and disciplines or has been partially or totally ignored. In some cases, individuals who are unqualified to manage these problems are left to deal with them. Others with more ability are often over-utilized and receive this responsibility as an unwelcome additional duty. These practices are counterproductive. There is, at present, a critical shortage of individuals with the necessary training and interest to cope with environmental hazards in institutional settings.

Today, legislation and accreditation bodies are forcing the emergence of health and safety managers in a wide variety of institutional settings. However, in most small institutions, their economy of scale makes it impossible to employ specialists in each of the fields that comprise institutional environmental health and safety (IEHS). Likewise, consultants are very expensive to retain on an on-call basis to remedy problems and provide little in terms of program continuity. In some cases, even outside experts are not fully trained or aware of the specific equipment or technology that is used within a given facility.

Specialized training in institutional environmental control offers a systematic approach to solving problems, preventing adverse incidents, and coordinating a program of risk management. Qualified IEHS professionals will have the capability to respond to many types of problems and are flexible enough to meet specific needs. They can provide both immediate and long-term benefits because many of the problems and concerns facing institutions are related and, to some degree, predictable. But, more importantly, these problems are often preventable when an effective IEHS program is implemented. Therefore, the purpose of this book is to provide the necessary tools for future IEHS specialists so they can anticipate, recognize, evaluate, and control risks affecting workers and those served by institutions.

INSTITUTIONS AS A MICROCOSM

An institution can best be described as a *microcosm*, or a smaller version of the larger community. In this microcosm, there are five elements that must be managed. These include:

- General environmental health
- Radiation protection
- Infection control
- Safety
- Industrial hygiene

While the community at large has environmental concerns such as the need for controlling air and water pollution or managing hazardous wastes, these are same concerns as in institutions. The following section describes each of these five elements. See the Appendix, "Institutional Environmental Health and Safety Matrix," for examples of tasks within each of these elements.

General Environmental Health

The general environmental health program in institutions encompasses the traditional subjects of air and water quality, waste management, food protection, pest control, general sanitation, and environmental management. However, in the institutional environment there are special concerns relating to each of these topics. For example, indoor air quality in certain high-risk locations, such as surgical suites used for bone marrow transplants, must meet stringent filtration, air exchange, and air pressure requirements. Failure to achieve these minimum requirements may result in life-threatening infections among severely immuno-compromised patients. (See Chapters 8 and 13 for more information.) Another example is potable water. In hospitals, water used in laboratory procedures or for hemodialysis must meet additional purity requirements. Failure to remove certain chemicals, such as chlorine, may result in a failed laboratory procedure or a dead dialysis patient.

Air Quality

The improper operation of medical waste incinerators or improper hood design may result in the release of toxic gases and fumes. Concern for toxic emissions resulted in the closure of many of these incinerators. The use of refuse compactors or certain laboratory procedures (for example, centrifugation) may result in the creation of microbiological aerosols. The inadequate separation of fresh air intakes and waste vents in buildings may also affect the quality of air in an institution. Indoor air quality is covered in Chapter 8. Many air quality issues are also industrial hygiene concerns, such as the control of ethylene oxide, nitrous oxide, or other hazardous gases and vapors.

Water Quality

Water used in institutions must meet at least the minimum requirements for potability; for some uses, it must receive special treatment, such as reverse osmosis when it is used in dialysis, pharmaceutical, and laboratory procedures. In healthcare institutions, provisions must be made for redundancy to assure continuous supplies of drinking water in the event of a disruption in the primary water supply.

Waste Management

Waste management in the healthcare environment offers unique challenges. The sheer volume of general refuse from institutions can present some serious problems associated with storage, handling, and disposal. The Environmental Protection Agency (EPA) places strict controls on the methods of disposal for certain types and amounts of hazardous waste. In the healthcare environment, there is special concern regarding the potential for the spread of infection from medical waste. The Medical Waste Tracking Act of 1988 (MWTA) was passed as the result of public concern over improper disposal of potentially infectious waste. While this two-year demonstration project, enforced under 40 CFR Part 259, is no longer in effect, most states have adopted similar strict provisions for the handling of medical waste. See Chapter 9 for more information on waste management.

Food Service

Food service sanitation in healthcare institutions must maintain a higher standard than in commercial food establishments because of the increased susceptibility of hospital patients to food-borne illness. An outbreak in an institutional setting usually has devastating consequences, not only in terms of morbidity but also in public relations. There are certain methods of providing nutrition to patients who cannot eat, such as total parenteral nutrition (TPN) and nasal-gastric (NG) tube feedings, which are unique to the healthcare setting. TPN and NG procedures require an even greater degree of scrutiny than conventional food sanitation.

Sanitation

Sanitation includes the physical cleaning of the institution and laundry services. Housekeeping supervisors may lack the technical and management skills necessary to implement quality assurance programs, including the selection and use of germicides or the evaluation of cleaning effectiveness. Institutional laundry operations include the use of potentially hazardous laundering formulae, contamination control concerns, and special testing requirements. These concerns must be addressed whether linen service is provided in-house or on contract.

Pest Control

The prevention of insect and rodent infestation in an institution is an obvious concern. Controlling insects and rodents includes sanitation concerns as well as the limited use of appropriate pesticides by certified pest control technicians or applicators. The job of the IEHS specialist in an institution is generally limited to monitoring contracts with these pest control companies.

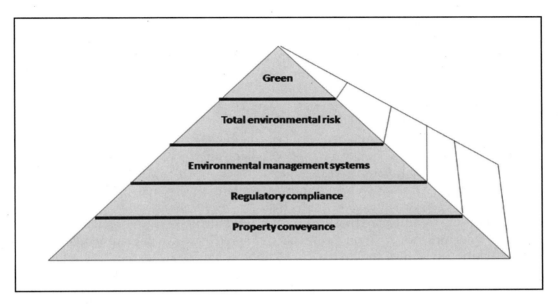

Figure 1.1 EPA's pyramid of audits. (Source: EPA)

Environmental Management

Institution managers must comply with myriad environmental regulations. However, regulatory compliance is only one part of an environmental management system (EPA 1997). The EPA describes this process in terms of a pyramid (Figure 1.1), where the lowest level is property conveyance, that is, the sale or transfer of real estate. The next level in the pyramid is regulatory compliance, followed by environmental management systems, and total environmental risk. The highest level, "green," represents a total commitment to pollution prevention through reducing waste generation, recycling, and reclamation. While the first two levels of the pyramid are mandated by law, the IEHS specialist should strive to reach the highest levels of environmental management.

In each of the above general environmental health activities, the responsible individual must have the necessary expertise to monitor contracts or to provide direct services where necessary. See Chapter 6 for more information on environmental management.

Radiation Protection

Radiation protection activities in institutions may include surveys of non-ionizing radiation (such as lasers or ultraviolet exposure) or ionizing radiation (such as diagnostic X-ray machine performance or nuclear medicine operations). Some of the ionizing radiation concerns include testing for shielding, patient entrance skin exposures, and monitoring quality assurance. In many cases, radiation safety evaluation will require the expertise of specialists.

Machine performance results should be analyzed and evaluated for compliance with the regulations of the Center for Devices and Radiological Health (CDRH) (FDA 2007) or appropriate state regulations. Shield design must be evaluated for compliance with the standards of the National Council of Radiation Protection and Measurements (NCRP 2004). Patient exposure results should be compared to national averages compiled by the Conference of Radiation Control Program Directors (CRCPD), and quality assurance programs are evaluated for compliance with criteria of CDRH. Nuclear medicine operations are evaluated for compliance with licensing requirements of the Nuclear Regulatory Commission (NRC 2007).

Employee dosimetry results must be well within the limits specified by NCRP in their *Report Recommendations on Limits for Exposure to Ionizing Radiation* (NCRP 1993). Any significant exposures must be investigated for potential causes. Control activities in radiation protection generally involve recommendations for machine preventive maintenance, recalibration, or repair; policy development or revision, and provision of training for radiology technicians or dental staff on various topics in radiation protection. In some cases it may be necessary to recommend changes in shielding design if barrier penetration is a concern.

Infection Control

Infection control activities in an institutional setting may be performed by IEHS personnel or other clinical professionals. In some cases, the infection control activity is conducted as a collateral duty by individuals with limited experience in epidemiology. The potential for healthcare-associated infections from microbiological agents is well recognized in public health literature. The risk of exposure to biological agents to staff, students, visitors, and inmates in non-healthcare settings, such as schools or correctional facilities, is less publicized but not any less real. Despite infection control programs, it is likely that outbreaks will continue to occur due to:

- Proximity and repeated exposures of susceptible hosts to virulent organisms introduced from the community or present within the institution
- Inadvertent exposure to contaminated products
- Introduction and use of new therapeutic devices before recognition of infection hazards
- Failure by employees to adhere to sanitary practices designed to prevent the transmission of organisms
- The emergence of antimicrobial resistance among institutional micro flora
- The increased use of invasive medical procedures and technology that potentially compromises patient immune systems
- The constraints placed on operational budgets for surveillance and control programs and personnel

The IEHS professional can perform a pivotal role in infection control. This role includes developing, implementing, and promoting isolation policies, aseptic techniques, laundry and housekeeping protocols, in-service training, employee health policies, and general infection control policies and procedures. Specially trained IEHS personnel may provide training for other environmental health and safety staff in the recognition and control of infection hazards in a variety of institutions. These individuals may also supplement a health facility's epidemiological response team and provide insight into the evaluation and control of other disease outbreaks related to the environment. Infection control is covered in Chapter 3.

Safety Management

Safety management in healthcare facilities is another activity that is often a collateral duty performed by personnel with little formal training in occupational health and safety. Safety management activities include:

- Emergency preparedness
- Hazard surveillance
- Injury and incident reporting and investigation
- Data analysis
- Systematic intervention
- Means to evaluate program effectiveness

Note that in 2008, the Joint Commission on Accreditation of Healthcare Organizations significantly changed their elements of performance for emergency preparedness. See Chapter 7 for more details.

A major focus of a safety management program is assuring compliance with legislation, regulations or standards, and containing workers' compensation costs. Specific tasks that must be completed include developing or revising policy, scheduling and evaluating drills, and providing orientation or in-service training to employees. Occupational injury incidence must be tabulated to identify possible trends.

A team approach involving environmental health and safety, clinical services, administrative services, and support services is most effective. A workers' compensation management team should review case files, look for trends, recommend rehabilitation programs, and identify possible restricted duty assignments. Control strategies may require redesigning a potentially hazardous situation, substituting a safer product or process, conducting training, or developing a new policy. Active safety management programs are required for all institutions. Healthcare safety is covered in Chapter 5.

Industrial Hygiene

Industrial hygiene includes a system for anticipating, recognizing, evaluating, and controlling environmental agents that may cause adverse health effects. These are referred to as the *tenets of industrial hygiene* (AIHA 2003). Depending on size and scope, industrial hygienists may work directly for the institution or may be consultants who are hired on contract. Hazards may be anticipated by becoming knowledgeable in different departments and processes, including any inherent hazards. This may require the review of policies and procedures relating to biological, chemical, and physical exposures to determine potential areas of vulnerability. In addition, anticipating hazards requires close, frequent communications with employees in these departments, so that concerns such as "near-misses" are brought to the attention of IEHS personnel. Hazards may be recognized by completing surveys for biological hazards, chemical hazards, noise, ventilation, and ergonomic assessments. The severity of a hazard may be quantitatively evaluated by comparing the results of surveys to national standards such as OSHA permissible exposure levels (PELs), American Conference of Governmental Industrial Hygienists (ACGIH) threshold limit values (TLVs), or other sources. PELs and TLVs are two types of occupational exposure limits, calculated as time-weighted average (TWA) exposures to chemical or physical agents. The allowable exposures are generally determined based on an eight-hour work day. For certain chemicals, which are highly irritating or cause an allergic sensitivity, short-term exposure limits (STELs) of fifteen minutes' duration or ceiling limits (never to exceed levels) are in place. Also, there may be action limits (set at one-half the occupational exposure limit or OEL) that require additional steps to be taken, such as use of personal protective equipment (PPE) or other means to reduce the exposure. Where no national standards exist, it may be possible to benchmark your facility's results to other "gold-standard" operations or by establishing an internal baseline of historical sample results. In other cases, qualitative assessments may be performed to determine if a procedure is being implemented in accordance with standard operating procedures. Once a hazard is determined to present a serious exposure risk, it may be necessary to implement control strategies. A key focus of this book is controlling environmental or occupational hazards using a *hierarchy of controls*. Ideally, steps can be taken to eliminate the hazard using engineering methods, such as redesigning an existing process or substituting safer processes. If that is not possible, administrative changes may be necessary, such as developing policies and providing training. The least desirable approach is to require employees to wear PPE. The hierarchy of controls is described later in this chapter in the section entitled, "Identifying, Implementing, and Evaluating Prevention or Control Strategies."

THE DISEASE TRIANGLE

Prudent management is directed at the development of an epidemiological approach to problem solving. Figure 1.2, the disease triangle, is a useful way to approach environmental or occupational hazards in the healthcare or other institutional setting.

This basic epidemiological concept is used in Figure 1.3, the healthcare model, to demonstrate that the agent could be an infectious microorganism, a toxic chemical, or a physical hazard, such as repetitive motion injuries. The

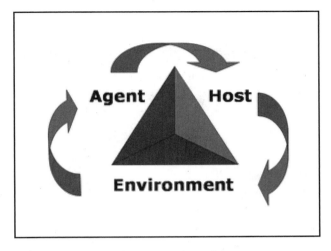

Figure 1.2 The disease triangle.

primary hosts are those caring for and served by the institution, and the environment is specific to the institutional setting. It is important to remember that in health care, there are important differences between workers and patients regarding exposures and medical-legal or regulatory issues. These differences are discussed below.

Another at-risk individual is the institutional manager. If there is a disease outbreak, a toxic release, or an unusually high workers' compensation problem, it is the manager's job that is on the line. It is also important to note that institutions may offer unique environmental sources for air, water, or food contamination not found in other settings, and healthcare facilities undergo frequent renovations and technological changes.

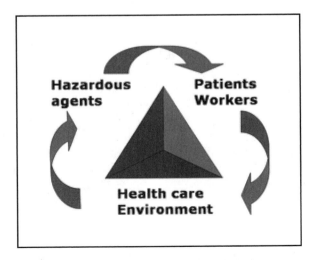

Figure 1.3 The healthcare model.

Employee Exposure Characteristics

Workers may come to the job with prior health conditions that increase their risk of injury or illness. For example, individuals with a human immunodeficiency virus (HIV) infection or other conditions that compromise the immune system will be at greater risk of becoming infected with tuberculosis or other infectious diseases.

Workers who are atopic or who have other respiratory diseases may not be protected when exposed to chemicals at or even below the allowable OELs. Certain tasks, such as cleaning and maintenance procedures, create exposure to cleaners and solvents. Changing the filters in biological safety cabinets or cleaning suction traps (devices designed to prevent solid materials such as bone fragments or dental amalgam from entering the plumbing system) may be particularly hazardous tasks.

Laboratory or clinical procedures may be inherently hazardous. Centrifuging blood or other body fluids may release infectious aerosols, and preparing and administering special medications such as chemotherapy drugs may release toxic aerosols. Even mundane activities, such as running copying machines in the business office, may release ozone or particulate aerosols that can adversely affect sensitive individuals.

Patient Exposure Characteristics

Patients in hospitals are expected to have a poor prior health status. They may be infected with HIV or other serious infections, and therefore are both more susceptible to other infections and may be a source of infection for others. Patients may have poor respiratory clearing mechanisms or other conditions that put them at an increased risk. In addition, special procedures, such as bone marrow transplants or chemotherapy treatments, may further increase susceptibility. Finally, unlike workers, patients are continually exposed to the agent as long as they are in the institution. This is an important consideration because OELs are based on recovery times when exposure ceases. There is no recovery time while a patient is hospitalized.

The IEHS professional may not be aware of special patient risk factors due to confidentiality. For example, a patient with an HIV infection may be at greater risk from a contaminated ventilation system, but this information is generally not public knowledge. In the occupational setting, the ethical requirements to inform a worker exposed to a hazard are clear. In the healthcare setting, there may be conflicts between potential malpractice risk and the responsibility to inform. In this case, the IEHS specialist must consult with both the institution's risk management staff and the patient's clinician if there is reason to believe that a patient has been exposed to a chemical or biological hazard.

Types of Agents

We typically think of an *agent* as an infectious microorganism. However, this is only one type of agent. *Biological agents* may be viable or non-viable, such as an endotoxin that is created from the cell fragments of a bacterium. Biological agents may arise from human sources (for example, tuberculosis bacteria, HIV, and hepatitis B or C virus) or from environmental sources (for example, *Legionella* bacteria and molds or fungi). Some of these biological agents, such as *Legionella*, require some degree of immune system impairment to cause an infection (OSHA 2007). However, in the case of *Legionella*, being a cigarette smoker may be sufficient to increase the risk of infection. A recent concern is the vulnerability of healthcare facilities to bioterrorism from the deliberate release of anthrax spores or other biological hazards (NIOSH 2002).

Other examples of agents are the many chemicals found in institutions. They may pose a health risk from inhalation or skin contact. Physical agents include heat, radiation, noise, and acute or cumulative trauma. *Ergonomic hazards* are a type of physical agent having serious consequences in healthcare settings, both in terms of morbidity and cost. *Psychological stress* is an agent that may have environmental components due to overcrowding, excessive noise, or exposure to other hazardous agents. For many healthcare providers, psychological strain can result from job demands, such as heavy workload and lack of control. *Workplace violence* is an agent involving a combination of physical and psychological hazards. Each of these agents may be analyzed and controlled in an institutional environment.

Emergent Agents in Healthcare Institutions

Chapter 2 provides an overview of the most serious biological, chemical, or physical agents in health care. A particular concern are emerging or re-emerging pathogenic agents. Severe acute respiratory syndrome (SARS) is an example of a newly emerging pathogen, and multi-drug resistant tuberculosis is a re-emerging older pathogen. The list of emergent agents will change over time. It is important to note that while there may be differences among these agents in terms of their modes of transmission and other factors, there are similarities in our approach to controlling them. In each case, a formal risk assessment must be performed; once the extent of the risk is known, a written exposure control plan must be developed. This plan will often include training, surveillance, and the implementation of some type of control. A key concern is selecting the most appropriate control or controls for a given problem.

Why should IEHS specialists get involved in disease control? Obviously, a strong background in epidemiology is important in evaluating the risk factors of biological hazards. It is expected that all IEHS specialists are well versed in the principles of epidemiology and use this knowledge to help others in the investigation and control of disease outbreaks. Few clinical professionals or others in an institution have been trained in the principles of epidemiology.

Hazardous Materials and Waste Management

Hazardous materials and wastes management is one of the most complex issues affecting the institutional environment. Hazardous materials come in a wide range of toxicities and forms (gaseous, liquid, or solid). These materials must be safely managed from the point of receipt into the facility to the final disposal—the so-called *cradle-to-grave* concept.

These materials and wastes are regulated by a multitude of state and federal agencies with potentially overlapping jurisdictions. For example, the Department of Transportation (DOT) and the Nuclear Regulatory Commission (NRC) both regulate the handling and shipping of radioactive materials and waste. To comply with these regulations often requires in-depth education and training of employees in worker right-to-know, community right-to-know and hazardous spill response. Occasionally, the wastes involve a combination of special concerns such as medical, radiological, or chemical hazards. Each of these concerns may require a specialized approach for waste management.

Identifying, Implementing, and Evaluating Prevention or Control Strategies

Prevention programs, such as those for environmental and health and safety, are most successful when nothing happens: in other words, no one becomes ill, and no one is injured. This can present a problem in times of economic hardship. Administrators may be pressured into downsizing or cost cutting to achieve short-term savings, even when prevention programs provide long-term savings. This is a serious problem because there is a tendency to discount the value of savings accrued in the future. It is important to understand the value of a prevention program to an administrator, to an organization, and to the community. It is even more important to make the value of prevention programs known to these target audiences.

Types of Prevention

There are actually three types of prevention: *primary*, *secondary*, and *tertiary*. *Primary prevention* means that we *stop* the event from occurring. Vaccinating a person against hepatitis B virus would be a medical example of primary prevention. An occupational health example of primary prevention would be to substitute a nonhazardous chemical for one that is hazardous. We prevent the potential for injury by removing the hazardous chemical.

Secondary prevention means that we *limit* the damage from the event. A medical example of secondary prevention would be to take an x-ray of a patient and discover early evidence of a cancerous lesion. By early detection, it may be possible to intervene and prevent the patient from developing advanced cancer. An environmental health example of secondary prevention would be to drill monitoring wells around a hazardous waste landfill to detect any traces of toxic leachate. If there is evidence of leachate, this means there is a need to dig up the landfill and remove the leaking containers before there is serious contamination of the groundwater.

Tertiary prevention means we *treat* the damage from the event. A medical example of tertiary prevention would be to rehabilitate a worker with a back injury to some level of performance. An environmental example would be a clean-up of a major hazardous waste spill before it harms large numbers of people or the environment. Tertiary is considered a form of prevention because it prevents additional cost to the individual, society, and the employer.

Active Versus Passive Prevention

Normally, we think of something that is active as good and something that is passive as bad. This is not necessarily true when it comes to prevention. Passive prevention strategies are always present and require no action by the protected person. For example, an automobile airbag is always present and only deploys (hopefully) when needed. Active prevention requires an action by the person to receive protection. For example, a car seatbelt must be buckled each time the person gets into the car. Active prevention strategies that require a single action are considered to be more effective than those requiring repeated actions. For example, once a machine guard is installed, it is always available for use, although someone may decide not to use it. If possible, prevention strategies that are passive are preferred. If this is not possible, active approaches that require fewer actions to be protective are the next best alternative.

Control of Hazardous Conditions

According to the tenets of industrial hygiene, we anticipate, recognize, evaluate, and control hazards (AIHA 2003). Once a decision to act is made, there may be several choices available. OSHA recommends a *hierarchy of controls*, which ranks the methods of handling a hazard.

In the hierarchy of controls:

- The first and most desirable type of control to consider is to make an engineering change or in some way modify the environment to eliminate the potential for harm.
- The next best choice is to administratively change the work practice to reduce the hazard.
- The control of last resort is to require employees to use PPE. This is always the least desirable approach because the hazard is still present and the burden of responsibility for implementing the control is placed on the individual worker.

If an engineering change that eliminates the risk is not possible, other options must be considered. Haddon's Matrix is one useful means to sort through these options. This approach to assist in identifying the appropriate control was developed by William Haddon, the first director of the National

Table 1.1. Haddon's Matrix for Automobile Crash

	Human	Vehicle	Environment
Pre-event	Alcohol use, fatigue	Tires, brakes, visibility	Visibility of hazard
Event	Seat belt use, osteoporosis	Air bag	Break-away utility poles, pull-outs
Post Event	Physical condition	Fuel tank protection	Access to emergency service

Highway Safety Administration (NHSA), which later became the National Highway Traffic Safety Administration (NHTSA) (Robertson 1992). According to Haddon's Matrix, controls may be implemented before a hazard is present, while the hazard is present, or after the damage has occurred. The approach corresponds to the idea of primary, secondary and tertiary prevention that was presented earlier. In addition, the control can target people, equipment or supplies, or the physical or social environment.

Using an automobile crash as an example, during the pre-crash phase, keeping drunks off the road or forcing truckers to take rests can improve traffic safety. Also, drivers who have cars with good breaks, tires and clear windshields will reduce traffic problems; another control would be to make sure that four-way intersections are free of visibility obstruction. During the crash, wearing a seatbelt and having strong bones can help the person survive. Also, having a car equipped with an air bag, and having break-away utility poles and truck pull-outs can reduce the chance of serious injuries. Finally, after the crash, your chance of survival is better if you are already in good physical condition. Preventing fuel tank ruptures can prevent an explosion after the crash, and getting the injured persons quickly to the medical facility can improve the chance of survival. While Haddon's Matrix was designed for traffic safety, it can be applied to a wide range of environmental health and safety problems.

Two examples are presented below that demonstrate how the tenets of industrial hygiene and Haddon's Matrix can work together in solving an environmental or occupational health issue.

Example 1: Control of Communicable Diseases in a University Daycare Center

Anticipate the problem: Review public health reports on gastrointestinal illness in small children in your community during the previous year.

Recognize the problem: Contact local pediatricians regarding the incidence of these diseases in the community.

Evaluate the problem: Compare your community's vulnerability for large-scale outbreaks to others in the state.

Control the problem: Apply Haddon's Matrix as follows:

Using Haddon's Matrix to select the best control (see below for examples)

Table 1.2 Haddon's Matrix for University Daycare Center

	Human	Vehicle	Environment
Pre-event	Vaccinations Education	Hand washing sink & supplies	Room separations Disease control policy
Event	Monitor hand washing Staffing levels	Monitor glove use, protective paper & disinfection	Use isolation area for sick child
Post-event	Medical clearance	Proper disposal of medical waste	Conduct an investigation Review policy & design concerns

Prior to an outbreak:

- **Person:** If available, require vaccinations for specific diseases of concern. Educate the daycare staff on the most frequent diseases of concern.
- **Equipment and supplies:** Be sure there is a hand-washing sink and supplies in key locations, such as the immediate vicinity of the diaper-changing table.
- **Physical environment:** Be sure that the facility is designed to allow for separation of age groups and separation of children from the kitchen.
- **Social environment:** Be sure that there is a comprehensive policy that addresses environmental health and infection control concerns, including drop-in policies.

During an exposure incident:

- **Person**: Monitor hand washing of staff and children during critical periods. Be certain that proper staff-to-child ratios are maintained, as required by state and/or municipal regulations.
- **Equipment and supplies:** Monitor for the use of gloves, disposable paper during diaper changing and proper disinfection procedures for high-risk areas and toys.
- **Physical or social environment:** Implement appropriate isolation policy for a sick child.

After an outbreak:

- **Person:** Allow sick staff or children to return to the facility only when cleared by a physician.
- **Equipment and supplies**: Dispose of any medical waste properly.
- **Physical or social environment:** Conduct a formal investigation, including a review of the adequacy of facility design, such as facilities to isolate potentially infectious children until they are returned to their parents. Review the adequacy of the facility's infection control policy and staff response to the policy.

Once the controls have been implemented, it will be necessary to reassess their effectiveness in preventing the problem. If the intervention did not completely address the problem, other approaches should be examined and evaluated upon implementation.

Example 2: Anticipating, Recognizing, Evaluating and Controlling a Problem

Reviewing the literature on problems associated with anesthesia equipment, you learn that one of the gases used, nitrous oxide, is a potent oxidizer that may degrade rubber. You are concerned that this property may cause gas leakage in equipment used in the dental and surgical departments. Therefore, you first visit the dental clinic and conduct an industrial hygiene survey. You immediately discover that nitrous oxide levels significantly exceed the exposure limits recommended by ACGIH. During the survey you identify a number of issues that may have led to this condition. These include leaks at the fittings and cracks in the breathing bag. You also discover that vacuum flow-rate used to capture nitrous oxide is below that recommended by the manufacturer. You prepare a written report and submit the results to the directors of the dental, clinical and plant engineering departments. The next step is to refer the problem to the health and safety committee, which will assign a team to resolve the major issues. An important question is: What are possible underlying causes that contributed to this problem?

In this case study, key team members will include the dental director, the clinical engineer, the plant engineer, and the health and safety officer. In this hypothetical scenario, the dental team is assigned responsibility for completing a procedural checklist prior to administering the nitrous oxide. This checklist will include an inspection of the system for obvious leaks and checking to see that the scavenging flow rate (local exhaust system) is in the desirable range. The clinical engineering program will be responsible for conducting monthly high- and low-pressure checks of the delivery and scavenging system, including leaks in the piped system and manifold. Plant engineering will be responsible for monitoring the general ventilation rates annually, and the health and safety manager will monitor emissions on a quarterly basis using passive dosimetry. The results of monitoring will be shared with the affected staff and included in their employee medical files. Also, the health and safety officer will assist the dental team in training its staff on the hazards of nitrous oxide. An important issue is the need to set a reasonable timetable for corrections. In this scenario, it was projected that these activities could be implemented within 30 days. The effectiveness of the program to limit exposure to nitrous oxide should be evaluated on an annual basis and, if necessary, changes should be made.

There are exceptions to the hierarchy of controls. For example, the control of tuberculosis in a healthcare facility first requires the implementation of an administrative procedure to quickly identify potential cases so they can be isolated and treated. Also, if a hospital lacks proper isolation facilities, the appropriate administrative control is to not accept such patients into the facility.

Are prevention and control different? Not really, because in preventing something, the focus is on the event or the hazard; in controlling something, the focus is on the type of intervention. In each case, the goal is to prevent or limit damage to someone or something.

SUMMARY AND CONCLUSIONS

This chapter describes the basics of an IEHS program. There will be positive or negative outcomes resulting from our efforts (or lack thereof) in addressing problems in the institutional environment. If the program is proactive, positive outcomes may include:

- **Continued accreditation:** Accreditation organizations expect to see programs that include continuous quality improvement, and the quality of the environment of care is one of the most important considerations in achieving successful accreditation.

- **Secure funding:** Healthcare programs that meet either the requirements of the Joint Commission or the federal Centers for Medicare and Medicaid Services (CMS) can continue to receive reimbursement for Medicare and Medicaid charges. This is a significant part of the total operating budget for many institutions, and facilities that fail their accreditation survey would be in serious financial danger.

- **Prestige:** In the U.S., consumers have choices when selecting a healthcare facility. Institutions that are accredited for certain services will have a competitive advantage over facilities that lack this status. Therefore, proactive programs can use accreditation as a marketing ploy to increase their market share.

On the other hand, if the program fails to address serious issues, negative outcomes may include:

- **Poor safety climate:** If workers feel that their jobs present a health risk, they will have reduced morale.

- **Litigation:** Individuals who believe they were harmed while in an institution may file a lawsuit to recover damages. In some cases, these judicial awards are far in excess of the cost of preventing the injury in the first place.

- **Workers' compensation payments:** Employees are entitled to reimbursement for loss of salary or medical costs associated with a work-related illness or injury. While these direct costs may be substantial, indirect costs due to decreased productivity and lower morale may be higher. Decreased productivity and lower morale are especially important issues. When a worker is injured or becomes ill on the job, it is likely that there will be a decrease in both productivity and morale. Units that are short-handed will have a difficult time providing the same level of service as a fully staffed unit, and new hires may be less productive during their initial assignments due to a learning curve. The bottom line is that when a coworker is disabled, production and morale on that unit will suffer.

A case in point about the importance of a proactive IEHS program was the emerging threat of blood-borne infections. As workers became infected, there was a demand for action. There was a perception of a slow response by the health-care industry to protect workers from hepatitis B and HIV. The failure to act resulted in OSHA's promulgation of the *Bloodborne Pathogens Standard* (OSHA 2006). This standard meant that each workplace with the potential for occupational exposure to blood-borne pathogens must have a written program that meets the regulation's minimum requirements. Programs that did not meet these minimum requirements were subject to citations and fines. The prevention of blood-borne pathogens is covered in more detail in Chapter 2.

A similar situation nearly occurred with the proposed tuberculosis standard. The proposed OSHA standard was recently withdrawn; however, it may reappear sometime in the future. There are other examples of the consequences of failing to promote a safe and healthy environment in institutional settings.

It should be clear from the above that a comprehensive IEHS program offers many benefits to managers of institutional settings. The remainder of this book will describe each of the components of this program in more detail and provide the reader with practical approaches to problem solving.

Review

1. Explain why hospitals are sometimes called microcosms.

2. What are some problems that are common to different classes of institutions (healthcare versus corrections and educational/daycare)?

3. What are some unique environmental health and safety problems that affect hospitals?

4. How is the disease triangle useful in our study of environmental health and safety problems affecting hospitals?

5. A proactive institutional environmental health program provides rewards and a reactive program results in penalties. What are some examples of rewards and penalties?

Reference List

American Industrial Hygiene Association (AIHA). 2003. *The Occupational Environment: Its Evaluation, Control, and Management.* 2d ed. Fairfax, VA: American Industrial Hygiene Association.

DiBenedetto, D. V. 1995. "Occupational Hazards of the Health Care Industry: Protecting Health Care Workers." *AAOHN.J.* 43:131–137.

Environmental Protection Agency (EPA). 1997. "Environmental Audit Program Design Guidelines for Federal Agencies." Report # 300-B-96-011. Washington, D.C.: Environmental Protection Agency.

Foley, M. 2004. "Caring for Those Who Care: A Tribute to Nurses and Their Safety." *Online.J.Issues Nurs.* 9:2.

Food and Drug Administration. 2007. 21 CFR Part 1000, *Radiological Health* (retrieved August 11, 2008) (http://www.accessdata.fda.gov/scripts/cdrh/cfdocs/cfCFR/CFRSearch.cfm?CFRPart=1000&showFR=1).

Harrington, J. M. 1990. "The Health of Health Care Workers: The Ernestine Henry Lecture 1990." *J.R.Coll.Physicians Lond* 24:189–195.

National Council of Radiation Protection and Measurement (NCRP). 1993. "Limitation of Exposure to Ionizing Radiation." Report # 116. Bethesda, MD: National Council on Radiation Protection and Measurements.

———. 2004. "Structural Shielding Design for Medical X-Ray Imaging Facilities." Report # 147. Bethesda, MD: National Council on Radiation Protection and Measurements.

National Institute for Occupational Safety and Health (NIOSH). 2002. *Guidance for Protecting Building Environments from Airborne Chemical, Biological, or Radiological Attacks* (Publication No. 2002–139). Cincinnati, OH: NIOSH-Publications Dissemination.

Newman, M. A. and Kachuba, J. B. 1991. "Protect the Health of Your Health Care Worker." *Hosp.Health Serv.Adm*, 36:537–543.

Nuclear Regulatory Commission. 2007. 10 CFR 20, *Standards for Protection Against Radiation* (retrieved August 11, 2008) (http://www.nrc.gov/reading-rm/doc_collections/cfr/part020/full-text.html).

Occupational Safety and Health Administration (OSHA). 2006. 29 CFR 1910.1030, *Bloodborne Pathogens.* (retrieved August 8, 2008) (http://www.osha.gov/pls/oshaweb/owadisp.show_document?p_table=STANDARD&p_id=10051).

———. 2007. "Legionnaires' Disease." (retrieved August 8, 2008) (http://www.osha.gov/dts/osta/otm/legionnaires/disease_rec.html).

Robertson, L. S. 1992. "The Problem, History, and Concepts." In Robertson, Leon S., ed. *Injury Epidemiology: Research and Control Strategies*, pp. 3–22. New York: Oxford University Press.

Shortridge-McCauley, L. A. 1995. "Reproductive Hazards: An Overview of Exposures to Health Care Workers." *AAOHN.J.* 43:614–621.

Spurgeon, A., Harrington, J. M., and Cooper, C. L. 1997. "Health and Safety Problems Associated with Long Working Hours: A Review of the Current Position." *Occupational and Environmental Medicine* 54:367–375.

Weaver, V. M. 1997. "Chemical Hazards in Health Care Workers." *Occup.Med.* 12:655–667.

CLASSROOM ACTIVITY

Compare and Contrast Prevention and Control Strategies

Scenario: This is your first day on the job as the Environmental Health Officer at the Abnormal County Health Department. The public health nurse (PHN) just called your office to report that over the past week there were 6 cases of *Salmonella* diarrhea infections in the Institute for Lower Education Day Care Center, and she is asking for your help in investigating and controlling the outbreak. All of the cases were toddlers except one five-year old. Your first step is to ask the PHN for more information on the outbreak. (Your instructor will play the part of the PHN.)

On your own, write a lab report in memo format to Ms. Smith, PHN, answering the following questions:

1. Briefly the describe epidemic including the agent, the hosts, the environment and possible means of transmission (no more than one or two sentences for each).
2. Describe any patterns, e.g., age breakdown, in the outbreak.
3. Is this a point source or propagated outbreak?
4. Give an explanation for the five-year-old child's case.
5. Using Haddon's Matrix, describe a control program to prevent future outbreaks. Do not actually insert a table in your memo but add it as an attachment.

CHAPTER 2

Healthcare Occupational Hazards

George Byrns, Lee Shands and Christopher Janicak

Learning Objectives

1. Identify the four major classes of hazards affecting healthcare workers.

2. Identify the departments most affected by each type of hazard.

3. Describe the health effects associated with exposure to these hazards.

4. Describe methods of anticipating or recognizing these hazards.

5. Discuss methods of evaluating the severity of these hazards.

6. Discuss the most effective means of controlling these hazards.

According to the most recent Bureau of Labor Statistics (BLS) Report, there were approximately 14 million workers involved in some aspect of health care in 2006 (BLS 2006). The Occupational Safety and Health Administration (OSHA), in its *OSHA Technical Manual,* lists a large number of potential health hazards in a typical healthcare facility (OSHA 1995). Some examples of these occupational hazards include exposure to radiation, toxic chemicals, biological hazards, heat, noise, ergonomic strain, and psychological strain (Weaver 1997; Rogers 1997). Until relatively recently, occupational hazards had been ignored because hospitals and other types of healthcare facilities were presumed to be safe by enforcement agencies. Also, healthcare management has been slow to take action against these hazards because workers were assumed to be responsible for their own protection; the primary concern was the protection of patients. These false perceptions have been debunked, and enforcement agencies, such as OSHA, have cited healthcare facilities for failure to recognize hazards and protect workers. Most disturbing is that these hazards are largely preventable; however, the number of occupational injuries and illnesses to healthcare workers has remained significantly higher than industry averages (BLS 2006).

There are many federal and state agencies involved in health care. Some of the most important are OSHA, the Food and Drug Administration (FDA), the Centers for Disease Control and Prevention (CDC), NIOSH, the Centers for Medicare and Medicaid Services (CMS) (formerly the Health Care Financing Administration (HCFA)), the Environmental Protection Agency (EPA) and the Nuclear Regulatory Commission (NRC). State and local agencies are also involved in health care, such as departments of health and environmental protection. Also, there are a number of voluntary agencies involved in health care, including: the Joint Commission on Accreditation of Healthcare Organizations (known simply as the Joint Commission or JCAHO), the National Fire Protection Association (NFPA), the National Safety Council (NSC), the American Institute of Architects (AIA), and the American Society of Healthcare Engineering (ASHE), which is part of the American Hospital Association (AHA). Since accreditation through the Joint Commission qualifies a facility for Medicare/Medicaid funding, administrators are often more concerned with compliance with these "voluntary" standards than those of OSHA or other enforcement agencies. The fact that there is often overlapping jurisdiction among these agencies and organizations makes regulatory compliance a significant challenge for most healthcare organizations.

COMMON FEATURES IN A COMPREHENSIVE INSTITUTIONAL PROGRAM

A comprehensive institutional environmental health and safety (IEHS) program that is designed to manage these hazards must have the following features, discussed below.

Management Support

There must be written evidence of management support for any environmental and occupational health and safety program. Evidence of such support includes the appointment of a health and safety director and employee health coordinator, establishment of a health and safety committee, and the provision of resources to manage these programs.

Hazard Identification and Evaluation

There must be a systematic means of identifying and evaluating hazards. This must include periodic surveys of both environmental hazards and employee knowledge of safety and health. Other sources of hazard identification information would include the results of medical surveillance of employees (for adequacy of immunizations, biologic indices, and exposure monitoring), review of chemical inventories and the master Material Safety Data Sheet (MSDS) files. Hazard identification also includes reviewing information from various sources for new hazards. Hazard surveys and surveillance is covered in Chapter 10.

Hazard Control Programs

The *hierarchy of control*, as described in Chapter 1, must be followed when addressing healthcare hazards, using an engineering method to modify the environment, thus eliminating the hazard. If this is not possible, another approach involves enforcement of administrative controls, such as policies and procedures, to reduce the potential effects of the hazard. The control of last resort is to encourage the appropriate use of personal protective equipment (PPE). This is always considered the least useful approach because the burden of control is placed on the worker. The worker must know which kind of PPE to use, when to use it, its limitations, and so on. The most serious drawback of the use of PPE is that it does nothing to remove the hazard from the environment.

Program Monitoring

Accrediting organizations and enforcement agencies expect to see a process of continuous quality improvement to address known or potential risks. There must be a systematic approach to setting IEHS program priorities and monitoring progress in meeting these priorities. Program priorities should be based on the significance of the issue: hazard severity; the probability that the issue will occur; and the cost of addressing the issue. Another factor to be considered is whether the issue might result in a fine, law suit or loss of accreditation. Priority setting is covered in more detail in Chapter 10. At a minimum, the IEHS program manager should develop annual program priorities, with quarterly progress reports.

Recordkeeping

Accrediting organizations and enforcement agencies also expect to see written documentation to substantiate the presence of a comprehensive IEHS program. Examples of records that must be kept include: survey reports, evaluations, training, and employee medical records. The length of time that this information must be maintained varies by the type of record. For example, certain types of medical exposure records must be maintained for the duration of employment plus 30 years. Occupational and environmental information may be maintained in an electronic database as long as it is readily accessible when requested by surveyors or others who have a right of access.

CATEGORIES OF HEALTHCARE HAZARDS

The four major categories of healthcare hazards are: chemical, biological, physical or ergonomic, and psychological. The study of healthcare hazards is complicated because some of them, such as low back pain (LBP), involve multiple, interacting risk factors (Burdorf et al. 1997). Examples of each of these will be discussed below. While there are unique risk factors for each of these hazards, there are also commonalities in both the risks and the approaches to problem resolution.

Chemical Hazards

The effects of chemical hazards will be either acute or chronic, depending on a variety of factors. The most important factors that determine the effect of a chemical on the body are its dose, route of exposure, physical state and toxicity (NSC 2005). The health status of the exposed individual is also important, as well as the presence of other chemicals in the environment. A hazardous situation may result if multiple chemicals affect the same organ system or act synergistically and magnify the health effect. A worker with poor health who is exposed to an aerosol containing a high concentration of one or more toxic volatile chemicals is likely to have an acute reaction. On the other hand, someone with good health, with a dermal exposure to a chemical with low toxicity and low percutaneous absorption rates, may have a reaction only if there is chronic exposure. Therefore, it is important to not only assess the toxicity of a chemical, but also evaluate the pathways of exposure and the behavior and health status of the worker to determine the degree of risk (AIHA 2003). The following section describes some of the more important hazardous substances found in health care.

Asbestos

Asbestos is a class of fibrous silicates which, according to OSHA, must be at least 5 μm in length, and the ratio of the length to the diameter of the fiber must be greater than or equal to 3:1 (OSHA 1995). Three of the more common types of asbestos include *chrysotile, amosite,* and *crocidolite.* OSHA defines materials as being asbestos-containing if they have greater than 1% asbestos content. The hazards of inhalational exposure to asbestos have been well documented and include: *asbestosis,* a type of pneumoconiosis that results in fibrosis of the lung and emphysema; lung cancer, and *mesothelioma,* another form of cancer that affects the pleural lining surrounding the lung. Older buildings may contain asbestos in a variety of locations including: pipe lagging insulation, floor and roof tiles, ceiling tiles, spray-applied fire proofing, and outside siding.

Asbestos is normally hazardous only when it is in an airborne state. *Friable asbestos,* containing materials such as spray applied fireproofing, can be reduced to dust under hand pressure when dry. These materials present a greater risk of becoming airborne than non-friable materials, such as asphalt-shingle roofing or vinyl floor tiles. The facility maintenance staff is most likely to have the greatest potential for occupational exposure due to routine repair activities such as repairing leaking pipes, conducting inspections, working above suspended ceilings, or other tasks. Another group that may be at risk is the housekeeping staff when using a high speed floor buffing unit (Edwards et al. 1994). During floor buffing, some of the bound asbestos is released due to the friction activity of the buffer and is aerosolized.

Occupational exposure to asbestos must be kept below the OSHA standard for both eight-hour time-weighted averages (TWAs) and during 30-minute excursion periods. A full discussion of the OSHA regulation (OSHA 1995) is beyond the scope of this book. However, a worker who was exposed at or above the occupational limits must be assessed for airborne exposure and undergo a medical evaluation. Control of asbestos involves removal or controlling-in-place through encapsulation or enclosure. Removal is expensive and, if done incorrectly, can result in significant contamination of the workplace. It is currently recommended to control asbestosis in place rather than removal. Individuals who work around or contact asbestos-containing materials must receive special EPA- or state-certified training in asbestos. Likewise, individuals that inspect or sample for asbestos must also have completed required EPA training. When working with asbestos, it is critical to follow proper procedures, such as keeping the material wet, using the appropriate type of PPE based on the airborne concentration, and using special vacuums equipped with high efficiency particulate air (HEPA) filters.

Cryogenic Agents

Cryogenic liquids have a boiling point below $-238°F$ ($-150°C$). In controlled situations, cryogens can be used to remove skin lesions or growths. Cryogens are used in both the liquid and compressed gas forms in health care. The ability to produce extremely low temperatures is the reason for their use; however, this property poses occupational hazards as well. Inadvertent contact with the skin can cause severe burns. Safe handling of liquid cryogenics (usually liquid nitrogen) requires that the staff be familiar with the nature and hazard of the material. Safety precautions during handling include using appropriate PPE (face shield, plastic apron, insulated gloves with gauntlet cuff and pants worn outside shoe tops) and a long-handled dipper when transferring the liquid to smaller containers.

Compressed gases, such as nitrous oxide (N_2O) and carbon dioxide (CO_2), may also be used as cryogenic agents (NIOSH 1999a). The compressed gases, when allowed to expand, reach very low temperatures. In a cryosurgical unit, the gases expand in the tip of a probe, causing the tip to freeze at a low temperature. The frozen tip is placed upon the lesion or growth that is to be removed. Cryosurgical units, if not vented to the outside atmosphere, can result in room concentrations of the cryogenic gas of several thousand parts per million (ppm). Nitrous oxide levels from cryosurgical units can be controlled through proper preventive maintenance of the unit to control leakage and venting of the discharge gas from the unit to the outside atmosphere. Substitution of CO_2 for N_2O as a cryogenic agent is not always advised. The freezing temperature of CO_2 ($-79°C$) is higher than N_2O ($-89°C$) and can result in inadequate depth of freeze during lesion removal. Cryosurgical units may be used by gynecologists to remove cervical lesions, by general practitioners or dermatologists to remove skin lesions, and by ophthalmologists for eye surgery.

The health hazards associated with N_2O exposure are discussed in the "Waste anesthetic gases" section below.

Disinfectants

Disinfectants used in health care have a wide range of physical and health hazards (Rutala 1996). The following is a brief overview of the uses and hazards associated with chemical disinfectants. Chemical disinfection is covered in more detail in Chapter 4.

Alcohol. Ethyl or isopropyl alcohol are flammable and may de-fat the skin, causing chapped hands; however, they are considerably less toxic than other germicides and may be used as skin antiseptics.

Formaldehyde. Formaldehyde and glutaraldehyde are both strong irritants following both dermal and inhalation exposure. Formaldehyde as an aqueous formalin solution has long been used for tissue preservation and as a high-level germicide. (Formalin is a saturated mixture of 37% formaldehyde in water which often contains another substance such as 6-13% methanol.) Its use has been significantly reduced over time because of its extremely irritating properties. Potential for formalin exposure can be found throughout the hospital during tissue specimen collection, in the pathology laboratory, especially during specimen preparation, and in the mortuary. One special concern is disinfection of hemodialysis machines, since the presence of residual formaldehyde in the machine may have life-threatening consequences if used on a patient. Formaldehyde is also a suspected carcinogen. Exposure should be minimized through product substitution (such as steam sterilization instead of cold sterilant use), reducing usage quantities to minimal levels required, and proper rinsing after use, proper enclosure, and exhaust ventilation. A common method of reducing the quantity of formalin on hand is to utilize prefilled specimen containers.

OSHA requires specific monitoring, and employee training for formaldehyde exposure above the action level or STEL (short term exposure level). An example of a special ventilation design to protect the embalmer from exposure to formaldehyde is the down-draft autopsy or embalming table in Figure 2.1. This design directs formaldehyde gas away from the worker's breathing zone, into the exhaust system and out of the building.

Glutaraldehyde. Glutaraldehyde formulations have been used for many years as high-level disinfectants or cold sterilizing agents, depending on contact time. Some formulations require the addition of an activator to achieve full potency. Glutaraldehyde used for disinfection purposes usually comes in a 2% solution. These solutions lose potency over time and especially with repeated use. Glutaraldehyde is also used in a much higher concentration (30–50%) as a hardening agent in x-ray film developing or as a tissue fixative in histology or pathology (NIOSH 2001).

Glutaraldehyde is considered to be highly toxic to humans via inhalation, ingestion, or skin contact and allergic sensitization can occur. Skin sensitization has been documented in endoscopy nurses, x-ray technicians and others (OSHA 2006a). The most serious health effect from exposure is occupational

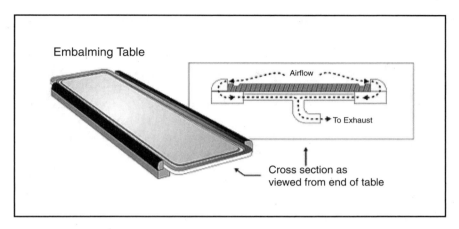

Figure 2.1 Embalming table. (Source: Dick Carlson of NIOSH)

asthma. Because workers were sensitized at low exposures, the American Conference of Governmental Industrial Hygienists (ACGIH) lowered the Threshold Limit Value (TLV) to 0.05 ppm as a ceiling level in 1995. In order to achieve this ceiling level, the best solution is to eliminate or minimize the use of the product. The first step in reducing exposure is to make sure that the glutaraldehyde is used appropriately. For example, it should not be used as a cold sterilant for items that do not require sterilization or that can be steam sterilized. Glutaraldehyde usage in radiology may be eliminated by installing glutaraldehyde-free, x-ray film processing units or digital radiography systems. Substituting equipment that can be steam sterilized for those pieces that require cold sterilization may also be feasible. Using glutaraldehyde as surface disinfectant should be prohibited because it can generate exposures above the TLV level. At a minimum, glutaraldehyde solutions must be tightly covered at all times or used in an area with good ventilation to capture any vapor release (Rutala 1996). In all cases, glutaraldehyde should only be used in locations with total exhaust, not recirculated, ventilation. When glutaraldehyde is used as a tissue fixative, it is important that procedures be done inside a fume hood. The hood should be checked to be sure that the sash is at the proper height and that hood face velocities are between 80 and 100 feet per minute (fpm) (ACGIH 2007). These hood velocities should be considered minimums, and some have recommended velocities in the range of 100 to 150 fpm. The use of glutaraldehyde in automatic disinfecting units significantly reduces, but does not eliminate, exposures.

In terms of worker protection from formaldehyde and glutaraldehyde, it is safer to use local exhaust ventilation than respirators. It is also important to avoid skin contact. Gloves should be made of nitrile or butyl rubber because glutaraldehyde has a tendency to penetrate latex (NIOSH 2001). Other forms of PPE, such as goggles, face shields, and gowns, may be necessary to protect the eyes and skin of workers. See "Additional Resources" at the end of this chapter for more information.

Ortho-phthaladehyde (OPA). There have been recent efforts to replace glutaraldehyde with alternatives because of exposure concerns. Ortho-phthaladehyde (OPA) is a relatively new germicide that was cleared in 1999 by the FDA for use as an instrument disinfectant (Rutala and Weber 2001). It is similar in action to glutaraldehyde but has several advantages over glutaraldehyde: It requires no activation; it is more stable than glutaraldehyde; and it has a lower vapor pressure, so it is less likely to be volatilized. One disadvantage is that it will stain unprotected skin a gray color. The most serious issue with OPA is that it is a potent skin sensitizer. For example, it should never be used for reprocessing of urological instruments to be used on patients with a history of bladder cancer because of reports of anaphylactic-like reactions (Hamasuna et al 2004). OPA also appears to be toxic to aquatic environments and may require neutralizing with glycerin before it is discharged to the sewer. Some other alternatives include steam sterilization for heat-stable instruments or hydrogen peroxide and ozone sterilizers for heat-sensitive instruments. Concern for the greater dermal and aquatic toxicity of OPA complicates the decision to switch from glutaraldehyde.

Regardless of where these chemicals are used, they should be included in the healthcare facility's hazard communication training program. Topics to be included are an explanation of the MSDS, possible health effects, locations where it is used, methods of minimizing exposure, and steps to take in the event of a spill.

Halide Compounds. Halide compounds containing chlorine or iodine are fast-acting, broad-spectrum germicides. While they are relatively non-toxic, they may be irritating to skin or corrosive to metals and other equipment. Exposure to chlorine can result in respiratory irritation, and high exposures can lead to pulmonary edema. Another potential hazard exists when chlorine solutions are mixed with basic compounds and chlorine gas is released. PPE should be used when working with chlorine. Chlorine is not generally used for routine surface or instrument disinfection due to the corrosive nature of the chemical, with one exception; a one-to-ten dilution of household bleach and water is frequently used to disinfect surfaces after a blood spill. Tincture of iodine is a mixture of alcohol and iodine that may be used as a skin antiseptic. Other products, called *iodophors,* which are a combination of iodine and a solubilizing agent, may also be used as a skin antiseptic.

Phenolic Compounds. Phenolic compounds are used as general-purpose surface disinfectants because they are non-flammable and are effective in killing a relatively wide range of bacteria. However, these chemicals are severely irritating to the skin, are toxic to the liver and kidneys, and will permanently destroy skin pigment (see Figure 2.2). This chemical is readily absorbed through intact skin and is especially toxic to infants, causing a potentially life-threatening condition called *hyperbilirubinemia.*

For the above reasons, this chemical should not be used in any areas where newborns may be present. It is also not approved for use on any food contact surfaces.

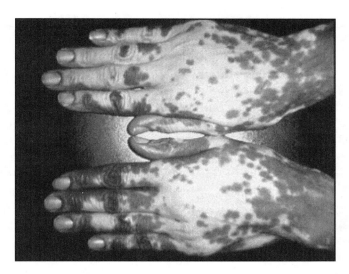

Figure 2.2 Phenol damage to skin pigment.
(Courtesy of NIOSH)

Quaternary Ammonium Compounds (Quats). Quaternary ammonium compounds (Quats) are more frequently used for general surface disinfection because they are less toxic than phenolic germicides. Exposure to quats in use-dilution concentrations can cause mild irritation, but exposure to concentrated solutions can cause burns to the skin and the mucous membranes. Therefore, exposure to even these less toxic germicides should be controlled through the use of PPE.

Ethylene Oxide (EtO). Ethylene oxide (EtO) is a flammable, highly reactive chemical (C_2H_4O) used in health care as a sterilizing agent for heat sensitive devices. EtO is a liquid when in cartridges or cylinders but is a gas when used in the sterilizer, due to a boiling point of 5.3°F. EtO is a respiratory irritant, causing watery eyes, salivation, and shortness of breath. Other acute effects can include nausea, vomiting, headache, diarrhea and cyanosis. EtO can also cause reproductive effects, mutagenicity, neurotoxicity and sensitization, and ACGIH has listed it as A2 (suspect human carcinogen) (ACGIH 2008).

The hazards associated with EtO are such that OSHA issued a permissible exposure limit (PEL) of no more than 1 ppm as an eight-hour TWA or 5 ppm averaged over fifteen minutes (OSHA 2006b). As in the case of other hazardous substances that are regulated by OSHA, potentially exposed workers must be monitored to assure that their exposures are below the TWA or excursion level (an OSHA equivalent of a STEL). With EtO, two samples taken at least seven days apart must be below the 5 ppm excursion level to avoid the medical monitoring and other provisions of this standard. A medical surveillance program is also required for all employees who are or may be exposed to EtO at or above the action level (0.5 ppm), without regard to the use of respirators, for at least 30 days a year.

If employees are exposed to levels exceeding the PEL, employers are required to implement notification and control measures. One important measure is to develop a written program to reduce employee exposure to or below the PEL. Wherever occupational exposures to airborne concentrations of EtO are reasonably expected to exceed the PEL, the employer is required to establish that area as a regulated area. As a first form of protection, engineering controls should be developed and implemented. If the engineering controls are unavailable or insufficient, work practice controls should be employed, and, as a last resort, PPE should be used to supplement other more effective measures. Exposure control plans must be reviewed at least every twelve months, and updated as necessary to reflect significant changes in the compliance program.

EtO sterilizers can utilize either 100% EtO or a freon/EtO mixture, depending on the design. Due to environmental concerns, usage of the freon/EtO mixture is disappearing. In sterilizers utilizing 100% EtO, the gas is supplied from small canisters containing only enough gas to sterilize a single load. Using the small canisters can reduce the fire hazards associated with EtO by allowing the bulk of the gas to be stored in a flammable gas cabinet in an area away from most employees. Due to the design of the sterilizers that use EtO cartridges, the cartridge fits into the sterilizer, eliminating tank connections, fittings, and piping, as well as the potential for leakage. Additionally, the small cartridges contain considerably less gas that could be released during a spill.

Residual EtO must be removed from the sterilized items to prevent the possibility of skin or respiratory reactions from contact (NIOSH 1989). The sterilized items are generally placed in an aerator for twelve hours, which allows the items to be heated slightly to increase the off-gassing and to vent the gas to the outside atmosphere. Transferring sterilized items to the aerator presents a greater risk of overexposure of employees to EtO. Units that are combination sterilizer/aerator units remove this exposure potential. Using combination units increases the time between sterilizer runs and may not be acceptable for larger facilities unless more than one combination unit is available.

Employee exposure to EtO can occur in a variety of areas (NIOSH 1989). When the EtO is supplied in large cylinders, potential exposure occurs during tank change-outs, from leakage in the fittings, and from lines supplying the gas. Pressurized sterilizers use a water-sealed vacuum pump to evacuate the chamber. The water must be discharged into the plumbing with an air gap to prevent back siphonage. This discharge area can result in greater employee exposure and should be equipped with a local exhaust ventilation "capture" box. To reduce employee exposure, the EtO sterilizer should be flush with the work area wall, allowing all fittings, tanks, and vacuum discharge lines to be in a separate room away from the normal work area. EtO exposure can be minimized during transfer of items from the sterilizer to aerator by slightly opening the sterilizer door less than two inches at the end of the cycle, and allowing the initially high levels to dissipate for fifteen minutes before the items are transferred. The area directly above the sterilizer door should be equipped with an exhaust ventilation slot hood to remove the excess gas. Items should be moved in a basket to allow the transfer to occur quickly and not further expose the staff by handling each item separately. EtO sterilizers that utilize cartridges operate under negative pressure, reducing the potential for leakage, but the discharge line is under pressure and is therefore a possible leakage source. In all cases, placing the sterilizers and aerators in a separate work room will help to reduce employee exposure. EtO sterilizers, aerators, and associated equipment/tank rooms should be under negative pressure. EtO sterilizer rooms should be equipped with alarms to alert operators if proper negative pressure is not maintained.

EtO is an air pollutant that is regulated by the EPA. Currently, the EPA does not require emissions controls for release of EtO for facilities that use less than one ton of EtO per year (EPA 2008a). To reduce exposure to EtO, the use of the sterilizer should be limited to only those items requiring sterilization that cannot withstand high-temperature steam sterilization or other safer methods of reprocessing. See Chapter 4 for additional information on EtO and examples of safer alternative methods.

Hazardous Drugs

A wide variety of drugs are administered in the healthcare setting for the treatment of infectious disease or chronic conditions such as cancer. Potential side effects for both patients receiving these drugs and employees who are exposed to them have been documented for many of these drugs (NIOSH 2004). In fact, even exposure to low concentrations of some drugs can be hazardous to workers who contact them. A special concern is *antineoplastic agents,* which are drugs with proven ability to destroy neoplasms (cancer cells). Substances that kill cancer cells will also kill or damage normal cells. NIOSH provides detailed guidance to assist in the recognition and control of many of these hazardous drugs (NIOSH 2004). Exposure to hazardous drugs may occur in the form of aerosols during preparation; during administration, when air bubbles are released from the syringe; through accidental injection; or from surface contamination of skin, during a spill or patient voiding cleanup. These exposures can cause symptoms such as skin irritation, reproductive system damage, and cancer. The three groups that should be monitored most closely for occupational exposure are pharmacy, nursing, and housekeeping personnel. Control of these exposures primarily includes the following:

- Use of class II Type B1 or B2 biological safety cabinets during the preparation of the agent to be certain that any air exhausted from the hood passes through a HEPA filter. (The difference between a B1 and B2 hood is that B2 is a total exhaust system.)
- Use of needle-less intravenous drug administration sets.
- Enforcement of procedures to prevent the release of aerosol or spills.
- Medical monitoring of exposed workers.

- Use of appropriate PPE to minimize inhalation or skin contact.
- Return expired or unused hazardous drugs to the pharmaceutical company for disposal.

Hydrogen Peroxide

The problems associated with EtO toxicity and destruction of ozone encouraged the development of other methods of achieving a higher level of disinfection and cold sterilization. Hydrogen peroxide plasma is an example of one of the alternatives to ethylene oxide. This product is primarily being used to disinfect endoscopes. It has extremely irritating properties and should be used in enclosed systems that are completely evacuated before opening. See Chapter 4 for other examples of alternatives.

Latex

The term *latex* refers to a product that is manufactured from a milky fluid derived from the rubber tree, *Hevea brasiliensis* (NIOSH 1997b). It is estimated that between 5–18% of healthcare workers are allergic to latex, and latex exposure is one of the leading causes of occupational asthma (Amr and Suk 2004). There are three types of reactions from exposure to latex containing materials: irritant contact dermatitis, allergic contact dermatitis, and latex allergy. *Irritant contact dermatitis* is not a true allergy but a skin reaction due to the irritating properties of wearing latex gloves or other products. *Allergic contact dermatitis* is a delayed hypersensitivity reaction due to contact with chemicals used in the manufacture of the latex product. The last, *latex allergy,* is an immediate hypersensitivity reaction due to exposure to certain proteins in the latex. These reactions can range from mild skin redness to anaphylactic shock and death.

While the risk associated with latex gloves has been well-documented, there are many products found throughout healthcare departments that contain latex. The control of latex allergy typically involves a combination of worker education and screening, substitution with latex-free products, worker relocation, and good housekeeping. (For more information on control of latex allergy, see Classroom Activity 1 at the end of this chapter.)

Lead-based Paint

Lead-based paint usage was banned for residential use in 1978 due to the health affects from exposure to lead, especially to children. Lead exposure affects the brain and nervous system, causing behavioral problems, reduced IQ and attention span, and hyperactivity. Lead also damages the kidneys, gastrointestinal tract, reproductive system, and blood-forming organs. Most recently, there has been concern that lead may be a carcinogen (NIH 2004). Lead-based paint is still available and used in marine applications, as steel primers, for structural steel coatings, and for roadway/parking lot stripping. Lead-based paint poses a hazard when it is no longer intact, and paint chips or paint dust can be ingested or inhaled. Special concerns arise from the potential for a small child to ingest lead paint chips or to "mouth" objects painted with lead-based paint. Occupational concerns regarding lead exposure from lead-based paint arise when the paint is removed (such as during heat striping), sanded or during spray application of paint containing lead. Workers disturbing lead-based paint, including sampling, must meet specific training requirements (EPA 2008). A myriad of occupational and environmental regulations including federal, state and local requirements apply to lead-based paint. Specific regulations regarding child-occupied facilities are aimed at protecting children from lead-based paint hazards in daycare centers, kindergarten classrooms, pre-schools and similar facilities.

Mercury

Mercury has a long history of use in healthcare settings (Monroe 2006). In dentistry, it is used in combination with silver to create an amalgam for tooth restorations. Elemental mercury (Hg) is used in many types of equipment in healthcare facilities. Some examples of these devices include: basic thermometers, sphygmomanometers (blood pressure measurement devices), batteries, Coulter counters in the laboratories, Maloney and Hurst bougies (esophageal dilators), Van Slyke apparatus (which measures carbon monoxide levels in the blood), Miller-Abbot and Cantor tubes (which are used to clear intestinal obstructions), and mercury switches. The dilators are commonly found in operating rooms, gastrointestinal labs, and endoscopy departments. Mercurochrome contains mercury, as do other chemical reagents used in the clinical laboratory department. Employee exposure to mercury is usually the result of an accidental spill or breakage, such as broken thermometers or sphygmomanometers. Since mercury is used in so many types of medical devices, biomedical technicians and engineers may have significant exposure to mercury during repair work (Goldberg et al. 1990). Maintenance staff may be exposed to mercury from improper disposal in the past. This can occur when mercury is improperly flushed down a sink drain or dental vacuum. The mercury settles out in the drain or vacuum trap and the maintenance staff is exposed when working on the line.

Elemental mercury is a metallic element that is liquid at room temperature. It is odorless and vaporizes easily. Elemental mercury also tracks and disperses easily, making spills difficult to clean up. Mercury exposure can occur from inhalation of mercury vapors, absorption through intact skin and ingestion. Exposure to mercury vapors results in absorption of approximately 75% of the inhaled dose. The toxicity of mercury depends on the amount absorbed and absorption depends on the chemical form of the mercury. When elemental mercury is ingested, approximately 0.01% is absorbed, compared to nearly 100% absorption of methyl mercury. The biological half-life for mercury is generally 60 days.

Short-term exposure to high levels of mercury can result in severe respiratory irritation, digestive disturbances, kidney failure and cardiovascular collapse. All are potentially fatal. Short-term exposure to mercury levels of 1 to 3 mg/m^3 for 2 to 5 hours can result in headaches, metallic taste in the mouth, chills, tremors, abdominal cramps, diarrhea, nausea, vomiting, tightness in the chest and difficulty breathing, fatigue, and lung irritation. These symptoms may have a delayed onset of a number of hours.

Long-term exposure to low levels of mercury can result in the classic *mad hatter syndrome*. Makers of felt hats who used mercury in the processing were first noticed to have developed this syndrome, which is characterized by emotional instability, irritability, excitability, and a tendency to weep. The exposure also causes tremors of the hands and feet, inflammation of the gums, excessive salivation, anorexia, and weight loss. Sensitization dermatitis is also possible from long-term, low-level exposure.

The best method to reduce the employee exposure hazard is to eliminate the use of mercury-containing equipment. However, total removal of all mercury-containing items may not be feasible, especially if the facility includes a dental clinic that uses mercury-based amalgam. It is essential that easily broken items, such as thermometers and sphygmomanometers, be replaced with non-mercury-containing equipment. Until all mercury is eliminated from the facility, staff should be trained on proper spill response. Specialized spill cleanup kits and equipment should be kept on hand for spill response. Large spills may require a hazardous materials response team. Direct-reading mercury vapor monitors can be used to evaluate the initial vapor concentration and completeness of a spill clean up. Employee exposure levels can also be determined through urinalysis and personnel air sampling.

A memorandum of understanding was signed between the EPA and the American Hospital Association (AHA) in 1998 to virtually eliminate mercury waste and reduce the use of mercury in all forms by one-third from health care by 2005 (EPA and AHA 1998). See "Additional Resources" at the end of this chapter for more information.

Methyl Methacrylate

Methyl methacrylate is a colorless, flammable liquid with a pungent, bitter odor. It is used to make dental or medical prosthetic devices and as an adhesive in certain surgical procedures such as total hip replacement. It is an eye and mucous membrane irritant and can cause allergic and irritant dermatitis. There is evidence that healthcare workers exposed to this chemical compound become sensitized and may develop allergic contact dermatitis and occupational asthma (Massachusetts Department of Public Health 1997). The OSHA PEL for this chemical is 100 ppm (OSHA 2006c). Fortunately, this compound has an extremely irritating odor, and this property increases the likelihood that mixing will be performed in a fume hood and that workers will take steps to minimize exposure. Because of these irritating and sensitizing properties, ACGIH recommends that 8-hour exposure be limited to 50 ppm with a STEL of 100 ppm (ACGIH 2008).

Radiology Film Developing Chemistry

Radiographic film processing is commonly conducted in medical imaging departments, operating rooms, and dental clinics. Digital radiology is making advancements and, when used, does not require film processing chemistry.

However, most radiographs are still recorded on film and require a processing system.

Automatic radiographic film processing equipment contains tanks for the developing solution, fixing solution, and rinse water. The developer contains chemicals that reduce the silver bromide ions on the film. The developer may also contain chemicals that control the speed of the processing, a preservative, and a hardening agent. Fixing chemicals include a neutralizer, an agent to remove undeveloped silver bromide ions, a preservative, and a hardening agent. Many of the compounds in the chemical solution may cause health effects; these include: acetic acid, diethylene glycol, glutaraldehyde, hydroquinone, potassium hydroxide, sodium sulfite, phenidone (1-phenyl-3-pyrazolidone), aluminum sulfate, and ammonium thiosulfate (Byrns et al. 2000). These compounds and others are mixed in various concentrations and combinations in the processing chemistry, depending on the manufacturer. The health effects of glutaraldehyde are discussed elsewhere in this chapter. *Hydroquinone* affects the eyes, respiratory system, skin and central nervous system. Hydroquinone is a known dermal sensitizer and may cause leukoderma, an absence of pigment in the skin. ACGIH also designates this chemical as an A3, which means it is a confirmed animal carcinogen (ACGIH 2008).

The potential for exposure to all of the processing chemicals may be increased because the process is heated, resulting in increased volatility. Mixing of the processor chemical components results in sulfur dioxide release from the decomposition of sulfite. Sulfur dioxide is a respiratory irritant, which may cause a persistent cough; chronic exposure may result in bronchospasm. Another byproduct of the breakdown of the processing chemistry is ammonia, a respiratory irritant. The potential health effects from synergism between the compounds in the processing chemicals themselves or from mixing with the byproducts are unknown. Additionally, the discharge from the processor is usually filtered to remove the silver ions from the waste stream prior to release into the sewer system. The silver recovery system can also be a source of chemical decomposition products and must be properly maintained. Automatic processors require cleaning on a regular, frequent basis. Employees must come into close contact with the chemicals while cleaning film cross-over rollers, processing racks, and chemistry tanks, as well as when mixing the processing solutions.

Reducing employee exposure to processing chemicals and reducing the potential for sensitization requires proper equipment installation, adequate ventilation, and appropriate work practices. The room where the processing equipment is located must meet the minimum AIA guidelines for ventilation (AIA 2006). The minimum rate should be ten air changes per hour, under negative pressure with all air exhausted directly to the outside atmosphere away from any supply inlets. Additional local exhaust ventilation directly above the processor may be needed to control emissions from the processing chemicals. The manufacturer's guidelines must be followed for proper processing equipment installation. An exhaust duct should be connected to the film dryer to discharge contaminates directly to the outside atmosphere. In some departments, the chemical replenishment tanks may be located outside the darkroom and would require local exhaust hood ventilation to control vapor release. An automixer can be used in place of the replenishment tanks, and this reduces employee exposure during the mixing of the solutions. Employees should always use appropriate PPE, including chemical-resistant gloves and aprons, when cleaning the processor rollers, racks or tanks or when mixing chemical solutions.

In reducing employee exposure, the focus should be on processing equipment and ventilation design and installation. Ambient and personal sampling may not be useful, due to the potential for sensitization to the processing chemistry. Sensitized individuals may react to exposure to chemicals at levels far below the current standards and recommended levels. Furthermore, negative air sampling results may give a false impression of safe conditions.

Solvents

Solvents and other volatile organic compounds are used by several departments in a hospital. Maintenance personnel use solvents for paint thinners and cleaners. In addition, clinical laboratories use xylene and other solvents in histopathology and other procedures. The purpose of *histopathology* is to receive, examine, section, and stain tissue for eventual microscopic examination by a medical pathologist.

Exposure routes for solvents can be dermal or respiratory, with inhalation the most significant risk. Inhalation risks are more common and can often permit higher amounts of the chemical to enter the body; however, a problem could occur if adequate attention is not given to skin protection. The toxicities differ depending on the compound. For example, the PEL for acetone is 1000 ppm as an eight- hour TWA, and for xylene, only 100 ppm (OSHA 2006c). Most are dermal or respiratory irritants, and some affect the central nervous system; a few, such as benzene and methylene chlorine, are even suspected of being carcinogens. In 2007, ACGIH lowered its TLV for toluene to 20 ppm as an eight-hour TWA because of concern that is was a reproductive toxin (ACGIH 2008).

The best policy in dealing with hazardous chemicals is to substitute a less hazardous product for a more hazardous product or change the process to reduce risk; for example, using water-based instead of oil-based paints. Other approaches include enclosure and use of general and local ventilation. Histopathology labs should have a minimum of six room air changes per hour to control exposures to solvents and other airborne hazards (AIA 2006). However, in histopathology, toxic chemicals, such as formaldehyde and xylene, are most effectively captured using a local exhaust (LEV) system, and failure to use an effective system could result in significant exposures (Edwards and Campbell 1984). The key to an effective LEV system is to have the hazard source as close to the hood opening as possible, ideally *within* a fume hood. It is also important to place LEV units in locations that avoid cross currents that can interfere with capture. The face velocity of these hoods should be checked annually to assure a minimum of 100 cfm/ft^2 (ACGIH 2007); some recommend velocities as high as 150 cfm/ft^2.

While less preferred than ventilation or other engineering controls, respiratory protection and protective apparel are sometimes the best or only method for protecting workers from exposure to solvents. For example, respirators may be necessary when engineering controls have not been implemented, are not economically feasible or when some operation must be done and controls are under repair. If respiratory protection is used, a full respiratory protection program is required, following OSHA (OSHA 2006d).

Waste Anesthetic Gases

Halogenated anesthetics, such as *enflurane, halothane, isoflurane, desflurane, methoxyflurane, and sevoflurane,* are used in the operating suites. *Nitrous oxide* is also used in the operating theater for anesthesia and in the dental clinic for conscious sedation (McGlothlin et al. 1994). It has also been used as a cryogenic agent. (See the section on cryogenics above.) Studies have shown an association between waste anesthetic gas exposure and the following: cancer; reproductive effects, such as spontaneous abortion and congenital anomalies; neurologic effects; renal damage; and liver disease (NIOSH 1994). Anesthetic agents can cause irritation, confusion, drowsiness, and a decrease in audio-visual performance.

Reducing employee exposure to waste anesthetic gases involves scavenging equipment that removes the excess gases from the room environment and exhausts them to the outside atmosphere (NIOSH 1994). A mask equipped with scavenging equipment means that it is connected to a local exhaust line, which is usually tied into the medical/surgical vacuum system or into a separate, parallel waste anesthetic gas disposal system. The National Fire Protection Association (NFPA) has established standards for waste anesthetic gas disposal systems (NFPA 1999). Equipment leakage needs to be reduced or eliminated through an on-going, proactive preventive maintenance program, such as annual leak tests of gaskets and connectors. Careless work practices can lead to waste anesthetic gas exposure through spillage during filling of a vaporizer, starting the flow of anesthetic before the delivery system is properly in place, and use of poorly fitting face masks and endotracheal tube cuffs. Maintaining nitrous oxide levels to the lowest possible level in the dental clinic requires properly maintained and utilized scavenging exhaust system and auxiliary room exhaust ventilation to pull any leaked nitrous oxide away from the staff members and out of the room air. Auxiliary local exhaust capture devices have recently come on the market that surround the head of the patient and can reduce nitrous oxide levels during dental surgery or ambulance transport.

In addition to concerns about inhalation of waste anesthetic gases, there may also be some patient safety issues (ISSA 1993). While the risk of complications following anesthesia are low, halothane and other anesthetics are detoxified in the liver, and some patients may develop mild to severe hepatotoxicity after receiving the agent. Another concern is that these agents may potentate the toxic effects of acetaminophen on the liver. It is, therefore, critical that patients be warned to avoid taking acetaminophen after exposure to anesthetics because of the potential for severe liver damage.

The vapors of anesthetic agents such as enflurane, halothane and isoflurane can be monitored with charcoal tubes. Nitrous oxide can be monitored with a direct-reading infrared analyzer or by passive dosimeters.

Records of all air samples should be kept, and results should be noted in the medical records of the corresponding workers.

Workers exposed to anesthetic gases should have complete medical histories on file. These should include family, genetic, and occupational histories and the outcomes of all pregnancies of female workers or of the wives of male workers. Baseline data should be obtained on the hepatic, renal, and hematopoietic systems. Exposed workers should also be monitored periodically for liver and kidney function (NIOSH 1988).

Biological Hazards

Healthcare workers may be exposed to a large number of potentially infectious agents; this is especially true of workers in the microbiology section of a clinical laboratory (Herwaldt 2001). Also, exposure to non-viable biological material may result in allergic or toxic reactions. For example, dead gram-negative bacteria may release endotoxins, a lipopolysaccharide component of the outer cell membrane, and certain molds have been shown to produce mycotoxins (penicillin is an example of one type of mycotoxin). The following is a brief discussion of some of the more common biological hazards. See Chapter 3 for more information on biological hazards.

Antibiotic-resistant Strains

Antibiotic resistance is a growing concern in health care. Methicillin-resistant *Staphylococcus aureus* (MRSA) and vancomycin-resistant enterococcus (VRE) are two examples of problem bacteria that are difficult to treat in the healthcare setting. While in most cases, these diseases are of greatest concern for nosocomial spread among patients, multi-drug-resistant tuberculosis (MDR-TB) can infect anyone, especially those with compromised immune systems.

The CDC is taking steps to address this serious problem through their *Campaign to Prevent Antimicrobial Resistance in Healthcare Settings* (CDC 2005a). The aim is to prevent antimicrobial resistance in healthcare settings by centering on four main strategies: prevent infection, diagnose and treat infection, use antimicrobials wisely, and prevent transmission. In most cases, control of antibiotic-resistant strains, such as MRSA and VRE, involves isolation of infected individuals and enforcing proper hand-washing among all healthcare providers. Control of airborne diseases, such as MDR-TB, requires the use of mechanical exhaust ventilation and PPE such as respirators.

Blood-borne Diseases

OSHA established the *Bloodborne Pathogens* Standard (OSHA 2006e) to eliminate or reduce the risk of occupational exposure to hepatitis B virus (HBV), hepatitis C virus (HCV), human immunodeficiency virus (HIV), and other biological agents transmitted through contact with blood. Table 2.1 shows the job title and number of confirmed or suspected work-related HIV infections in the U.S.

Table 2.1 Healthcare Personnel with Documented and Possible Occupationally Acquired AIDS/HIV Infection, by Occupation, 1981–2006 (CDC 2007)

Occupation	Documented	Possible
Nurse	24	35
Laboratory worker, clinical	16	17
Physician, nonsurgical	6	12
Laboratory technician, nonclinical	3	–
Housekeeper/maintenance worker	2	13
Technician, surgical	2	2
Embalmer/morgue technician	1	2
Health aide/attendant	1	15
Respiratory therapist	1	2
Technician, dialysis	1	3
Dental worker, including dentist	–	6
Emergency medical technician/paramedic	–	12
Physician, surgical	–	6
Other technician/therapist	–	9
Other healthcare occupation	–	6
Total	57	140

While there have been relatively few cases of work-related transmission to healthcare workers, this infectious agent causes a lot of fear because at present there is no cure. HIV is a retrovirus with a ribonucleic acid (RNA) core that replicates in two types of white blood cells (WBCs) called *macrophages* and in T4 lymphocytes. Figure 2.3 demonstrates the way cells are infected with HIV. When it binds to CD4 receptor sites on one of these WBCs, the virus releases RNA into the cell for replication.

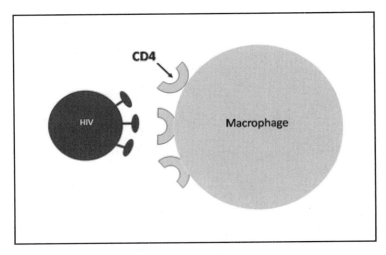

Figure 2.3 HIV infecting a macrophage.

It is important to recognize that HIV is not spread by casual contact, since only blood, semen, vaginal secretions, and breast milk have been implicated. Other important factors in transmission include the size of the inoculum, the susceptibility of the host, the virulence of the strain, and the stage of infection of the source case. The sero-conversion rate from an HIV-contaminated needle-stick is approximately 0.3%. In other words, the risk of becoming infected from a needlestick is about 3 in a 1000. The risk of acquiring an HIV infection from blood exposure to mucous membranes is even less, only about 0.1%.

The second major blood-borne disease pathogen of concern is HBV. HBV integrates into the host DNA; the result may be a carrier for life. Those who become chronic HBV carriers are at a high risk of developing liver cancer or other fatal liver diseases. The CDC estimates that chance of developing an HBV infection from a contaminated needlestick is between 37 and 62%. HBV infection may also result from skin contact with contaminated blood. This means that the risk of acquiring an HBV infection following exposure is much greater than that of HIV.

The third blood-borne disease of concern is HCV. The prevalence in healthcare workers is assumed to be the same as the general population (about 1–2%). A frightening aspect of HCV is that 75–85% of cases develop chronic disease, and 10–25% of these develop cirrhosis or liver cancer. Fortu-nately, the risk of contracting HCV is less than HBV (about 1.8% develop infections after a contaminated needlestick or percutaneous exposure).

The basic approach in controlling blood-borne disease is to use the OSHA *standard precautions;* this approach assumes that all patients are potentially infected with a blood-borne pathogen, and that steps may be taken to protect oneself from exposure to blood or other potentially infectious body fluids. Vac-cination is the single most important way of protecting oneself from HBV infec-tion. As of this writing, there are no effective vaccines for either HIV or HCV.

Overview of OSHA Standard

In order to prevent occupational transmission of blood-borne diseases, OSHA promulgated the *Bloodborne Pathogens Standard* (OSHA 2006e). Implementa-tion of an exposure control plan is described in detail in this standard. It has two aspects of assessing risk, one based on *job classification* and the other based on *task classification.*

To determine exposure based on *job classification*, each healthcare facility must identify those job classifications with routine exposure to blood, and those jobs with some exposure. For example, a surgeon would be assumed to have routine exposure, whereas a housekeeper could have some exposure. In a healthcare setting, relatively few employees, such as clerical staff, would be assumed to have no exposure.

The second approach to exposure determination is through *task classifica-tion.* All tasks presenting occupational exposure to blood, without regard to the use of PPE, must be listed; for example, a housekeeper collecting refuse or soiled laundry would be performing a hazardous task because of the poten-tial for contact with a contaminated needle or other sharp object. The OSHA standard describes the general methods of implementation of a blood exposure control plan to be through the use of *body substance isolation (BSI)* or *universal precautions (UP)*. These two approaches have been combined under an approach called *standard precautions*. The OSHA standards also describe some specific methods of implementation, using engineering controls or changes in work practices that are designed to reduce or prevent occupational exposure to blood. The standard states that, "Engineering or work practice controls shall be used to prevent occupational exposure. Where exposure remains, personal protective equipment shall be used " (OSHA 2006e).

Some examples of engineering controls or improved work practices include:

- Hand-washing facilities must accessible and the need for hand-washing must be stressed.
- Needles must not be bent or recapped except with a mechanical device or with a one-hand scoop technique prior to disposal. Also, needles used for surgical suturing should be of a blunt-tip type to reduce the chance of punctures.
- Sharps shall be placed in a puncture-proof, labeled container.
- Certain tasks, for example, mouth pipetting or handling contact lenses in the work area, are prohibited.
- Food or drink shall not be stored with potentially infectious materials.
- All procedures shall minimize splash or spraying of infectious materials.
- Specimen containers must be leak-proof and labeled with a biohazard warning before transport.
- Contaminated equipment must be disinfected or labeled as potentially contaminated before transport to biomedical service for repair.

Other requirements of the standard include:

- PPE that is appropriate to prevent contact with infectious materials under conditions of normal use must be provided at no cost to exposed employees.
- Any EPA hospital-grade disinfectant may be used to clean blood spills. A 1-to-10 dilution of household bleach and water is frequently used because it is fast-acting and inexpensive. A complete discussion of disinfection is provided in Chapter 4.

A key feature of the standard involves HBV vaccination. According to OSHA, vaccine must be offered within ten days of assignment to any employee with the potential for exposure, and employees who decline must sign a statement of waiver, called a *declination statement*. If vaccination is declined, the employee may accept later.

There also must be post-exposure evaluation and follow-up procedures. All exposure incidents must be investigated and documented. A confidential medical evaluation shall be provided immediately after exposure. With consent, a sample of the source's blood, as well as the employee's, shall be tested. The employee's sample is designed to provide a baseline for later comparison. The post-exposure procedure shall also include a healthcare professional's written opinion. This opinion describes the vaccination status of the affected employee and the need for additional evaluation and follow-up with an explanation of any suggested treatments. The employee must be informed of the results of all tests and provided with a copy of the results and the written opinion within fifteen workdays.

Another important part of the standard is the need for communication of hazards to employees. This communication includes the use of warning labels and training. Warning labels shall be affixed to:

- Containers of regulated medical waste. (OSHA specifically allows the use of red bags as substitutes for warning labels.)
- Refrigerators or freezers with potentially infectious materials.
- Containers used to ship specimens.

When communicating hazards to employees, training shall be provided at no cost and during work hours to at-risk employees. This training shall be given at the time of initial job assignment and repeated annually. Training shall also be modified to cover new tasks or procedures affecting exposure, and it shall be geared to the educational and language level of the employee. An important but frequently overlooked provision is that the training must be interactive and the trainer must be knowledgeable. This means that just showing a video once a year is not adequate.

As with all OSHA standards, there are recordkeeping requirements. All employee medical records dealing with blood exposure shall be kept for the duration of employment plus 30 years, and training records shall be maintained for 3 years.

There were some changes to the OSHA standard due to the *Needlestick Safety and Prevention Act* that took effect in April of 2001. All healthcare facilities must evaluate safer needle devices during the annual review of the exposure control plan, and employees must be included in choosing the safer devices. Also, OSHA requires the maintenance of a log of any injuries due to contaminated sharps.

Implementation of the blood-borne disease exposure control plan may be a shared responsibility of the infection control and IEHS programs.

Influenza, Measles, Mumps, Rubella, and Varicella

While these viruses are not generally considered to be *environmental* agents of disease, they present biological health hazards in many institutions. They are all included under the CDC, diseases for which immunization is strongly recommended, because there have been documented cases of nosocomial spread, and vaccination has been demonstrated to reduce the risk (CDC 1997). Also, the effects of diseases such as mumps on susceptible adults and rubella or varicella on susceptible pregnant workers have serious health consequences. In addition to vaccination, some strategies for managing clusters of vaccine-preventable infections in hospitals include:

- Isolation of infected patients;
- Appropriate use of ventilation to create negative pressure and move the air away from susceptible people;
- Testing employees to determine susceptibility;
- Furloughing exposed susceptible workers or screening these persons daily for symptoms; and
- Temporarily reassigning susceptible workers to non-patient-care areas.

Pandemic Influenza

Avian influenza (H5N1) is a likely candidate as the next pandemic because it is highly pathogenic and has crossed species and infected humans. *Pandemic influenza* is a special case because no one knows when the next major outbreak will occur, the general public will have little or no immunity to it, and it would spread across the world quickly (OSHA 2007b). It is anticipated that such a world-wide outbreak would overwhelm the healthcare systems and result in massive morbidity and mortality. A main concern for OSHA is that healthcare providers may become victims of the disease, thus exacerbating the problem (OSHA 2007b). One of the challenges in the control of pandemic influenza is that little is known regarding its mode of transmission. For example, it is unknown if the disease will be spread primarily via droplets or if airborne transmission is possible. The survivability of the virus on surfaces is also unknown. See Chapter 3 for more details on modes of transmission.

The role of the IEHS professional in combating pandemic influenza will be primarily in assisting in making the initial risk assessment, and by providing guidance for respiratory protection, disinfection, and barrier isolation, including the use of ventilation as a control. Preparing for the next pandemic influenza outbreak should be a critical component of the hospital's emergency preparedness program. See Chapter 7 for more information on emergency preparedness.

Legionella

Legionella pneumophila bacteria are ubiquitous in nature and can be found in 20–40% of freshwater sources (Fields 1997). According to the CDC, approximately 8,000–18,000 people are infected with *Legionella* disease each year, and 23% are nosocomial. It is likely that the true number is higher because it is estimated that only 2%–10% of cases are reported. The symptoms are fever, chills, and a cough; some patients also have muscle aches, headache, tiredness, and a loss of appetite. There are two types of disease associated with *Legionella* infection, a milder form called *Pontiac Fever*, and a more severe form called *Legionnaire's Disease*. The death rate from Legionnaire's Disease is about 10–15%; however, a substantially higher case fatality rate occurs during nosocomial outbreaks.

While people of any age may be infected with *Legionella*, the illness is most often associated with middle-aged and older persons, particularly those who smoke cigarettes. Also at increased risk are persons whose immune system is suppressed by diseases such as cancer, kidney failure requiring dialysis, diabetes, or AIDS. Those taking drugs that suppress the immune system are also at higher risk.

While *Legionella* is prevalent in water supplies, it is difficult to detect environmentally, and air sampling is of limited value. Even if the organism is detected, this does not prove causation. In the event of a nosocomial outbreak, sampling should target any sources with potential for aerosol release (CDC 2003). When sampling for *Legionella*, at least one liter of water should be collected in a sterile bottle that has be treated with 0.5ml of 0.1N *sodium thiosulfate* (to neutralize any residue chloride that could prevent bacterial growth) (Barbaree et al. 1987). Due to variations in laboratory methods, specific requirements for sample collection should be obtained from an accredited analyzing laboratory prior to sample collection. In addition, the laboratory should pre-treat the sample with acid or heat to prevent overgrowth by other species. The insides of faucet aerators and showerheads should be swabbed and tested as well. The CDC recommends that if samples must be transported, they should be placed in a cooler until they reach the laboratory. In order to prevent *Legionella* outbreaks, waterlines should be flushed periodically; no dead-end piping should be permitted. Hot water systems should be maintained at greater than or equal to 50°C (122°F) or less than 20°C (68°F) at the tap. Dental water lines operated between 20°C (68°F) and 37°C (98.6°F) can be of particular concern; these may need special disinfection. Other routine preventive maintenance activities include following standard operating procedures for cooling towers, evaporative condensers, and whirlpool spas, including general cleaning and treatment with a biocide. It is also important that respiratory therapy equipment never be rinsed in tap water. OSHA has a water treatment protocol in response to a Legionnaire's Disease outbreak (OSHA 1996d). They recommend using either a *chlorine shock treatment* at a minimum of 50 ppm or heat flushing the system at a minimum of 60°C. A good option is using chlorine dioxide solution because it is less corrosive than standard chlorination, and it is effective in destroying the biofilms in piping that harbor the *Legionella*.

Mold

Mold and mold spores are ubiquitous in outdoor and indoor environments, and exposure to low concentrations of mold generally does not result in adverse health effects. However, certain individuals may be sensitized to either viable or non-viable mold and develop allergic reactions. As the concentration of airborne mold increases, the likelihood of sensitization increases. Certain molds also produce mycotoxins, but their health effects are currently the subject of research. In the healthcare setting, exposure to even low concentrations of mold may result in infections to individuals with impaired immunity, such as patients with AIDS, uncontrolled diabetes, burns, or those taking immune suppressive drugs (OSHA 2003). Exposures to *Aspergillus* mold have resulted in infections and death in these highly susceptible individuals.

There are no federal regulations regarding safe or unsafe levels of mold exposure, so efforts should be directed towards prevention. Moisture control is critical to the prevention of mold growth on surfaces. Therefore, any major spills, plumbing leaks or rainwater infiltration into a building must be promptly corrected. Any patches of visible mold growth should be disinfected with a hospital-approved germicide. A special concern is to avoid the accumulation of mold inside the ventilation system. This issue is covered in more detail later in Chapter 8.

Severe Acute Respiratory Syndrome (SARS)

Severe acute respiratory syndrome (SARS) is a coronavirus that was first reported in Asia in February 2003, and caused severe respiratory illness in over two dozen countries before it was contained. More than 8,000 people were infected with SARS, and 774 died. In the U.S., only eight cases were documented and, in each case, the individuals had traveled to countries known to have SARS present (CDC 2005b). The infection is spread is by person-to-person contact and by inhaling respiratory droplets when an infected person coughs or sneezes. There is also evidence that the virus can be spread indirectly when a person touches a surface contaminated with infectious droplets and then touches his or her mucous membranes. It is not known at this time if the disease can be spread by other means. The symptoms are: high fever, headache, mild body aches, and respiratory distress. Some patients develop a cough; most eventually develop pneumonia (CDC 2004a).

Both the CDC and OSHA offer guidance in developing infection control programs to protect workers and other patients from exposure to SARS (CDC 2004b; OSHA 2003). In general, the process is similar to prevention of tuberculosis infection, which is described below. Key features include a system to rapidly identify and isolate persons suspected of being infected with SARS in rooms with proper negative exhaust ventilation. Individuals in contact with SARS cases must wear protective gowns, gloves, eye protection, and respirators equipped with N95 or better filters. While there were few cases of SARS, causing relatively little impact on the U.S. healthcare system, it clearly demonstrated the potential for a global spread of an emerging pathogen. It is unknown at this time if SARS or another exotic respiratory pathogen will reach the U.S. in the near future, but it is clear that programs must be in place to quickly identify the existence of such a hazard and to contain it.

Tuberculosis (TB)

Epidemiology and Pathogenesis of TB. The potential for transmission of pulmonary or laryngeal TB in healthcare institutions to patients and workers has long been recognized (CDC 2005c). Transmission of multi-drug-resistant TB in healthcare facilities and correctional institutions has been a special concern. A proactive infection control program that involves risk assessment and appropriate engineering, administrative, and personal protective controls are necessary to prevent the spread of this disease. The minimum elements of an infection control program are described in Chapter 3.

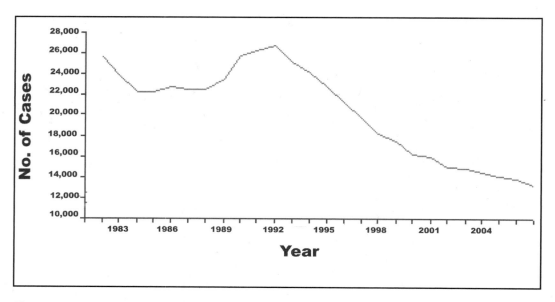

Figure 2.4 Reported TB Cases, United States, 1982–2007. (CDC 2008c)

The incidence of TB was steadily falling until 1985. Figure 2.4 shows that from 1985 to 1992, this trend was reversed. There were a number of reasons for this reversal. First, this TB increase coincided with the HIV epidemic, since infection with HIV significantly increased the susceptibility to TB infection. Second, TB is highly prevalent in many foreign countries, and recent immigrants may have imported TB to the U.S. Third, TB is a disease of poverty and poor living conditions. During this period, there was a rise in homelessness, and TB may have spread in homeless shelters or other areas where the homeless congregated. Also, these individuals were prone to discontinuing therapy, thus contributing to the development of multi-drug-resistant strains. Lastly, and probably most importantly, the earlier success in the control of TB meant that some public health programs were decreasing or eliminating their TB programs. As a result, when a new crisis arose, the public health community was ill prepared to deal with it.

The individuals most at risk of infection with TB include those living in inner cities and correctional facilities, homeless persons, American Indians and Alaskan Natives, the elderly, and anyone with a compromised immune system, especially HIV patients. Figure 2.5 shows that the incidence of TB varies by state. TB is spread when particles become airborne from coughing, sneezing, speaking, or spitting; the inhaled particles reach the alveoli, causing infection. This generally requires prolonged, close contact with an infected person; however, the causative agent *Mycobacterium tuberculosis* is capable of remaining viable for prolonged periods in the air. When the *M. tuberculosis* organism reaches the alveolus, the immune system usually limits the disease spread, and in some cases, the organism may remain dormant for years (CDC 2005c). This is referred to as *latent TB infection (LBTI)*. Persons with latent TB would be expected to have a positive skin test but would show no symptoms and would not be infectious.

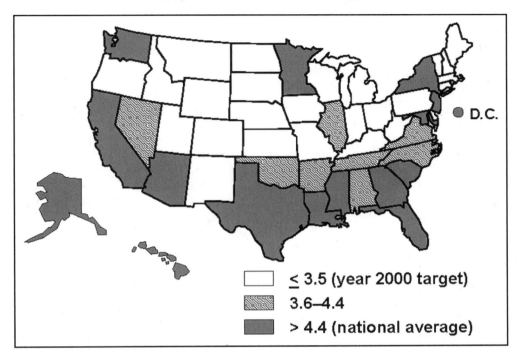

Figure 2.5 Rate of TB Cases by State/Area (per 100,000 people),
United States. (Source: CDC 2008c)

Approximately 5–10% of people infected with *M. tuberculosis* develop active TB
disease, and the risk of developing an active case is greatest during the first
two years after exposure. Individuals with weakened immune systems, especially
those who are infected with HIV, have nearly an 8% chance of developing
active disease each year they are infected. The signs and symptoms of active TB
disease are coughing for more than two weeks, fever, weight loss, night sweats,
blood tinged sputum, and loss of appetite.

The major risk factors for transmission of *M. tuberculosis* within a hospital
are the prevalence of TB in the community, the types of patients that are
served (for example, a clinic that provides treatment for HIV infected patients
would be at a greater risk for TB spread), the healthcare worker's occupation
(for example, respiratory therapists or triage personnel), whether healthcare
workers are infected with HIV or have weakened immune systems, the presence of high-risk procedures (described below), and the adequacy of TB controls (also described below).

Identification and Control of TB. OSHA provides uniform inspection procedures and guidelines for compliance safety and health officers to be followed
when conducting inspections and issuing citations under Section 5(a)(1) of the
OSH Act and pertinent standards for employees who are occupationally
exposed to tuberculosis (OSHA 1996a).

Requirements are established for the development of protocols for the
early identification of tuberculosis cases, medical surveillance of employees,

worker training, engineering controls, and PPE requirements (OSHA 1996a). The determination of an unsafe or unhealthful environment is based on whether a facility meets the intent of the CDC (CDC 2005c).

The general recommendations to prevent the spread of TB follow OSHA's *hierarchy of controls* (discussed in Chapter 1), with an important exception. The most effective means of controlling TB is early identification, followed by isolation and effective treatment (CDC 2005c). A written *exposure control plan* (ECP) describes all aspects of the program, including a formal risk assessment that must be in place in each facility. This risk assessment should be implemented and revised annually for the entire facility. This assessment documents the number of TB cases seen in the last five years, lists any changes in the prevalence of TB in the community, identifies the status of the TB surveillance and control programs, and highlights areas that need special attention. The risk assessment should list and describe the location of any high-risk procedures that are preformed in the facility. Examples of high-risk procedures include sputum induction, administration of respiratory therapy treatments of *pentamidine* or any other cough-inducing procedure, such as bronchoscopy and suctioning. Additional critical information for the risk assessment is the number of TB patients seen and the presence of any employee skin test conversions during the prior year. Based on this risk assessment, CDC defines a facility's risk category for TB as:

- **Potential ongoing transmission:** This describes a temporary situation with evidence of person-to-person transmission of TB. This is the most serious risk category.
- **Medium risk:** A larger healthcare facility (greater than 200 beds) is defined as having a medium risk if six or more TB inpatients were seen in the preceding year. Smaller facilities (200 beds or less) are defined as medium risk if three or more TB inpatients were seen in the previous year. In outpatient settings, outreach or home-based healthcare settings, three or more TB patient contacts are considered to be medium risk.
- **Low risk:** Large facilities are classified as low risk if they had less than six TB inpatients in the previous year, and smaller facilities are low risk if they had less than three TB inpatients in the previous year. Outpatient operations are low risk if they had less than three TB patients in the previous year (CDC 2005c).

In order to identify potential TB cases, administrative procedures must be in place to assure that healthcare workers know TB signs and symptoms. This is especially important for workers in triage, reception, emergency services, and the outpatient department. In addition, there must be rapid access to TB testing, for example the ability to do a smear for the microscopic examination of acid fast bacilli (a special staining technique for TB), microbiological culturing for TB, and drug sensitivity.

The other important feature of early detection is the TB testing program. All staff with the potential for exposure to TB must be tested to determine their TB status. The frequency of testing depends on the risk category, as described above. The CDC recommends testing every eight to ten weeks in high-risk facilities with the potential for ongoing transmission. The minimum frequency is baseline testing of exposed persons and repeat testing after known exposures. Currently, the most frequently used test is based on a subcutaneous injection of purified protein derivative (PPD). A positive result is based on measuring the amount of induration around the injection site after 48–72 hours. There is a certain amount of subjectivity in this test because individuals with HIV or other conditions that affect the cellular immune system will have a much reduced skin reaction. In 2001, a test called *QuantiFERON-TB test (QFT)* was approved by the FDA; this is a whole-blood test for diagnosing latent TB infection that involves an antigen/antibody reaction (FDA 2001); this test was replaced in 2005 with the *QuantiFERON-TB Gold test (QFT-G)* (CDC DTBE 2007). The advantage of these tests is the elimination of subjectivity in interpreting the results. Some of the disadvantages are that the blood must be analyzed within twelve hours, and there are a limited number of laboratories with the capability of running the test. Whichever test is used, the results must be recorded in the employee's medical file.

The prevention of transmission of TB within a healthcare facility requires certain key design and operational features. First, there must be at least one isolation room in each inpatient facility; more may be required, based on the results of the facility's risk assessment. Isolation anterooms are not required but may increase effectiveness by creating a negative pressure airlock. There may also be a need for a special isolation room in the outpatient department. This isolation room could be used to perform high-risk procedures, such as collecting sputum. Alternatively, a special booth equipped with local exhaust may be used, especially when administering aerosolized treatments that induce coughing. There should also be separate waiting areas to segregate individuals suspected of having respiratory infections from other patients.

Rooms that are used for patients suspected of respiratory infections should be under negative pressure isolation. This simply means that more air is exhausted to the outside atmosphere than is supplied to the room and that the air direction is away from staff entering the room. In addition, all the air in these rooms should be changed at a minimum air exchange rate per hour (ACH). According to the CDC, existing isolation rooms must provide at least six ACH; in new construction, the minimum rate is twelve ACH. Special local exhaust booths used for sputum induction or aerosol treatments should have at least twenty ACH.

Operational features that are designed to reduce the transmission of TB include the use of surgical masks on suspected TB cases and encouraging the use of tissues by patients to control the release of aerosols from coughing or sneezing. Some other administrative controls include proper scheduling of appointments and procedures; for example, scheduling the well-baby clinic at different times than a chest clinic to avoid mixing of sick and well patients. Other examples include keeping TB patients in the isolation room with the doors closed, and keeping the number of visitors to a minimum.

Respirators should be used to protect workers from occupational exposure to TB in high-risk situations. While the OSHA Standard, *Respiratory Protection for TB*, was rescinded on December 31, 2003, there are still strict standards covering the selection and use of respirators found in the OSHA *Respiratory Protection* Standard (EPA 2006e). In addition, NIOSH has a standard that specifies the categories of non-powered, air-purifying respirators (CDC 2005b). The three categories are:

- Class 100: 99.97% efficiency (HEPA);
- Class 99: 99% efficiency; and
- Class 95: 95% efficiency

NIOSH recommends that staff members with close contact with TB patients, such as those conducting sputum inductions, utilize a respirator with at least a Class 95 designation. OSHA also requires that any new TB conversions among workers be listed on the OSHA Log and that information regarding the conversion must be documented in the employee's medical file.

There are some special concerns regarding TB patient transport. Active cases should never be transported on common carriers, and only patients on effective therapy should be transported. Staff accompanying TB patients must use an approved respirator.

Physical and Ergonomic Factors

There are a variety of physical or ergonomic hazards in health care. Basic safety issues such as slips, trips, falls, fires, explosions, and electrical hazards are covered in Chapter 5. This section covers hazards associated with poor ergonomics and exposure to ionizing radiation, non-ionizing radiation, noise, and heat.

Ergonomics

Work-related musculoskeletal disorders (MSDs) account for one-third of all occupational injuries and illnesses reported to the Bureau of Labor Statistics (BLS) by employers each year (BLS 2006). Disorders such as carpal tunnel syndrome and low back pain constitute the largest ergonomic problem affecting these healthcare workers. While a proposed OSHA standard on ergonomics has been withdrawn, MSDs are typically the number one workers' compensation problem in healthcare facilities, and the costs of this problem cannot be ignored.

Low Back Pain (LBP). The first step in addressing the problem of MSDs is to identify who is at risk. NIOSH compiled evidence of risk factors for MSDs such as low back pain (LBP) (NIOSH 1997a). There was strong evidence linking heavy physical work and awkward postures with LBP, as well as individual factors, such as age and prior history of back injury, psychological factors, such as workplace stress, and organizational factors, such as degree of job control (Burdorf et al. 1997). The problem has been determining the relative importance of each of these risk factors in causing LBP, which is complicated due to the overlapping of these factors. For example, a job that is physically strenuous may also be psychologically stressful, so it is difficult to untangle the effects of each (Byrns et al. 2002).

While the prevalence of LBP in workers increases with age, the risk of newly developing LBP is greatest with younger, least experienced worker (Byrns et al. 2004; Bigos et al. 1986). While it is known that a person's spinal discs degrade with age, a worker's age is highly correlated with years of experience (Hoaglund and Byl 1997; Byrns et al. 2002). Is the increase in prevalence due to individual factors (i.e., a degraded spine), or physical factors (i.e., accumulative exposure to strenuous activity)? A study by Byrns and others found a strong association between cumulative years of exposure and LBP, whereas an individual's age did not appear to play a role (Byrns et al. 2004). This is an important question because the effects of cumulative physical strain can be prevented, whereas age effects cannot. In the case of the increased incidence of LBP in younger, less experienced workers, the cause is probably due to a lack of knowledge about proper procedures; this also should be preventable. Whatever the cause, it is critical that the initial onset of LBP be prevented because the number one risk factor for future LBP is a history of LBP, so this becomes a recurrent, debilitating problem (van Poppel et al. 1998).

Researchers have found that the failure to use mechanical patient lifts contributes to the prevalence of LBP in nursing personnel (Engkvist et al. 2000; Owen and Garg 1999; Lynch and Freund 2000). A particularly serious concern is manually lifting of morbidly obese or bariatric patients. A bariatric patient has a body mass index of 40 or greater. Researchers found that hospital nurses who reported that they did not use a mechanical lift because the patient's weight exceeded the rated capacity of the lift were 3.5 times more likely to have severe LBP than those who did not answer in this manner (Byrns et al. 2004). Another extremely hazardous procedure is lifting a fallen person from the floor. In a study of lifting patterns in nursing homes, workers who manually lifted residents who had fallen were 3.8 times more likely to have severe LBP than those who routinely use mechanical lifts for this procedure (Byrns et al. 2007).

According to NIOSH, there is no evidence that worker training in proper lifting or the use of back belts is effective in preventing this problem (NIOSH 1997a). In our initial research, more frequent exercise appeared to prevent LBP (Byrns et al. 2004). Using a longitudinal design, we were able to show that those in pain are less likely to exercise than those who are pain free (Byrns et al. 2005). In contrast to the conclusions that emerged from the first cross-sectional study, these findings did not support a protective relationship between frequent exercise and prevention of LBP. This conclusion is consistent with research conducted by de Looze and others, who found that having greater muscle strength was not protective against developing LBP (de Looze et al. 1998). This is not surprising, given that manual patient lifting exceeds safe manual lifting criteria established by NIOSH (Steinbrecher 1994).

The most effective method of preventing MSDs is the use of automation where possible; for example, using forklifts to move materials and mechanical

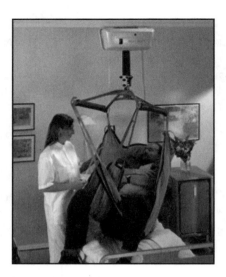

Figure 2.6 ARJO Maxi Sky 1000 ceiling-mounted, patient-lifting device. (Used with permission from ARJO)

lifting devices to move patients. There are a number of friction-reducing, lateral-transfer aids, which may be effective in reducing muscle strain from moving patients; for example a device that uses jets of air. Some healthcare facilities have installed ceiling-mounted lifts in all adult patient rooms. Figure 2.6 shows one of these devices that operate on tracks, allowing the patient to be moved from the bed on to a chair, stretcher, or into the toilet room. The cost of implementing this type of system would be much less during the construction phase for new facilities or during major remodeling projects. However, savings from workers' compensation or the need to hire and train replacement workers may make these devices cost-effective even for existing facilities.

However, simply providing mechanical lifting equipment may not be enough. In an earlier study, we found that only about 10–11% of registered nurses (RNs) reported using mechanical lifts on a daily basis. In Table 2.2, we compared manual lifting patterns at two nursing homes and found that the facility with a rigorously enforced "no-lift" policy (site #2) did significantly less manual lifting than at a facility where they had a limited, voluntary lifting policy (site #1) (Byrns et al. 2007). In this same study, it was also found that nursing personnel who reported that they did not use a mechanical lift had 2.8 times (1.0–7.6 95% CI, p = 0.041) more LBP than those who routinely used the lifts.

The results in Table 2.2 demonstrate the need for a written policy that is rigorously enforced to promote the use of mechanical lifts and discourage manual lifting of patients or nursing home residents.

Table 2.2 Comparison of Lifting Patterns at Two Nursing Homes

Lifts & Transfers at Site #1 Compared to Site #2	Odds Ratio	95% C.I.	p-Value
Manually lifted residents	2.9	1.2–7.0	0.017
Manual lift of fallen resident (ambulatory)	10.3	4.1–25.6	<0.001
Manual lift of fallen resident (non ambulatory)	4.7	1.9–11.9	0.001
Transfer from bed to stretcher	2.9	1.2–7.2	0.018
Transfer from bed to toilet	2.4	1.1–5.3	0.035

A final complication in the study of LBP is that there is evidence that worker psychological stress contributes to musculoskeletal pain (Bigos et al. 1991; Bongers et al. 1993; Hoogendoorn et al. 2001; Houtman et al. 1994). Psychological stress may affect LBP due to increased muscle tension, guarded movements, or disuse syndrome (Waddell 1998). Researchers have found that jobs that are high in physical and psychological demand, low in the control of job performance, and low in the availability of social support tend to be more stressful than jobs with the opposite characteristics (Karasek et al. 1998). Karasek's *Job Content Questionnaire* is a useful way of measuring each of these potential job stressors (Karasek 1985).

The Veteran's Administration Patient Safety Center provides detailed guidance for those wishing to establish a policy that restricts manual lifting of patients (VA 2003).

Carpal Tunnel Syndrome. In *carpal tunnel syndrome*, in which pain is caused by the compression and entrapment of the medial nerve in the wrist, there are certain known risk factors that must be addressed. According to NIOSH, women are three times more likely to suffer this disorder because the tunnel itself is smaller than in men. The risk is also greater in those individuals doing assembly work; for example, central services technicians who assemble surgical packs. In the case of workers involved with data entry, such as patient registration and medical records, carpal tunnel syndrome may be a concern; however, other problems, such as eyestrain and neck pain, may also result from poor workstation design (NIOSH 1999b). Prevention of these problems involves attention to environmental factors, such as the positioning of the monitor and mouse, the type and adjustment of the chair, and proper lighting to eliminate glare. In addition, the need for rest breaks should be emphasized.

Heat. Heat stress can be a life-threatening condition (AIHA 2003). Fortunately, there are few areas in health care that have the potential of causing heat stress. The location most likely to have higher thermal exposures is the hospital laundry (OSHA 2002). In most cases, excessive heat should be controlled through the combination of local exhaust ventilation and general dilution ventilation.

Ionizing Radiation. Ionizing radiation has important uses in the healthcare setting, both for diagnosing and treating medical conditions; it may also be used in the form of electromagnetic radiation or a radioisotope. Radiation is all around us: in soil and rock, for example, uranium, thorium, radon, radioactive potassium (K^{40}), as well as in high-energy photons and charged particles from cosmic sources. Radiation may also be artificially produced in nuclear power reactors and accelerators. It is important to remember that, in medicine, artificially produced radiation is considered a *risk-benefit*, which means that while there are known risks associated with exposure to radiation, and the overall benefit in diagnosing or treating an illness or injury exceeds the potential harm.

To be classified as *ionizing*, radiation must contain enough energy to ionize matter (at least 12 eV of energy). Radioactive elements spontaneously change to a lower energy state and emit radiation (NIOSH 1988). Some examples of ionizing radiation particles are: alpha, which originate from the disintegration of unstable nuclei and contain two protons and two neutrons; beta, which are also ejected from nuclei and have a negative charge like electrons; protons; and neutrons. *Alpha* particles cause little external damage, but if inhaled or ingested, can cause considerable harm. *Beta* particle emissions have relatively low penetration but may have sufficient energy to cause skin or eye injury. *Proton* or *neutron* emission is generally associated with nuclear accelerators and should not be a concern in healthcare facilities.

Two types of electromagnetic radiation are *gamma* or *x-rays*, which are photons of energy that may be highly penetrating. *X-radiation* is created when a stream of high-speed electrons are directed at a metal target (usually a hard substance like tungsten). When the electrons slow down or strike orbiting electrons of the target material, a photon of energy is produced. *Gamma radiation* is similar to x-radiation except the source of the photon is the nucleus of an unstable radioisotope. The amount of penetration of x-rays or gamma rays depends on the photon's energy level.

There are a number of units of measure used in radiation. The measure of radioactivity is either the *Curie* ($3.7 * 10^{10}$ decays per sec.) or the *becquerel* (1 decay per sec.). The unit used in measuring x-rays and gamma rays exposure is a *Roentgen* (0.000258 coulomb/kilogram). Radiation dose is measured in *radiation absorbed dose* (rad) or *Grays* (1 Gray = 100 rads). Since some forms of radiation cause more damage internally than externally, a special unit called *radiation equivalent man* (rem) is used as a measure of the biological effect from a dose of radiation to body tissue. The International System of Units' (SI) equivalent of rem is the *Sievert* (1 Sievert = 100 rem). Examples of this adjustment for biological effect are:

- ▪ 1 rad of X-, gamma, or high energy beta = 1 rem
- ▪ 0.1 rad of neutrons or high energy protons = 1 rem
- ▪ 0.05 rad of alpha = 1 rem

One of the most important theories in radiation protection is the *non-threshold effect*, shown in figure 2.7.

A *threshold theory* states that some amount of radiation dose will produce no biological effect because of the body's ability to repair damage. According to the *non-threshold theory*, any amount of radiation will produce an effect; the

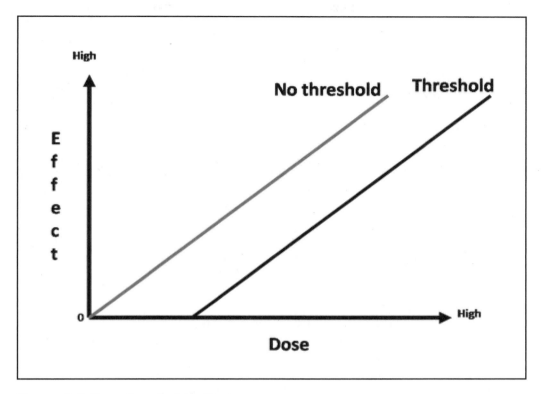

Figure 2.7 Non-threshold effect.

greater the dose, the greater the effect. Most authorities follow the non-threshold theory and recommend that all exposures to radiation be kept as low as reasonably achievable (ALARA).

The amount of biological effect is due in large part to the amount of linear energy transfer (LET) produced by the specific kind of ionizing radiation. Radiation with high LET, such as alpha particles, will release all of its energy in a contact with tissue, whereas radiation with low LET, such as a gamma rays, releases little of its energy as it passes through tissue. Radiation damage can cause either acute or chronic effects. Acute or somatic effects are the result of direct tissue damage from large single dose. For example, an exposure of 100 rem may produce nausea, weakness and a temporary decrease in red blood cells. Higher levels may be fatal. Chronic effects are the result of low-level, long-term exposure, creating damage to the DNA, as well as having genetic effects (AIHA 2003). Chronic effects, such as cancer, may be minimized by following the concept of keeping exposures ALARA.

Reduced exposures to patients can be achieved by having properly trained radiological technologists, using properly calibrated and maintained equipment, and implementing a good quality control program that minimizes the need to repeat radiological procedures. The OSHA occupational standard for ionizing radiation is a maximum, per calendar quarter, of 1.25 rem to: the whole body, head and trunk; active blood-forming organs; lens of eyes; or gonads (OSHA 1996b). Exposure to employees can likewise be reduced by developing and implementing appropriate standard operating procedures; installing structural shielding; and using PPE, such as leaded aprons and gloves.

One important radiation-monitoring instrument is a *dosimeter*, such as a film badge, thermo-luminescence detector (TLD), or a pocket dosimeter. These provide an integrated exposure. *Ionization meters* measure the ionization of air caused by gamma and x-rays, but some may pick up ionization caused alpha and beta particles. *Geiger-Mueller (G-M) counters* are very sensitive to low levels of beta, gamma, and x-rays and are used for screening surveys. For example, clothing may be scanned before someone is allowed to leave a controlled area where radioisotopes are used. *Scintillation counters* measure light flashes cause by interaction between radiation and crystals. These instruments are very sensitive and may even measure alpha emissions.

There is increased concern over the hazards associated with treating victims of a radiation attack in the emergency room. The Joint Commission has standards that address decontamination of patients with either chemical or radioactive contaminants (JCAHO 2009). This issue is covered in greater detail later in Chapter 7. The other issue is the potential hazard of releasing patients after therapy with radionuclides. These patients have been treated for cancer or other serious conditions and may still be emitting radiation after leaving the hospital. The risk will depend on the type of radionuclide and the dose administered to the patient (radiation for therapy would be riskier than diagnostic procedures). The risk also depends on whether or not there are infants or small children at the patient's home. Fortunately, most radiation used in medicine has a short half-life. For example Iodine-131 has a half-life of only eight days. In this case, the patient may be no longer emitting hazardous levels of radiation after a period of time.

Noise. Sound is generated by a vibrating surface or turbulent fluid flow that forms high and low pressure areas. Sound is transmitted via a wave that has properties of frequency, wavelength and velocity. The frequency of the wave is measured in Hertz (cycles per second). The wavelength of the sound can affect the effectiveness of shielding to reduce sound levels. The velocity of the sound wave is determined by the medium in which it is being transmitted. All sound waves travel the same speed in air, but are faster in water, wood and other denser media.

An extremely large range of sound pressures can be perceived by the human ear. This range of pressures is too unwieldy to use as the actual scale of measurement. As a result, sound pressure is measured in a relative scale know as a *bel.* The usual unit for measuring sound power levels is the *decibel,* a logarithmic scale. Sound level meters generally have two scales. The dBA scale discriminates against very low frequencies to better approximate the insensitivity of human hearing for these types of sounds. The C scale is used in high intensity noise levels, and it does not discriminate against low frequency noise. Older sound level meters may also have a B scale that was intended to be used on medium level sounds.

Hearing loss can occur for a number of reasons, including a blockage of the auditory canal, trauma, diseases, drug-induced damage, natural aging, and exposure to high sound levels (Berger et al. 2000). *Presbycusis,* or the hearing loss that occurs from aging, is normal and generally affects the higher frequency sounds. Younger people can hear sounds in the range of 20 to 20,000 Hertz (Hz), whereas people over 60 may have difficulty hearing sounds above 12,000 Hz. Hearing loss in the frequency range for human speech of 300 to 4000 Hz is considered to be the most debilitating.

Noise-induced hearing loss can be an insidious problem that occurs from damage to the hairs in the Organ of Corti in the inner ear. Hearing loss is generally the result of chronic exposure to noise. This is a problem because noise damage may cause no noticeable pain, and the hearing loss is permanent. Temporary hearing loss can often precedes permanent loss. Temporary threshold shift in the level of hearing can result from exposure to brief, but high, sound levels. Usually the shift in the level of hearing gradually returns to normal after a rest period of 14 to 16 hours. Exposure to hazardous levels of occupational noise also results in a temporary threshold shift, usually in the higher frequency range of 4000 Hz and above. The long-term effect of repeated and extended noise exposure is permanent hearing loss. The process of developing permanent hearing loss may be accelerated if the noise exposure is extremely intense or if the recovery from the temporary threshold shift is not complete before the next noise exposure begins.

A hearing conservation program is mandated for noise exposures that exceed 85 dBA as an eight-hour TWA (OSHA 2006f). The ACGIH has established 85 dBA as the eight-hour TLV for noise exposure with a 3 dBA noise doubling standard (ACGIH 2008). This is more restrictive than the OSHA standard of 90 dBA as the eight-hour PEL with a 5 dbA noise doubling (OSHA 2006f). Both standards state that no noise exposure should exceed 140 dB. However, even the ACGIH guidelines will not protect all exposed workers from hearing loss. OSHA's hearing conservation program includes five areas: exposure monitoring, audiometric testing, hearing protection, employee training and recordkeeping. Locations that are suspected of high noise levels should be monitored with sound level meters to accurately determine exposure levels and ways to address noise level control. OSHA requires that sound level meters be used in the SLOW response setting (Berger et al. 2000), and all noise in the 80 to 130 dBA ranges must be measured. Hand-held sound level meters can be used to pinpoint noisy locations and specific equipment. However, due to the variation in the duties of most healthcare workers, accurate assessment of the worker's noise exposure requires measurement with a noise dosimeter that is worn by the employee throughout the workday. Sound level meters and dosimeters use similar technology, and both must be calibrated per the manufacturer's requirements. The calibration should be checked before and after use with a calibration check device; however, these devices are not a substitute for proper calibration. Employees are entitled to observe the monitoring, and receive a copy of their dosimetry results. A third device, called an *octave band analyzer (OBA),* is sometimes used to determine the predominant frequencies of the noise source. Knowing the noise's frequency can be helpful in determining the best control strategy. The OBA must be calibrated in a manner similar to the other noise-monitoring devices.

Audiometric testing should include a baseline and annual audiograms. Baseline audiograms ideally should be obtained before the employee begins work in the high noise level area and after the employee has had a rest period from occupational and non-occupational noise to allow any temporary threshold shifts to return to normal. The audiometric program must be monitored by a healthcare professional, and audiograms conducted by trained technicians using equipment that meets OSHA requirements (OSHA 2006f). Hearing protection must be offered to all employees exposed to noise levels greater than 85 dBA as an eight-hour TWA. NIOSH recommends that all employees exposed to noise levels of 85 dBA or above be provided hearing protection, regardless of the duration of the noise exposure. Employees must have a variety of hearing protection devices to choose from and be provided training on the proper use and care of the device. The employer must supervise the initial fitting of the hearing protection device and assure their correct usage. Simply buying a box of ear plugs and putting them in the maintenance shop does not constitute a hearing protection program. Employee training and motivation is critical for the hearing conservation program to be effective. Employees need to be properly motivated to actively participate in the program. Employee training should include information on the effects of noise; the purpose, pros and cons, selection and effectiveness of various hearing protective devices; the audiometric testing procedures and the purpose of the audiometric program. A copy of all sound level surveys and audiometric testing must be kept in the employee's employee health file.

High occupational noise levels in the healthcare setting may be found in the maintenance department. Some notably noisy areas include the boiler room, mechanical room, emergency generator during operation, carpentry shop and heating, ventilation and air-conditioning (HVAC) system compressors and fans. One of the potentially noisiest hazards involves emergency transport of patients and helicopter pads. High noise levels have also been measured when employees use grounds-keeping equipment, such as lawn mowers, weed-eaters, and leaf-blowers. Medical transcribers wear headphones that can produce peak noise exposures up to 110 dB. This level of exposure can result in a violation of the OSHA PEL after fifteen minutes of exposure. Sterile Processing Department employees working with compressed air in the decontamination area to dry medical instruments can often experience high peak noise levels (100 dB), although levels seldom exceed OSHA exposure limits over the course of the workday. Irritating and annoying noise levels can often be identified in the dental and dietary areas, although the levels are usually not hazardous. Engineering and administrative controls should always be implemented first before considering the use of hearing protectors. If hearing protection is necessary to reduce noise exposures, a proactive program with employee and supervisory input is required to insure hearing protection is used properly. Complete in-depth coverage of all elements of noise measurement, evaluation and hearing conservation programs is beyond the scope of this book. Many good resources are available on this topic from NIOSH, AIHA and OSHA (Berger et al. 2000; NIOSH 2007a; OSHA 1981).

Non-ionizing radiation. *Non-ionizing radiation (NIR)* is increasingly used in the healthcare industry for a variety of diagnostic and therapeutic procedures; some uses are direct, such as ultrasonography; others are indirect, such as microwave tissue processing. It is important to remember that NIR is a form of electromagnetic (EMF) radiation, which means that there is an electrical charge and a magnetic field moving perpendicularly to it (AIHA 2003). For longer wavelength NIR, the electrical and magnetic fields can be measured separately. These fields cannot be distinguished in short wavelength NIR. Another important issue in electromagnetic radiation is its energy level. EMF with energy levels greater than 12 eV is considered to be *ionizing radiation,* which is capable of ionizing other matter. While we generally consider ultraviolet (UV) radiation to be NIR, a portion of the UV band produces energies above 12 eV and is considered to be ionizing radiation.

UV-A has been used extensively to cure resin-based materials in industrial and dental procedures. Dental personnel are shielded from the emissions; however, the safety of irradiating the oral mucosa is not fully known. Both UV-A and B have been used in phototherapy on patients with psoriasis or other skin conditions. While these treatments have been effective, these bands of UV (particularly UV-B) have been linked with induction of skin cancer. The C-band of UV has a long history of use in germicidal lamps in microbiological laboratory hoods and in tuberculosis isolation rooms. Unlike UV-A and B, the risk of UV-C appears to be primarily related to photoketatoconjunctivitis (snow blindness) and photodermatitis (skin reddening) (First et al. 2005). The use of UV-C should be closely monitored to assure that the intensities of the lamp are sufficient to be germicidal and that employees are protected from the optical effects of UV-C. Maintenance and housekeeping personnel involved in replacing and dusting these lamps must be cautioned about the need for eye protection when the lamps are on. This requires the purchase of safety goggles equipped with lenses of the correct optical density to block the UV rays. A final issue associated with optical NIR is the potential for suppression of melatonin (MLT) by exposure to light at night (LAN). Some have suggested that this may be a factor in increased rates in breast cancer (Pauley 2004). This is an extremely complex and controversial issue that is beyond the scope of this book.

Another major concern is the effects of NIR on patients who have pacemakers or metal implants. The strength of the magnetic resonance imaging (MRI) emissions is such that there is the potential for disruption of the pacemaker signal, and metal implants may be dislodged. Because of the potential danger, facilities that use MRI must have ferrous iron policies. This means that all individuals must be screened for the presence of metal objects or even credit cards (since the MRI will demagnetize them) before entering the procedure room. Recently, there have been advances in the development of new bioabsorbable interference materials that will not be affected by MRI emissions. Another unintended consequence of NIR use is cell phone interference with medical devices. There has been concern that cell phone transmissions may interfere with the function of critical medical equipment, such as mechanical ventilators and automated IV pumps. Again, technological improvements are reducing this risk. In some cases, the interference in the form of electrical noise may be less drastic than shutting down a ventilator, but may still be hazardous to the patient. This electrical noise may complicate the interpretation of diagnostic tests. This interference has also been a problem with MRI emissions and electromyography (EMG) tests. The basic issue is the difficulty in shielding magnetic fields. Therefore, when planning a new facility, it is important to consider locating MRI equipment as far away as possible from other sensitive equipment, such as EMG units. There is currently a need for better research regarding potential effects of NIR, including any potential interference with medical equipment (Ahlbom et al. 2004).

OSHA's *Nonionizing Radiation Standard* applies to electromagnetic radiation, which is restricted to that portion of the spectrum commonly defined as the radio frequency region and includes the microwave frequency region. The non-ionizing standard and its requirements applies to all radiation originating from radio stations, radar equipment, and other possible sources of electromagnetic radiation used for communication, radio navigation, and industrial and scientific purposes (OSHA 1996c). See "Additional Resources" at the end of this chapter for more information on UV and other NIR concerns.

Lasers. Lasers are used in health care and in research for positioning and for surgical procedures. It is important to remember that there is a wide range of hazards associated with their use, and ANSI classifies lasers from type I to type IV based on their potential hazard (ANSI 2005). Lasers used for patient positioning are considered to be non-hazardous, whereas Types III B and IV are classified as hazardous because even a brief exposure may cause harm. They can be especially dangerous to the eyes and could cause a serious injury or skin burns. Despite the use of lasers in movies and theatrical displays, hazardous laser light is often not visible to the naked eye, and people have been burned by placing a hand into a beam accidentally.

The primary method of controlling exposure from lasers is through the use of engineering methods, such as guarded switches and interlocks to prevent turning on the laser accidentally. The other approach is through the use of administrative controls in the form of standard operating procedures and warning labels. One individual should be designated as the laser safety officer, and that individual should monitor compliance with laser safety policy throughout the facility. Training and standard operating procedures for use of lasers within health care is a paramount aspect of a laser safety program. Healthcare organizations should establish minimum training requirements and credentialing of physicians for the laser type and surgical procedure they intend to use. This not only allows individuals who are responsible for the case to understand fundamental laser physics but it also empowers them with the knowledge and means of dealing with hazards associated with laser use. Laser goggles or other types of PPE are used as a last resort when engineering and administrative controls are not sufficient. In order to reduce ocular exposure hazards, these goggles must be selected for the appropriate optical density (OD). OD is determined using a logarithm scale; thus, a pair of goggles with an OD of 3 is ten times more protective than goggles with an OD of 2.

Lasers present additional hazards such as ignition of combustible materials, electrical shock, and hazardous aerosols from tissue destruction. Patient injuries or death are a particular concern when lasers are used during surgeries. The Joint Commission lists reducing the risk of surgical fires as one of its 2008 patient safety goals (JCAHO 2008). In January 2003, the Joint Commission issued a Sentinel Event Alert on preventing surgical fires (JCAHO 2003). In particular with lasers, endotracheal tubes have caught fire and melted when anesthesia providers did not use specially shielded tubes. (This means that the plastic tube is wound with a filament that deflects the laser beam.) Laser misfiring or inattention when testing the laser beam can result in igniting flammable materials, such as drapes, or can bounce off reflective surfaces and cause direct injury to staff or patients.

Steps should be taken to assure that alcohol or other flammable materials are not ignited during laser operative procedures. Electrical hazards will also be minimized if the equipment is part of a routine preventive maintenance program.

During a surgical procedure, a smoke plume is created. According to NIOSH, this plume may ". . . contain toxic gases and vapors such as benzene, hydrogen cyanide, and formaldehyde, bioaerosols, dead and live cellular material (including blood fragments), and viruses" (NIOSH 1998). The smoke is a respiratory irritant, and may affect the vision of the surgeon. The smoke not only has an unpleasant odor, but has been shown to be mutagenic. NIOSH recommends a combination of general room ventilation and local exhaust ventilation (called a smoke evacuator) to control the release of this plume. In addition, staff exposed to this laser plume should be required to wear N-95 respirators.

Additional information on laser safety can be found in the "Additional Resources" section at the end of this chapter.

Psychological Factors

It has long been known that excessive psychological stress may be linked with health disorders (Seward 1997; Cartwright and Cooper 1997). Some of the health conditions include gastrointestinal ulcer, mental disorders and substance abuse, muscle pain, allergies, and even cancer. The link with allergies and cancer is thought to be due to the effects of stress hormones on the immune system. It also should be noted that rather than the cause, stress may serve as a promoter of pre-existing disease. There may also be a relationship between stress and an increase in injuries, especially among so-called "accident-prone" individuals. Too little stress can also be a problem. Workers in jobs such as security or housekeeping with low levels of mental stimulation may have an increased likelihood of inattention and injuries.

There are many theories that describe the causes of worker stress. One of the simplest is called the *demand-control model* (Karasek et al. 1998). Workers with high physical or psychological work demands who have little control over the performance of the job, such as receptionists, tend to be more stressed than individuals with lower demands and higher control, such as university professors. It has also been shown that the presence of social support can significantly modify the amount of stress in a particular job (Bosma et al. 1998). The control of psychological stress should target the work environment rather than the individual. Of course, individuals with stress-related conditions, such as alcoholism or drug abuse, should receive appropriate therapy. For a lasting solution, the conditions that caused the worker to adopt self-destructive habits must be identified and controlled. Workers need to believe that the workplace is safe, and that management cares about their safety. This is often described as the organization's *safety climate* (DeJoy et al. 2004). This requires managers to establish safety policies and procedures and provide sufficient resources for an effective safety program. The establishment of an effective safety program is covered in Chapter 5.

Nanotechnology

Nanotechnology involves engineered structures, devices, and systems that are typically in the range of 1–100 nanometers in diameter (NIOSH 2007b). These nanoscale materials are increasingly used in many applications, including medical care (Suri et al. 2007). The extremely small size of these materials causes them to react in unique and unexpected ways (Oberdorster et al. 2005; Holsapple et al. 2005). Potential exposure may occur through inhalation, dermal contact, or ingestion. There is evidence that low-solubility nanoscale particles are more toxic than larger particles on a mass-per-mass basis. Preliminary research by NIOSH found that low doses of certain nanotubes caused serious pulmonary damage in mice soon after exposure (NIOSH 2007b). Due to their small size, there may be concern for dermal exposure as well. NIOSH suggests caution until more is known about the potential health effects associated with exposure to nanoparticles (NIOSH 2007b). Some of their recommendations include:

- Implement risk management assessments to determine potential routes of exposure and adequacy of controls.
- Using engineering controls, such a local exhaust ventilation, to contain the release of these particles. Exhaust systems should be equipped with HEPA filters to prevent the release of nanoparticles to the environment.
- Use good work practices such as wet methods (keeping powdered material wet to inhibit the creation of airborne particles) and training to reduce the potential for exposures.

■ In situations where engineering and administrative controls do not eliminate the potential for exposure, NIOSH recommends that respirators equipped with HEPA filters be worn. Preliminary research shows that HEPA filters are effective in removing particles as small as 2.5 nanometers in diameter.

Nanotechnology is a field that is rapidly evolving and new information about risks is expected.

SUMMARY AND CONCLUSIONS

There are a variety of hazards in the healthcare environment. The categories of hazards are chemical, biological, physical, and psychological. While there are differences among these hazards, it is important to remember that the same approach should be used to manage them. The basic approach is to anticipate, recognize, evaluate, and control all healthcare hazards. It is also important to understand the difference between a hazard and a risk. A *hazard* is something with the potential to do harm. However, to be a *risk* there must be the likelihood of exposure. A 400-lb patient may be a hazard to healthcare personnel, but unless someone attempts to manually lift that patient, the patient's weight is not a risk to anyone. Therefore, the goal of the IEHS professional is to manage hazards in such a way that they do not become risks to workers, patients or the general public.

Review

1. Give an example of each of the major classes of hazards found in healthcare settings.
2. For each of the chemical hazards, list the health hazard(s), where it is found in a healthcare setting, the persons at risk, and control strategies:
   ■ Asbestos
   ■ Phenolic disinfectants
   ■ Ethylene oxide
   ■ Waste anesthetic gases
3. Explain why both viable and non-viable biological agents may be hazardous.
4. Explain why tuberculosis has re-emerged as a major concern.
5. Provide an example of each of the four major risk factors for low back pain.
6. Describe the control strategies for psychological stress.
7. What is nanotechnology, and why is it a concern?

Additional Resources

American Industrial Hygiene Association (AIHA). *Lasers* (retrieved August 11, 2008) (http://www2.umdnj.edu/eohssweb/aiha/technical/lasers.htm#Lasers).

Canadian Centre of Occupational Health and Safety (CCOHS). 2003. *Lasers—Health Care Facilities* (retrieved August 11. 2008) (http://www.ccohs.ca/oshanswers/phys_agents/lasers.html).

Environmental Protection Agency (EPA). *Lead in Paint, Dust and Soil: Basic Information: Health Effects of Lead* (retrieved August 11, 2008) (http://www.epa.gov/lead/pubs/leadinfo.htm#health).

Environmental Protection Agency (EPA). *Mercury: Information for Health Care Providers* (retrieved August 11, 2008) http://www.epa.gov/mercury/healthcare.htm

National Institute for Occupational Safety and Health (NIOSH). *Formaldehyde* (retrieved August 11, 2008) (http://www.cdc.gov/niosh/topics/formaldehyde).

———. *Glutaraldehyde* (retrieved August 11, 2008) (http://www.cdc.gov/niosh/topics/glutaraldehyde)

Occupational Health and Safety Administration (OSHA). *Formaldehyde* (retrieved August 11, 2008) http://www.osha.gov/SLTC/formaldehyde/index.html.

———. *Best Practices for the Use of Glutaraldehyde in Health Care* (retrieved August 11, 2008) (http://www.osha.gov/Publications/3258-08N-2006-English.html#glutaraldehyde).

———. *Legionnaires' Disease* (retrieved November 19, 2007) (http://www.osha.gov/dts/osta/otm/legionnaires/index.html).

———. *Non-ionizing Radiation* (retrieved August 11, 2008) http://www.osha.gov/SLTC/radiation_nonionizing/index.html.

Reference List

Ahlbom, A., A. Green, L. Kheifets, D. Savitz, and A. Swerdlow. 2004. "Epidemiology of Health Effects of Radiofrequency Exposure." *Environ. Health Perspect.* 112:1741–1754.

American Conference of Governmental Hygienists (ACGIH). 2007. *Industrial Ventilation—A Manual of Recommended Practice for Design.* 26th ed. Cincinnati, OH: American Conference of Governmental Industrial Hygienists.

———. 2008. *Threshold Limit Values and Biological Exposure Indices.* Cincinnati, OH: American Conference of Governmental Industrial Hygienists.

American Institute of Architects (AIA). 2006. *Guidelines for Design and Construction of Hospital and Health Care Facilities.* Washington, D.C.: American Institute of Architects.

American Industrial Hygiene Association (AIHA). 2003. *The Occupational Environment: Its Evaluation, Control, and Management.* 2d ed. Fairfax, VA: American Industrial Hygiene Association.

Amr, S. and W. A. Suk. 2004. "Latex Allergy and Occupational Asthma in Health Care Workers: Adverse Outcomes." *Environ. Health Perspect.* 112:378–381.

American National Standards Institute (ANSI). 2005. ANSI Z136.3-2005, *American National Standard for Safe Use of Lasers in Health Care Facilities.* Washington, D. C.: American National Standards Institute.

Barbaree, J. M., G. W. Gorman, W. T. Martin, B.S. Fields, and W. E. Morrill. 1987. "Protocol for Sampling Environmental Sites for Legionellae." *Appl.Environ.Microbiol.* 53:1454–1458.

Berger, E. H., L. H. Royster, J. D. Royster, D. P. Driscoll, and M. Layne. 2000. *The Noise Manual.* 5th ed. Fairfax, VA: American Industrial Hygiene Association.

Bigos, S. J., M. C. Battie, D. M. Spengler, L. D. Fisher, W. E. Fordyce, and T. H. Hansson, T. H. 1991. "A Prospective Study of Work Perceptions and Psychosocial Factors Affecting the Report of Back Injury." *Spine* 16:1–6. [published erratum appears in *Spine* Jun 1991; 16(6):688].

Bigos, S. J., D. M. Spengler, N. A. Martin, J. Zeh, L. Fisher, and A. Nachemson. 1986. "Back Injuries in Industry: A Retrospective Study." *Spine* 11:252–256.

Bongers, P. M., C. R. de Winter, M. A. Kompier, and V. H. Hildebrandt. 1993. "Psychosocial Factors at Work and Musculoskeletal Disease." *Scandinavian Journal of Work and Environmental Health,* 19:297–312.

Bosma, H., R. Peter, J.Siegrist, and M. Marmot 1998. "Two Alternative Job Stress Models and the Risk of Coronary Heart Disease." *American Journal of Public Health* 88:68–74.

Burdorf, A., M. Rossignol, F. A. Fathallah, S. H. Snook, and R. F. Herrick. 1997. "Challenges in Assessing Risk Factors in Epidemiologic Studies on Back Disorders. *American Journal of Industrial Medicine* 32:142–152.

Bureau of Labor Statistics (BLS). 2006. *Incidence rates of nonfatal occupational injuries and illnesses involving days away from work by selected worker and case characteristics and industry, All U.S., private industry, 2006* (retrieved August 11, 2008) (http://www.bls.gov/iif/home.htm).

Byrns, G. E., J. Agnew, and B. Curbow. 2002. "Attributions, Stress, and Work-Related Low Back Pain." *Applied Occupational and Environmental Hygiene* 17:752–764.

Byrns, G. E., G. Jin, C. M. Mallory, G. D. Reeder, and J. E. Harris. 2005. "Low Back Pain Among RNs: Advantages and Potential Pitfalls of Longitudinal Research in Low Back Pain among RNs." *Professional Safety* 50:41–48.

Byrns, G. E., D. Knoblauch, and C. M. Mallory. 2007. "Are All 'No-lift' Policies the same?" *AOHP Journal* 28:19–23.

Byrns, G. E., K. H. Palatianos, L. A. Shands, K. P. Fennelley, C. S. McCammon, A. Y. Boudreau. 2000. "Chemical Hazards in Radiology." *Applied Occupational and Environmental Hygiene* 15:203–208.

Byrns, G. E., G. D. Reeder, G. Jin, and K. A. Pachis. 2004. "Risk Factors for Work-Related Low Back Pain in Registered Nurses and Potential Obstacles in

Using Protective Equipment." *Journal of Occupational and Environmental Hygiene* 01:11–21.

Cartwright, S. and C. L. Cooper. 1997. "The Growing Epidemic of Stress." In *Managing Workplace Stress,* pp. 1–24. Thousand Oaks, CA: Sage Publications.

Centers for Disease Control and Prevention (CDC). 2004a. *Fact Sheet: Basic Information about SARS* (retrieved September 12, 2008) (http://www.cdc.gov/ncidod/sars/factsheet).

———. 2005a. *Campaign to Prevent Antimicrobial Resistance in Healthcare Settings* (retrieved September 12, 2008) (http://www.cdc.gov/.drugresistance/healthcare/default.htm).

———. 2005c. *Guidelines for Preventing the Transmission of Mycobacterium tuberculosis in Health-Care Facilities, 2005. MMWR* (RR-17) 45:1–141. Washington, D.C.: U.S. Government Printing Office.

———. 1997. *Immunization of Health-Care Workers: Recommendations of the Advisory Committee on Immunization Practices (ACIP) and the Hospital Infection Control Practices Advisory Committee (HICPAC). MMWR* (RR-18) 46:1–42 .

———. 2008. *National Tuberculosis Surveillance System; Highlights from 2007.* (retrieved December 3, 2008) (http://cdc.gov/tb/pubs/slideset/surv/surv2007/default.htm)

———. 2004b. *Public Health Guidance for Community-Level Preparedness and Response to Severe Acute Respiratory Syndrome (SARS) Version 2 (Supplement C: Preparedness and Response in Healthcare Facilities).* Atlanta: Centers for Disease Control and Prevention.

———. 2005b. *Severe Acute Respiratory Syndrome (SARS): Surveillance and Reporting* (retrieved August 11, 2008) (http://www.cdc.gov/ncidod/sars.report.htm).

———. 2007. *Surveillance of Occupationally Acquired HIV/AIDS in Healthcare Personnel, as of December 2006.* (retrieved August 11, 2008) (http://www.cdc.gov/ncidod/dhqp/bp_hcp_w_hiv.html#2).

———. 2003. "Water Sampling Strategies and Culture Techniques for Detecting Legionellae." *MMWR* (RR10) 52:43.

Centers for Disease Control and Prevention, Division of Tuberculosis Elimination (CDC DTBE). 2007. *QuantiFERON-TB Gold Test* (retrieved September 25, 2008) (http://www.cdc.dov/tb/pubs/tbfactsheets/QFT.htm).

de Looze, M. P., E. Zinzen, D. Caboor, P. Van Roy, and J. P. Clarijs. 1998. "Muscle Strength, Task Performance and Low Back Load in Nurses." *Ergonomics* 41:1095–1104.

DeJoy, D. M., B. S. Schaffer, M. G. Wilson, R. J. Vandenberg, and M. M. Butts. 2004. "Creating Safer Workplaces: Assessing the Determinants and Role of Safety Climate." *Journal of Safety Research* 35:81–90.

Edwards, A., J. R. Kominsky, and R. W. Freyberg. 1994. "Airborne Asbestos Concentrations During Spray-Buffing of Resilent Floor Tile." *Applied Occupational and Environmental Hygiene* 9:132–138.

Edwards, F. P. and A. R. Campbell. 1984. "Removal of Formaldehyde and Xylene Fumes from Histopathology Laboratories: A Functional Approach to the Design of Extraction Systems." *J.Clin.Pathol.* 37:401–408.

Engkvist, I. L., E. W. Hjelm, M. Hagberg, E. Menckel, and L. Ekenvall. 2000. "Risk Indicators for Reported Over-exertion Back Injuries Among Female Nursing Personnel." *Epidemiology* 11:519–522.

Environmental Protection Agency (EPA). 2008a. *Final Amendments to Air Toxics Standard for Ethylene Oxide Sterilization Facilities* (retrieved September 18, 2008) (http://www.epa.gov/ttn/oarpg/t3/fact_sheet/finaleorisk_fs.html).

———. 2008b. 40 CFR 745, *Lead: Renovation, Repair and Painting Program* (retrieved September 18, 2008) (http://www.epa.gov/fedregstr/EPA-TOX/2008/April/Day-22/t8141.pdf).

Environmental Protection Agency (EPA) and American Hospital Association (AHA). 1998. *Memorandum of Understanding between the American Hospital Association & the U.S. Environmental Protection Agency* (Pub 1-03) (retrieved August 7, 2008) (http://www.h2e-online.org/docs/h2emou101501.pdf).

Federal Drug Administration (FDA). 2001. *Summary of Safety and Effectiveness Data* (retrieved August 25, 2008) (http://www.fda.gov/cdrh/pdf/P010033b.pdf).

Fields, B. S. (1997). 'Legionellae and Legionnaires' Disease.' In *Manual of Environmental Microbiology* (pp. 666–675). Washington D.C.: ASM Press.

First, M. W., R. A. Weker, S. Yasui, and E. A. Nardell. 2005. "Monitoring Human Exposures to Upper-room Germicidal Ultraviolet Irradiation." *J.Occup.Environ.Hyg.* 2:285–292.

Goldberg, M., S. Klitzman, J. L. Payne, R. J. Nadig, J. McGrane, and A. K. Goodman, A. K. 1990. "Mercury Exposure from the Repair of Blood Pressure Machines in Medical Facilities." *Applied Occupational and Environmental Hygiene* 5:604–610.

Hamasuna, R., K. Nose, T. Sueyoshi, M. Nagano, Y. Hasui, Y. Osada. 2004. "High-level Disinfection of Cystoscopic Equipment with Ortho-phthalaldehyde Solution." *J.Hosp.Infect.* 57:346–348.

Herwaldt, B. L. 2001. "Laboratory-Acquired Parasitic Infections from Accidental Exposures." *Clin.Microbiol.Rev.* 14:659–88.

Hoaglund, F. T. and N. N. Byl. 1997. "Musculoskeletal Injuries." In J. LaDou, ed. *Occupational & Environmental Medicine*, 2nd ed., pp. 64–88. Stamford, Connecticut: Appleton & Lange.

Holsapple, M. P., W. H. Farland, T. D. Landry, N. A. Monteiro-Riviere, J. M. Carter, N. J. Walker. 2005. "Research Strategies for Safety Evaluation of Nanomaterials, Part II: Toxicological and Safety Evaluation of Nanomaterials, Current Challenges and Data Needs." *Toxicol.Sci.* 88:12–17.

Hoogendoorn, W. E., P. M. Bongers, H. C. de Vet, I. L. Houtman, G. A. Ariens, W. van Mechelen. 2001. "Psychosocial Work Characteristics and Psychological Strain in Relation to Low-Back Pain." *Scand.J.Work Environ.Health* 27:258–267.

Houtman, I. L., P. M. Bongers, P. G. Smulders, and M. A. Kompier. 1994. "Psychosocial Stressors at Work and Musculoskeletal Problems." *Scandinavian Journal of Work and Environmental Health* 20:139–145.

International Section on the Prevention of Occupational Risks in Health Services (ISSA). 1993. *Safety in the Use of Anesthetic Gases: Consensus Paper from the Basic German and French Documentation: Working Document for Occupational Safety and Health Specialists* (ISSA Prevention Series No 2042 (E)). Hamburg, Germany: International Section on the Prevention of Occupational Risks in Health Services.

Joint Commission on Accreditation of Healthcare Organizations (JCAHO). 2003. "Preventing surgical fires." (retrieved August 6, 2008) (http://www.jointcommission.org/SentinelEvents/SentinelEventAlert/sea_29.htm).

———. 2008. *Questions about Goal 11 (Reduce surgical fires)* (retrieved August 6, 2008) (http://www.jointcommission.org/NR/rdonlyres/B84F6B36-0D86-4CF3-B436-1A41237F2F57/0/2008_FAQs_NPSG_11.pdf).

Karasek, R. 1985. *Job Content Questionnaire.* Los Angeles: Department of Industrial and Systems Engineering, University of Southern California.

Karasek, R., N. Kawakami, C. Brisson, I. L. Houtman, P. M. Bongers, and B. Amick. 1998. "The Job Content Questionnaire (JCQ): An Instrument for Internationally Comparative Assessments of Psychosocial Job characteristics." *Journal of Occupational Health Psychology* 3:322–355.

Lynch, R. M. and A. Freund. 2000. "Short-term Efficacy of Back Injury Intervention Project for Patient Care Providers at One Hospital." *AIHAJ.* 61:290–294.

Massachusetts Department of Public Health. 1997. "Work-Related Asthma Cases Reported to Massachusetts SENSOR, March 1992–December 1996." *SENSOR Occupational Lung Disease Bulletin.* (retrieved August 8, 2008) (http://www.mass.gov/Eeohhs2/docs/dph/occupational_health/sensorlung_disease_bulletins/astbull_feb97.pdf).

McGlothlin, J. D., K. G. Crouch, and R. L. Mickelsen. 1994. *Technical Report: Control of Nitrous Oxide in Dental Operatories* (NIOSH Publication No. 94-129). Cincinnati: National Institute for Occupational Safety and Health.

Monroe, C. D. o. H. 2006. *Reducing Mercury in Health Care: Promoting a Healthier Environment* Washington, D.C.: Environmental Protection Agency.

National Fire Protection Association (NFPA). 1999. *Standard 99C: Standard on Gas and Vacuum Systems.* Quincy, MA: National Fire Protection Association.

National Institute for Occupational Safety and Health (NIOSH). 2007a. *Assessment of Noise Exposures in a Hospital Kitchen* (HETA 2007-0183-3047). Cincinnati, OH: Department of Health and Human Services.

———. 1999a. *Control of Nitrous Oxide During Cryosurgery* (Publication No. 99-105). Cincinnati: National Institute for Occupational Safety and Health.

———. 1998. *Control of Smoke from Laser/Electric Surgical Procedures* (Publication No. 96-128). Cincinnati, OH: National Institute for Occupational Safety and Health.

———. 1989. *Ethylene Oxide Sterilizers in Health Care Facilities: Engineering Controls and Work Practices* (Current Intelligence Bulletin 52).

———. 2001. *Glutaraldehyde: Occupational Hazards in Hospitals* (Publication No. 2001-115). Cincinnati, OH: National Institute for Occupational Safety and Health.

————. 1988. *Guidelines for Protecting the Safety and Health of Health Care Workers* (Publication No. 88-119). Washington, DC: Government Printing Office.

————. 1997a. "Low Back Musculoskeletal Disorders: Evidence for Work-Relatedness." In National Institute for Occupational Safety and Health, Ed. *Musculoskeletal Disorders and Workplace Factors: A Critical Review of Epidemiologic Evidence for Work-Related Musculoskeletal Disorders of the Neck, Upper Extremity, and Low Back* (pp. 6-1–6-96). Cincinnati, OH: National Institute for Occupational Safety and Health.

————. 1997b. *NIOSH Alert: Preventing Allergic Reactions to Natural Rubber Latex in the Workplace* (Publication No. 97-135). Cincinnati, OH: National Institute for Occupational Safety and Health.

————. 1999b. *NIOSH Publications on Video Display Terminals: Third Edition* (Publication No. 99-135). Cincinnati, OH: National Institute for Occupational Safety and Health.

————. 2004. *Preventing Occupational Exposure to Antineoplastic and Other Hazardous Drugs in Health Care Settings* (Publication No. 2004-165). Cincinnati, OH: National Institute for Occupational Safety and Health.

————. 2007b. *Progress Toward Safe Nanotechnology in the Workplace: A Report from the NIOSH Nanotechnology Research Center* (Publication No. 2007-123). Cincinnati, OH: National Institute for Occupational Safety and Health.

————. 1994. *Request for Assistance in Controlling Exposures to Nitrous Oxide During Anesthetic Administration* (Publication No. 94-100). Cincinnati, OH: National Institute for Occupational Safety and Health.

National Institutes of Heath (NIH). 2004. *Report on Carcinogens*, 11th ed. (retrieved August 25, 2008) (http://www.ntp.niehs.nih.gov/index.cfm?objectid=32BA9724-F1F6-97SE-7FCE50709CB4C932).

National Safety Council (NSC). 2005. *Fundamentals of Industrial Hygiene.* 5th ed. Chicago: National Safety Council.

Oberdorster, G., A. Maynard, K. Donaldson, V. Castranova, J. Fitzpatrick, K. Ausman, K. 2005. "Principles for Characterizing the Potential Human Health Effects from Exposure to Nanomaterials: Elements of a Screening Strategy." *Part Fibre.Toxicol.* 2:8.

Occupational Health and Safety Administration. (OSHA). 1995. 29 CFR 1910.1001, *Asbestos.* (retrieved August 11, 2008) (http://www.osha.gov/pls/oshweb/owadisp.show_document?p=table=STANDARDS&p_id=9995).

————. 2006a. *Best Practices for the Safe Use of Glutaraldehyde in Health Care* (OSHA 3258-04N). Washington DC: US Department of Labor.

————. 2006e. 29 CFR 1910.1030, *Bloodborne Pathogens.* (retrieved August 11, 2008) (http://www.osha.gov/pls/oshweb/owadisp.show_document?p=table=STANDARDS&p_id=10051).

————. 2003. *A Brief Guide to Mold in the Workplace* (Rep. No. SHIB 03-10-10). (retrieved August 11, 2008) (http://www.osha.gov/dts/shib/shib101003.htm).

————. 1996a. *Enforcement Procedures and Scheduling for Occupational Exposure to Tuberculosis* (CPL 02-00-106) (retrieved August 11, 2008) (http://www.

osha.gov/pls/oshaweb/owadisp.show_document?table=DIRECTIVES& p=id=1586).

————. 2006b. 29 CFR 1910.1047, *Ethylene Oxide* (retrieved November 19, 2007) (http://www.osha.gov/pls/oshweb/owadisp.show_document?p=table= STANDARDS&p_id=10070).

————. 2002. *Hospital eTool* (retrieved November 20, 2007) (http://www.osha. gov/SLTC/etools/hospital/laundry.html#HearStress).

————. 2003. *Information Regarding Severe Acute Respiratory Syndrome (SARS)* (retrieved November 11, 2007) (http://www.osha.gov/dep/sars/ index.html).

————. 1996b. 29 CFR 1910.1096, *Ionizing Radiation.* (retrieved August 11, 2008) (http://www.osha.gov/pls/oshweb/owadisp.show_document? p=table=STANDARDS&p_id=10098).

————. 2007a. *Noise and Hearing Conservation* (retrieved August 6, 2008), (http://www.osha.gov/SLTC/noisehearingconservation/index.html).

————. 1996c. 29 CFR 1910.97, *Nonionizing Radiation Standard* (retrieved August 11, 2008) (http://www.osha.gov/pls/oshweb/owadisp.show_ document?p=table=STANDARDS&p_id=9745).

————. 2006f. 29 CFR 1910.95, *Occupational Noise Exposure* (retrieved August 11, 2008) (http://www.osha.gov/pls/oshweb/owadisp.show_document?- p_id9735&p_table=STANDARDS).

————. 1981. *Occupational Noise Exposure and Hearing Conservation Amendment* (CSP 01-01-016 - STP 2.21) (retrieved August 11, 2008) (http://www.osha. gov/pls/oshweb/owadisp.show_document?p_table=DIRECTIVES& p_id=1865).

————. 1995. *OSHA Technical Manual (OTM), Section III: Health Hazards* (TED 01-00-015 [TED 1-0.15a] (retrieved August 11, 2008) (http://www. osha.gov/dts/osta/otm/otm_iii/otm_iii_1.html).

————. 1996d. *OSHA Technical Manual (OTM), Section III:Appendix III:7-5 Water Treatment for Facilities That Have Experienced a Legionnaires Outbreak* (TED 01-00-015 [TED 1-0.15a] (retrieved August 25, 2008) (http://www. osha.gov/dts/osta/otm/otm_iii/otm_iii_7.html#app_iii_7_5).

————. 2007b. *Pandemic Influenza Preparedness and Response Guidance for Healthcare Workers and Healthcare Employers* (OSHA 3328-05) (retrieved August 11, 2008) (http://www.osha.gov/Publications/3328-05-2007- English.html).

————. 2006d. 29 CFR 1910.134, *Respiratory Protection* (retrieved August 11, 2008) (http://www.osha.gov/pls/oshweb/owadisp.show_document? p_id127168&p_table=STANDARDS).

————. 2006c. *Table Z – 1 Limits for Air Contaminants—1910.1000* (retrieved August 11, 2008) (http://www.osha.gov/pls/oshweb/owadisp.show_ document?p=table=STANDARDS&p_id=9992).

Owen, B. and A. Garg. 1999. "Back Injury Prevention in Health Care Part 2: An Ergonomic Approach to Reducing Back Stress in Nursing Person- nel." In W.Charney, ed. *Handbook of Modern Hospital Safety*, pp. 717–755. Boca Raton: Lewis Publishers.

Pauley, S. M. 2004. "Lighting for the Human Circadian Clock: Recent Research Indicates that Lighting Has Become a Public Health Issue." *Med.Hypotheses* 63:588–596.

Rogers, B. 1997. "Health Hazards in Nursing and Health Care: An Overview." *Am.J.Infect.Control* 25:248–261.

Rutala, W. A. 1996. "APIC Guideline for Selection and Use of Disinfectants; 1994, 1995. *Am.J.Infect.Control* 24:313–342.

Rutala, W. A. and D. J. Weber. 2001. "New Disinfection and Sterilization Methods." *Emerg.Infect.Dis.* 7:348–353.

Seward, J. P. 1997. "Occupational stress." In J. LaDou, Ed. *Occupational & Environmental Medicine*, 2 ed., pp. 585–601. Stamford, Connecticut: Appleton & Lange.

Steinbrecher, S. M. 1994. "The Revised NIOSH Lifting Guidelines: Application in a Hospital setting. *AAOHN.J.* 42:62–66.

Suri, S. S., H. Fenniri, and B. Singh. 2007. "Nanotechnology-based Drug Delivery Systems." *J.Occup.Med.Toxicol.* 2:16.

Veterans Administration (VA). 2003. *Patient Care Ergonomics Resource Guide: Safe Patient Handling and Movement.* (retrieved August 11, 2008) (http://www.va.gov/patientsafetycenter/resguide/ErgoGuidePtOne.pdf).

van Poppel, M. N., B. W. Koes, W. Deville, T. Smid, and L. M. Bouter. 1998. "Risk Factors for Back Pain Incidence in Industry: A Prospective Study." *Pain* 77:81–86.

Waddell, G. 1998. *The Back Pain Revolution.* Edinburgh: Churchill Livingstone.

Weaver, V. M. 1997. "Chemical Hazards in Health Care Workers." *Occup.Med.* 12:655–667.

CLASSROOM ACTIVITIES

Activity 1: Case Study Involving Latex Allergy

Scenario: You are the new health and safety officer at Happy Valley Hospital and the Director of Nursing just called telling you about 3 nurses who are complaining about skin rashes whenever they put on disposable gloves. She wishes to know what is causing the problem, and what needs to be done to prevent it.

Your assignment is to read the NIOSH Alert: *Preventing Allergic Reactions to Natural Rubber Latex in the Workplace* (NIOSH 1997b) and write a two-page memo to the Director of Nursing. This memo should:

- Identify the types of diseases caused by latex.
- Identify which healthcare products may contain latex.
- Identify other healthcare workers (other than nurses) who may be at risk from exposure to latex.

An Injury Control Approach—Haddon's Matrix

Human	Vehicle	Environment
Pre-event		
Event		
Post Event		

- Using Haddon's Matrix, list five recommendations to control this problem. Do not insert the table into your memo, but you may wish to include it as an attachment.

Activity 2: Tuberculosis Transmission Case Study

Start with the NIOSH video *Respirators: Your TB Defense,* narrated by Loretta Swit (approximately 16 min). This video can be ordered free of charge from NIOSH. Review the following scenario with your group members and attempt to answer the question below.

Scenario: You have been asked to investigate the nosocomial transmission of tuberculosis (TB) at the Happy Days Hospital located in Some City, NM. The hospital infection control nurse just informed you that four nurses converted from tuberculin skin test negative to positive during the annual surveillance clinic. One of the four nurses has active disease and has been hospitalized. This makes a total of five staff conversions for the year. The other staff conversion was also a nurse that occurred in March. This nurse was not an active case. In addition, there have been five active TB cases among local community members since the beginning of the year. All were treated at your facility, and two are still hospitalized.

This 100-bed facility is located in a relatively rural part of the state on a complex that includes employee quarters, the physical plant, and a collection of trailers and other temporary structures that serve as offices and some outpatient examination facilities. The hospital is staffed by 250 people, providing a wide range of services. While the hospital was originally designed with two operating rooms, difficulty in recruiting and retaining qualified surgeons resulted in the elimination of this service approximately ten years ago. These rooms are currently used for storage. General anesthesia is occasionally used in the obstetrical service for patients requiring a C-section.

1. Using CDC TB risk criteria, how would you classify this situation?
2. Since the beginning of the year, what was the total number of TB infections seen at this facility, and of that number, how many were active cases?

We currently do not have detailed information on the community-acquired cases. The four recent employee conversions were all identified during an employee health fair approximately one week ago. Our infection control nurse spoke with the nurse who is currently hospitalized, and she confirmed that she had been working on the unit that housed two of the community-acquired cases. The usual prevalence of TB cases treated at this facility until about two years ago was no more than one case of TB every other year or so. Last year two active cases were treated at this hospital.

Recently, there has been an increase in the number of immigrants who have been recruited to work on some of the larger farms in the areas. Most are from Mexico, and some are from Haiti.

Description of the physical plant. The hospital contains three floors. The first contains admissions and registration, outpatient services, emergency services, laboratory, radiology, outpatient pharmacy, food service, cafeteria, an employee health unit, and administrative offices. The second floor contains inpatient beds, arranged in four units. The third floor contains the obstetrical unit (including two delivery rooms, labor and a newborn nursery), the former operating unit, central services, a six-bed intensive care unit, recovery, respiratory therapy, and rehabilitation.

The hospital was originally built without a mechanical ventilation system, and air was delivered through open windows. In 1968, the first mechanical heating, ventilating, and air conditioning (HVAC) unit was installed, and this unit still services portions of the third floor. In 1981, a second HVAC unit was installed; it supplies air through fan-coil units to the rest of the hospital. This system passes exhaust air and incoming outdoor air through a rotary air-to-air heat exchanger, located on the roof, to transfer latent heat. Exhaust air and incoming supply air is mixed and re-circulated to conserve energy. Air conditioning for the hospital is accomplished using a chilled water system, and heating is done using steam from the boiler plant.

The hospital has one designated isolation unit on each of the four wings of the second floor. These rooms do not have a dedicated exhaust system. However, these rooms do include ultraviolet (UV) lamps located near the ceilings on all four walls. Housekeeping is encouraged to occasionally dust off the lamps. However, it is unknown when the lamps were last changed. All patient rooms have approximately two to three room air changes per hour and are under slightly positive pressure relative to hallways. High-risk procedures, such as sputum induction, are currently performed in standard exam rooms.

3. What is the current recommendation for dilution ventilation in rooms housing TB patients?

Status of the employee health program. All new employees receive a physical exam and care for work-related injuries and illnesses through the employee health unit. TB surveillance includes periodic PPD skin testing and chest x-rays for those with positive PPD results. The frequency of routine testing depends on staffing of the health unit. It had been over 1½ years since the last round of skin testing.

Patient screening protocol. Employees in patient registration and admissions and in outpatient triage have been trained to ask patients about key symptoms suggestive of TB. Those patients with suspicious symptoms undergo PPD skin testing, chest x-ray if appropriate, and sputum induction if needed.

Hospital employees coming in contact with suspected or confirmed TB cases are issued N95 respirators prior to entry into patient rooms. There is no fit-testing program.

4. Is the lack of fit-testing acceptable?

Homework assignment. Write a report that includes the following items:

1. A brief summary of the outbreak (no more than a paragraph).
2. The problems with TB prevention at this facility.
3. Recommendations to improve TB prevention at this facility.

CHAPTER 3

Introduction to Infection Control

George Byrns and Mary Elkins

> ## Learning Objectives
>
> 1 Define terms used in infection control.
>
> 2. Review significant risk factors for infection.
>
> 3. Identify the four most common types of hospital-associated infections.
>
> 4. Discuss the concept referred to as the chain of infections.
>
> 5. Explain the differences among the modes of transmission.
>
> 6. Describe infection surveillance methods.
>
> 7. Describe the minimum elements of an effective program.
>
> 8. Determine what constitutes success in infection control.
>
> 9. Explain the role of the institutional environmental health and safety professional in infection control.

Infection control and prevention (IC) in a healthcare setting requires a comprehensive, coordinated program designed to prevent and control nosocomial or healthcare-associated infections (HAIs). The Centers for Disease Control and Prevention (CDC) restricts the usage of the term *nosocomial* to infections acquired in hospitals, whereas HAIs refer to infections in any type of healthcare setting (CDC 2007a).

IC is a required, patient-focused function for any healthcare setting desiring to maintain accreditation by the Joint Commission on Accreditation of Healthcare Organizations (Joint Commission or JCAHO). The Joint Commission's description of IC states that there must be ongoing surveillance, data collection, and analysis of risks associated with the acquisition or transmission of infectious agents within the healthcare setting. Part of this IC program must include integrating with the community and recognizing that

IC is larger than just within hospital settings (JCAHO 2007). Therefore, IC also involves collaboration between healthcare professionals and community partners when confronting any infectious disease transmission, including the control or prevention of community-acquired infections (CAI). An example is the increase in CAI methicillin- (also called oxacillin-) resistant *Staphylococcus aureus* (MRSA) in jails or in contact sports such as wrestling in schools. The infection control professional (ICP) may provide educational assistance to the jail or school staff to underscore the importance of hand hygiene and environmental sanitation within institutional settings for the control of MRSA.

A recent concern is the need for multidisciplinary planning for pandemic influenza. A program aimed at the reduction of the spread of respiratory illness is the "Cover Your Cough" program developed by the CDC (CDC 2007b). This simple program is an effective tool that can be taught to school staff to help control the transmission of respiratory illness within the school or other institutional settings. Therefore, ICPs must be prepared to respond to potential disease threats not only in their healthcare setting, but also in their communities. This response may include development of educational hygiene programs, assistance with researching problems, policy development, or developing preventive measures for control.

IC programs focus on the epidemiology of infectious agents and methods of preventing their transmission (Bolyard et al. 1998). In some cases, IC activities have been based on traditions and scientifically unproven methods. A critical component of IC programs must be monitoring and evaluation of effectiveness to assure that the most optimal means of infection prevention or control are employed. Another important consideration is the protection of not only the patient but visitors and healthcare workers from the spread of infection. It is also important to recognize that certain patients, such as those receiving immunosuppressive drugs, and certain healthcare workers, such as laboratory personnel, are at an increased risk of acquiring HAIs. Prevention efforts should target these and other at-risk individuals. However, individuals not directly involved in patient care or diagnosis may also be at risk at certain times. For example, a maintenance worker may be required to enter an isolation room to repair defective equipment or perform service on a biological safety cabinet. An IC program must be both comprehensive and flexible enough to provide protection again infection under all of these diverse conditions.

STUDY OF THE EFFICACY OF NOSOCOMIAL INFECTION CONTROL

Formalized IC programs are a relatively recent development. Prior to the 1960s, there were few hospitals in the U.S. that had a formal program to identify and control nosocomial infections. In 1974, the CDC initiated the *Study of the Efficacy of Nosocomial Infection Control* (SENIC). This project was a stratified random sample of U.S. hospitals in 1970 and in 1976 comparing the types and status of IC programs (Haley et al. 1985). The study found that there were three main elements of effective programs:

1. A systematic method of conducting epidemiologic surveillance for infections
2. Relevant written policies and procedures
3. Competent personnel

The first point should be self-evident. Unless personnel search for the presence of infections, it is unlikely that anyone will find them and even less likely that these infections will be controlled or prevented. Second, there must be written policies and procedures for patient-care tasks to enable uniformity in implementation and to monitor compliance. This was particularly important for certain high-risk tasks, such as placement of urinary catheters that have high infection potential. Lastly, effective programs were only possible if there were properly trained personnel to implement them. Therefore all hospitals should employ competent IC professionals, and all hospital employees should be trained in proper IC procedures that pertain to their departments. Some other important information gleaned from this study was that in 1976, 37.7 million patients were admitted to U.S. hospitals; 2.1 million of these patients contracted infections while in the hospital. This corresponds to a 5.6 nosocomial infection rate per 100 patient admissions. Most importantly, the study found that 80% of all infections were of four types: urinary tract infections (UTIs), surgical site infections, pneumonias, and bacteremias.

It was important to note that 45% of patient infections were related to the use of medical devices. Not surprisingly, use of urinary catheters ranked number one. In addition, 71% of those with infections were patients who had surgery or other types of invasive procedures. While surgical-site infections were the most costly type of infection, nosocomial pneumonias had the highest death rate. In 1976, nosocomial infections caused 7.5 million extra hospital days, which accounted for nearly $1.0 billion (1976 dollars). In 2002 prices, the annual economic cost of HAIs is estimated to be $6.7 billion (Graves 2004). It has been well established that some patients will get infections while in the hospital despite of all efforts to prevent them because of their lowered immune system function. The SENIC researchers estimated that approximately 32% of all nosocomial infections were preventable. The major conclusions of the SENIC Study were:

■ The more intensive the surveillance and control program, the higher percentage of prevention that was possible.
■ If the program reduces just 6% of the infections, the cost of the IC program was justified.

The CDC estimates that annually, nearly two million patients in the U.S. become infected while in hospitals and about 90,000 of these patients die as a result of their infection. As in the past, urinary tract infections, pneumonia, surgical-site infections, and bloodstream infections comprise most of all healthcare-associated infections (CDC 2005).

The investigation of sentinel events is part of the Joint Commission's National Patient Safety Goals (Frain et al. 2004). The term *sentinel event* is used for an uncommon and worrisome occurrence. For example, if a patient dies or loses a limb due to MRSA and it was determined that infection occurred during a hospital stay, it would be considered a sentinel event. The goal of investigating sentinel events is to identify the credible root cause of the infection; thus, the focus of the investigation should be on processes and not on the outcomes. If a nurse or another healthcare provider fails to wash hands prior to performing a dressing change on a post-operative patient and the patient becomes infected with MRSA, one root cause might be a failure to enforce hospital hand-hygiene policy (assuming there is one). Or, the investigation may reveal that the nursing unit was shorthanded, and this staff shortage caused a lapse in hand-washing compliance. In this example, the root cause would be insufficient staffing levels. The issue of nursing shortages and increased HAIs is not hypothetical. Researchers have found a direct correlation between insufficient staffing levels and increases in HAIs (Stone et al. 2004). The ratio of registry nurses (also known as contract nurses) to in-house staff and skill levels were also important. Having lower ratios of registered nurses (RNs) to certified nursing assistants (CNAs) or having higher ratios of registry RNs to in-house staff were associated with increases in HAIs.

DISEASE TRANSMISSION

In order to fully understand the most effective means of preventing the spread of infections, it is necessary to understand the basic modes of transmission. Transmission of infections requires three elements:

- A source of infecting microorganisms
- A susceptible host
- A means of transmitting the microorganism

The concept of the *chain of infection,* displayed in Fig. 3.1, includes more than just the pathogenic agent, the host, and the mode of transmission. It recognizes that the agent has a reservoir serving as a continuing source of contamination and that the agent must escape from the reservoir in excretions or secretions (called a *portal of exit*) for transmission to take place. In order to infect a susceptible host, the agent must enter through mucus membranes, breaks in the skin, or other means (called a *portal of entry*). By assessing each element or link in the chain, it may be possible to identify the most optimal control strategy. Thus, if you break one link in the chain by

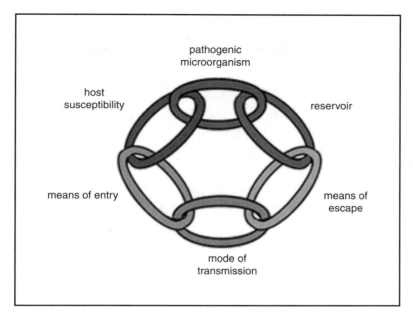

Figure 3.1 Chain of infection. (Courtesy of the University
of Minnesota Department of Environmental Health and
Safety)

eliminating the reservoir or immunizing the host, there is no possibility of
disease transmission (Kennamer 2002). In the previous example of transmission of MRSA from a caregiver to a post-operative patient, a break in the
chain of transmission could have been achieved by treating the source
(removing the reservoir), wearing gloves (preventing the means of escape),
or through hand washing (interrupting the direct transmission).

Sources of Infectious Agents

The most common source of infectious agents is the patient's own endogenous flora. These microorganisms typically do not harm us and are often beneficial because they may prevent the colonization of our skin or intestines
with pathogenic organisms. However, when a patient's immune system is
weakened or there are new portals of entry, such as central venous or urinary
catheters, these organisms become opportunistic pathogens. Other sources
of infectious agents include inanimate objects such as food, instruments, or
even environmental surfaces. For environmental surfaces to be a source of
infection, typically the patient's immune system must be severely compromised. Chapter 4 discusses the classification of environmental objects in
terms of infection risk.

Other patients, personnel, or visitors may serve as important sources of
cross-contamination. These infections are typically the most easily preventable

by rigorous adherence to personal hand washing and use of barrier techniques. Barrier techniques can range from simply using the proper personal protective equipment (PPE) to strict patient isolation.

Emerging Pathogens

A major concern in IC is the emergence of newly discovered microorganisms. In the early 1980s, the healthcare industry was greatly affected by the human immunodeficiency virus (HIV) epidemic. The control of HIV and other blood-borne diseases such as the hepatitis C virus has had a major impact on IC programs throughout the U.S. and elsewhere.

Another particular concern is the increasing prevalence of antibiotic-resistant strains of bacteria. Antimicrobial resistance developed soon after the discovery and use of penicillin. However, decades of inappropriate use of antibiotics have increased the spread of these dangerous pathogens. There are estimates that up to 3% of all infectious disease hospitalizations were due to just one of these organisms, MRSA (Kuehnert et al. 2005). They also estimated that about 10% of all septicemias were due to MRSA. There have been recent reports of an increased incidence of MSRA in the general community (Beam & Buckley 2006; CDC 2006). Once these drug-resistant organisms become established in a hospital, control becomes a challenge. HAI MRSA is of special concern because, unlike community-acquired strains, it is resistant to all antibiotics except Vancomycin. In 2002, the CDC reported the first case of Vancomycin-resistant *Staphylococcus aureus* (VRSA) in the U.S. (CDC 2002). This demonstrates a continuing trend of antimicrobial resistance. It is therefore critical to quickly identify and isolate patients carrying these organisms to prevent their spread.

The most recent concerns have been the potential spread of severe acquired respiratory syndrome (SARS) and avian influenza to the U.S. Both viruses quickly moved from the Far East to many other parts of the world. When SARS reached hospitals in Toronto, Canada, there was documented nosocomial spread, demonstrating the need for improvements in hospital preparedness (McDonald et al. 2004; Loutfy et al. 2004). These outbreaks have increased concern for another dangerous disease, avian influenza type A (H5N1). While this disease is currently limited to those with direct contact with infected poultry, a major concern is that this virus may mutate and become an airborne pathogen. If it does mutate, avian influenza could result in the next pandemic.

Susceptible Host

Patient susceptibility varies greatly, since some may be immune, others may develop into asymptomatic carriers, and some may develop clinical disease. The most important host factors affecting susceptibility are age, underlying disease, and current treatments (antimicrobial drugs, immunosuppressive agents, irradiation, surgery, anesthesia, and catheterization).

Means of Transmission

The five main routes of infection transmission are:

- Contact (direct or indirect)
- Droplet
- Airborne
- Common vehicle
- Vector borne

Each of these will be discussed below.

Direct Versus Indirect Contact

Contact transmission may be direct, for example, person-to-person contact, or indirect, as when a person contaminates an object and another person comes in contact with that object.

Droplet Versus Airborne

Microbes can be released into the air from human sources as droplets or droplet nuclei. Droplets produced by such activities as coughing or sneezing are relatively large in size (>5µm in diameter). Once released, they either settle out of the air or dry out and become *droplet nuclei*. It is estimated that these particles become desiccated after traveling no more than approximately three feet. The particles are now much smaller in size (<5µm) and are capable of going deeper into the respiratory system once inhaled. Fortunately, most microorganisms do not survive this drying process and cannot be transmitted greater than a distance of three feet. There are some notable exceptions; tuberculosis (TB) and measles survive the drying process and, because of the small size of the droplet nuclei, may remain suspended in the air for considerable periods of time. This is why it is critical to have patients with airborne infections isolated in rooms with proper mechanical exhaust (six room air changes per hour for existing facilities, and twelve room air changes per hour in new construction or renovations) (AIA 2006). These rooms must be under negative pressure relative to the corridor.

Other Sources of Airborne or Droplet Transmission

Soil, water, dust, and decaying organic matter may be released into the air, creating potentially infectious aerosols. For this reason, care must be taken during renovation projects and in the placement of building fresh air inlets. A special concern is the location of aerosol-generating equipment such as cooling towers. Water-borne disease may occur if these towers are located in close proximity to building fresh air intakes since they may be contaminated with *Legionella pneumophilia* bacteria (CDC 2003).

Vector and Vehicle Transmission

Vectors are living transmitters of disease. For example, West Nile virus requires a mosquito to transmit the viral agent from a bird reservoir or another infected host to a susceptible host. Vector-borne HAI transmission is rare in the U.S. However, this may not be the case in some developing countries where screened windows and other public health necessities may be absent.

Vehicles are non-living transmitters of disease. For example, inadequate disinfection or sterilization of medical devices may result in HAIs. (This issue is covered in Chapter 4.) Other potential vehicles include: contaminated food, water, and medications. These are uncommon causes of HAIs, but they may result in large-scale outbreaks. It is particularly worrisome if the contamination occurs at a pharmaceutical manufacturing plant because it may result in an international incident. Water systems may be contaminated with *Legionella pneumophilia*, and this can make even showering risky for certain susceptible patients. There is a wide variety of medical equipment that may serve as vehicles of disease, such as dialysis systems, hydrotherapy tanks, endoscopes and endoscope re-processors, and even dental lines. These may become contaminated with chlorine-resistant, gram-negative bacteria that may cause illness or death (CDC 2003).

STRUCTURE OF IC PROGRAMS

Below is a discussion of the role of the IC Committee and the key personnel and their tasks on the Committee.

IC Committee

A healthcare facility IC committee serves several important functions in the management of HAIs. First, this committee approves policies that establish optimal patient-care procedures to reduce the risk of infections. Once these policies are established, educational programs can focus on implementing these approved practices. Thus, the second important committee function is to oversee IC educational programs. Third, the committee has the responsibility of monitoring compliance with approved policies. This means that the committee must have a written authority statement from the governing body to allow it to take actions when it is deemed necessary. The last function of the committee is to serve as a mechanism for the exchange of information between programs and departments. It is often necessary to clarify who is responsible for certain key tasks; for example, is it the housekeeping department or nursing staff that is responsible for removing sharps containers from patient rooms when full? Failure to address such a mundane problem could result in a sharps-related injury.

Key Personnel and their Roles

The key members involved in IC are the IC committee chairperson and the ICP. Three other important members are the quality assurance coordinator, the employee health coordinator, and the hospital institutional environmental health and safety (IEHS) professional. The quality assurance coordinator should be involved because success in preventing HAIs is an important measure of the quality of patient care. The employee health program coordinator is important because of the role of the employee health program in preventing hospital staff from acquiring infections through vaccinations and by identifying employees who have been infected and referring them for treatment (CDC 1997; CDC 1998). Managing and controlling certain hazardous agents, such as blood-borne pathogens or TB, involve both the IC and the safety program. It is therefore critical that the IEHS professional work closely with the IC professional. Other important groups that should be represented on the IC committee are members are hospital administration, because of the committee's role in policy setting, and clinical staff, because IC decisions often directly affect patient management.

SPECIAL DEPARTMENTAL IC CONCERNS

Besides the general IC concerns found in hospitals overall, specific hospital departments have unique concerns regarding infection; such departments include:

- Central services (CS)
- Intensive care units (ICUs)
- Kitchen facilities
- Laboratories
- Laundry facilities
- Morgues
- Obstetrics (OB) and pediatrics
- Outpatient and emergency services
- Pharmacies
- Physical therapy (PT) and hydrotherapy
- Post-operative surgery
- Radiology

   Each of these departments and their specific IC issues are addressed below.

Central Services (CS)

The heart of an effective IC program is the CS department. This department is responsible for the disinfection and sterilization of instruments and supplies used throughout the hospital. The design of this department should be broken down into three distinct areas: decontamination, instrument reprocessing, and sterile storage. There should be physical barriers separating these three areas, and the ventilation system should assure the movement of air from the sterile areas, through the clean (reprocessing) areas, into the dirty (decontamination) area. The decontamination room should be under negative pressure, relative to the rest of the department and to the hallway (AIA 2006). A cart-washing room should be located between the decontamination area and the instrument reprocessing area to allow large equipment to be disinfected. Personnel assigned to the decontamination area must use proper personal protective equipment (PPE), including moisture-resistant gowns, gloves, and face shields. Those individuals working in clean areas should wear hair and shoe covers. Individuals assigned to clean and dirty operations must not move between these areas unless they don the appropriate clothing. Another concern in CS is the overuse of flash sterilizers for reprocessing surgical instruments. This becomes a problem when procedures are scheduled back to back, and there are insufficient numbers of surgical packs to meet the demand. A final issue is the difficulty in processing instruments that are suspected to be contaminated with prions. Prions are resistant to all conventional sterilization methods (Fichet et al. 2004). Disinfection and sterilization procedures used in CS are covered in Chapter 4.

Intensive or Special Care Units (ICUs)

Infections are a serious complication for patients in an ICU (CDC 2007a). These patients may require mechanical ventilators or other forms of life support and, as such, have lower immunity and multiple pathways of exposure (Ayliffe et al. 2000). Since these patients require more frequent nursing care, a serious concern is cross-contamination between patients from the staff, and, because such patients are immuno-compromised, opportunistic pathogens may pose a serious risk of infection. ICU design is critical in reducing the potential for infection. The arrangement of the units must allow for easy access between patients while maintaining barriers to the spread of infection. There must be at least one airborne infectious isolation room in each ICU.

Kitchen Facilities

IC in the hospital kitchen is the same as in any commercial food establishment, with one important difference. There must be stricter adherence to the principles of basic sanitation. An error in contamination prevention in a hospital kitchen would likely result in more severe illness and even death because the patient population is more susceptible than the general public. It is also important to prevent the kitchen staff from becoming infected because they can be a source of infection to the patients (Ayliffe et al. 2000).

In the past, a primary strategy in prevention of food-borne disease was to medically monitor food handlers. This approach was expensive and largely ineffective because timing of the examination was problematic. Over 30 years ago, the Food and Drug Administration developed a food safety program for astronauts called Hazard Analysis and Critical Control Point (HACCP) (FDA 2001). This program was designed to identify and monitor the highest risk food handling tasks to prevent food-borne diseases. (A serious gastrointestinal disease outbreak on a space craft would obviously be an undesirable event.) HACCP has since been applied to other food-handling industries and should be adopted in all hospitals. In order for HACCP to succeed, food service personnel must be thoroughly trained in contamination control techniques. There must be routine inspection of high-risk activities and complete documentation of these inspections.

Laboratories

The hazard of accidental exposure to infectious agents in the hospital laboratory has long been known (CDC and NIH 2007). However, with the ease of travel to developing countries, the presence of immigrants from countries where dangerous pathogens are endemic, and other factors, the risk of laboratory-acquired infections has increased (Herwaldt 2001). The mode of transmission and dose of exposure is often not known until the laboratory worker develops signs and symptoms of disease. Potential routes may include ingestion, inhalation of aerosols, contact with mucus membranes, and percutaneous injection.

To reduce the risk of infection, laboratories should adhere to rigorously enforced principles of biosafety. This includes development of biosafety protocols, as well as training for all laboratory personnel on these protocols. The CDC and National Institutes of Health (NIH) developed a system of biosafety levels from 1–4 (CDC and NIH 2007). Biosafety level 1 is equivalent to a high-school science laboratory, where only microorganisms that are not considered pathogenic to humans would be handled. Most hospital laboratories only deal with moderate-risk microorganisms and would be listed as biosafety level 2. The major concern here is the prevention of exposure to infectious aerosols from centrifugation or other procedures. Laboratories in larger teaching or research hospitals that work with *Mycobacterium tuberculosis* or other high-risk organisms should meet biosafety level 3. Since there may be serious disease consequences from auto injection or inhalation of aerosols, added safety measures must be implemented. Biosafety level 4 has special ventilation, multiple containment areas, and other features designed to handle exotic and dangerous pathogens such as the Lassa fever virus. Some specific preventive measures in these biosafety levels would include: frequent hand washing, use of appropriate PPE, and use of safety equipment. An example of safety equipment is a centrifuge safety cup, which prevents the release of aerosols during centrifugation of specimens.

One of the most important ways of protecting laboratory staff is through the use of biological safety cabinets (BSCs). There are three basic classes of BSCs. Class I is designed to protect the worker. Air from the cabinet is exhausted through a HEPA filter before being discharged into the room or to the outside. Class II has two HEPA filters, one of which protects the product inside the hood, and the other filters exhausted air. Class II Type B2 cabinets are not recirculating; 100% of the exhaust is directed to the outside. Class III is a glove box that is used for the most dangerous types of agents.

In addition to biosafety precautions, laboratory personnel should be vaccinated for certain infectious agents (Bolyard et al. 1998). The same approaches for biosafety and immunizations would be applied in animal research facilities as in clinical laboratories.

Laundry Facilities

Improper handling of soiled linen can pose a risk to healthcare workers, and inadequately disinfected "clean" linen can pose a risk to patients (Byrns and Bland 1980). Soiled linen should be handled as little as possible before placement into a laundry bag and stored in a properly ventilated storage room. The AIA recommends a minimum of ten room air changes per hour for soiled linen processing and storage rooms (AIA 2006). A special concern is that used sharp instruments may be left in the soiled linen, resulting in a sharps injury to laundry personnel.

Personnel handling soiled linen should wear PPE, including a moisture-resistant gown. The laundering process is usually effective in destroying most vegetative microorganisms because of high temperatures, pH changes, bleach treatment, and significant dilution. However, on occasion, errors in procedures or equipment malfunctions may reduce the biocidal effect of the laundering process. The laundry operation, whether it is operated in-house or through a contract, should be inspected to assure that proper procedures are in place and followed.

Morgues

A dead body may be the source of infection unless proper precautions are taken (Ayliffe et al. 2000). Potentially infectious aerosols may be released during autopsy or direct contact with mucus membranes or breaks in the skin may serve as sources of transmission. Researchers found that a TB patient did not transmit the infection to caregivers prior to death, but during a three-hour autopsy, the release of infectious aerosols resulted in positive skin tests for all five nonreactors (Templeton et al. 1995).

Control of infection can be achieved through the use of proper PPE, mechanical exhaust ventilation of the mortuary, and disinfection of instruments and surfaces. Also, the same down-draught autopsy table, which was described in Chapter 2 (see Figure 2.1) for the control of formaldehyde exposures, should protect post-mortem staff from exposure to infectious aerosols. Perhaps the most important control measure is to inform mortuary staff when they are dealing with the body of a patient who died from a communicable disease (Ayliffe et al. 2000).

Obstetrics (OB) and Pediatrics

Infection risks in OB depend on the stage of the patient's delivery (Ayliffe et al. 2000). Post-natal patients are at greater risk than antenatal (also called prenatal), and patients undergoing a Caesarean (C) section are at highest risk of infection. Colonization of the infant's skin with bacteria occurs immediately after birth, and the infant must be protected from contamination with pathogens. Strict adherence to hand washing is critical. In addition, perinatal patients (those up to 18 months old) have less developed immune systems than adults or older children. Outbreaks of respiratory syncytial virus (RSV), rotavirus and others can spread quickly through pediatric units. Cross-infection may be reduced by "rooming-in" the infant with its mother. However, an outbreak requires prompt isolation of suspected cases. In some cases, it may be necessary to *cohort* infants to stop an outbreak. This involves placing all infants born in a 24–48 hour period in one location with dedicated nursing personnel.

Children admitted to pediatrics may be incubating CAIs at the time of admission (Ayliffe et al. 2000). This presents a special risk to other patients and to employees. All employees in these units must have up-to-date vaccinations against the most common of these CAIs.

Outpatient Department (OPD) and Emergency Department (ED)

The risk of HAI transmission is less in the OPD and ED; however, there is a high risk of exposure to CAIs (Ayliffe et al. 2000). It is therefore important to have facilities available for the examination and treatment of patients suspected of having communicable diseases. These rooms should have at least six air changes per hour (ACH) in existing facilities and twelve ACH for new facilities and be under negative pressure relative to the corridor (AIA 2006). There should also be a readily available supply of gloves, gowns, and N-95 respirators on hand at all times.

Pharmacies

The major concern in the pharmacy is the protection of pharmaceuticals from contamination. This is particularly true of admixtures (intravenous solutions prepared by pharmacy personnel). There must be stringent policies to assure aseptic procedures in the preparation of admixtures, including proper labeling of the mixtures. In order to maintain a high level of asepsis, admixtures should be prepared inside of horizontal laminar flow hoods. See Figure 3.2. There has been a recent push for cleanrooms that that meet the requirements of Chapter 797 of the *USP Pharmacists' Pharmacopeia* for the preparation of all admixtures (USP 2008). Researchers found that there was no difference in admixture contamination rates between traditional sites using laminar flow hoods and preparations done in cleanrooms (Thomas et al. 2005). Instead they found that operator technique was the most important determinant of admixture contamination. This issue has important implications because construction of cleanrooms that meet Chapter 797 will be costly.

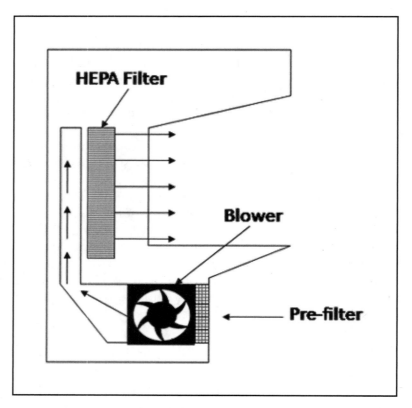

Figure 3.2 Horizontal laminar flow hood.

If the pharmaceutical is potentially hazardous, for example antineoplastic drugs, then a horizontal laminar must never be used. Instead, a biological safety cabinet (BSC) that protects both the worker and the product should be used. See Figure 3.3.

Physical Therapy (PT) and Hydrotherapy

The PT department receives patients from the community as well as all parts of the hospital, and physical therapists may go to other units to do treatments. Therefore, hand washing and equipment disinfection must be stressed. In addition, the hydrotherapy pool poses a significant risk for cross-infection. These devices may be the source of skin or respiratory infections due to *Legionella* (CDC 2003). See chapter 4 for information on the decontamination of hydrotherapy equipment.

Post-operative Surgery

The U.S. National Research Council developed a surgical classification system in 1964 (Berard and Gandon 1964). The four classes involve increasing risk of post-operative infection:

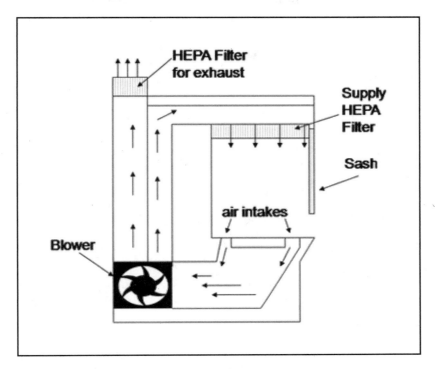

Figure 3.3 Class II biological safety cabinet.

- Class 1 (Clean): Elective surgery involving sterile tissue
- Class 2 (Clean-contaminated): Urgent surgery involving the respiratory tract or other non-clean site that does not involve heavily contaminated or infected tissue
- Class 3 (Contaminated): Surgery of the gastrointestinal tract or other heavily contaminated site with non-purulent inflammation
- Class 4 (Dirty): Surgery involving removal of purulent tissue

The use of pre-operative antibiotic prophylaxis has significantly reduced infection rates for the more risky procedures (Classes 3 and 4). However, proper timing before surgery is critical (Tan et al. 2006). The U.S. National Nosocomial Infection Surveillance (NNIS) system reported hospital infection rates to be: clean, 2.1%; clean-contaminated, 3.3%; contaminated, 6.4%; and dirty, 7.1% (Culver et al. 1991). It is also important to note that the source of surgical site infections is most commonly the patient's own skin (Ayliffe et al. 2000). This means that it is important to use proper skin antisepsis and to minimize the delay between pre-operative shaving and the start of surgery. While the operating room environment is less likely to be the source of infection, it is still important to assure that the ventilation system is operating properly, including the use of final filters of at least 90% efficiency (AIA 2006). For certain types of surgeries such as bone marrow transplants or total hip replacements, high-efficiency particulate air (HEPA) filters, which are 99.97% effective against particles that are 0.3 micrometers in diameter, are recommended. The direction of air should always be from sterile to clean and from clean to dirty areas (Ayliffe et al. 2000). A simple but effective measure to reduce post-operative infections is to provide feedback to surgical teams on their infection rates.

Radiology

There are similar concerns in radiology as in PT, since patients may come from all parts of the hospital for diagnostics and treatments (Ayliffe et al. 2000). In addition, individuals suspected of having communicable respiratory infections are likely to be referred for chest x-rays. This means that the potential for cross-infection is high. In addition, portable x-ray equipment may be used in other departments, including the operating rooms, and this may be a source of contamination in those areas. Prevention of cross-infection requires that the radiology staff be informed when a patient is suspected of having a communicable disease, and equipment must be disinfected when used in critical areas such as the operating rooms or after contact with an infected patient.

KEY COMPONENTS OF AN IC PROGRAM

The key components of an IC program are: surveillance, data gathering, data management, data reporting, assessment and control. Each of these is discussed separately below.

Surveillance

Surveillance is defined as, "the ongoing systematic collection, analysis, and interpretation, of health data essential to the planning, implementation, and evaluation of public health practice, as well as the timely dissemination of the data to those who need to know" (Thacker and Berkelman 1988). In the healthcare environment, infection surveillance must include both patients and employees. Employees must be included in surveillance because they may serve as both the source of an infection or the target of an infection. The type of surveillance system will vary based on the specific type of healthcare setting (the size and type of facility). In a large, acute-care facility, surveillance may target specific high-risk areas, whereas, in an extended care setting, it may be possible to do comprehensive surveillance of all units. An ambulatory care setting offers unique challenges because infections resulting from outpatient treatment will not be apparent until after the patient has left the facility. This means there must be a feedback system between free-standing ambulatory facilities and inpatient facilities, so that infections identified during a new admission are linked to the origin of the problem.

The CDC recommends that data from surveillance systems be used to (CDC 2001):

- Guide immediate action for cases of public health importance;
- Measure the burden of a disease (or other health-related event); including changes in related factors, the identification of populations at high risk, and the identification of new or emerging health concerns;
- Monitor trends in the burden of a disease (or other health-related event); including the detection of epidemics (outbreaks) and pandemics;
- Guide the planning, implementation, and evaluation of programs to prevent and control disease, injury, or adverse exposure;
- Evaluate public policy;
- Detect changes in health practices and the effects of these changes;
- Prioritize the allocation of health resources;
- Describe the clinical course of disease; and
- Provide a basis for epidemiologic research.

Steps in the surveillance process for a healthcare setting

1. **Assess Your Specific Population.** This assessment should consider the type of patients served, including those who may increase liability to the organization because of their high risk of getting an HAI. For example, the CDC recommends focused surveillance of patients at high risk for *aspergillosis* (CDC 2004a). Immuno-compromised patients, such as those undergoing chemotherapy or organ transplantation and patients with advanced HIV infection, are especially at risk for *aspergillosis*. Other factors to consider in establishing a surveillance program are the most common types of diagnoses in the area and the most frequently performed procedure. Possible sources for infection surveillance data collection include medical records, laboratory microbiology reports, surgical databases, and radiology reports.

2. **Determine the Surveillance Focus.** It is important to determine the focus of a surveillance program. Will the surveillance focus on processes that are high risk for infections or outcomes such as the number of infections? Ideally, a surveillance system will include elements of both. There must also be time frames for collecting data (monthly, quarterly, or annually) for both process and outcome surveillance, which should be described in a surveillance plan that is evaluated annually. The plan should also set goals for outcome and process surveillance, and finally, the surveillance plan should include clear definitions for what is being surveyed.

Data Gathering

The first step in data gathering is to develop a standard collection form to collect information on either processes (such as urinary catheterizations) or outcome data. Examples of critical outcome data are the total number of HAIs in patients and, if the facility is large enough, a breakdown by types of infections (urinary tract, surgical site, bacteremia, or respiratory). Surgical-site infections should also be categorized by risk category as described above under post-operative surgical site infection. The preferred denominator for reporting total HAIs should be the number of patient days per month, quarter or year. Surgical-site rates are calculated based on the number of patients receiving a particular type of surgical procedure. Surveillance of employee infections can include more than just HAIs. The number of tuberculin skin conversions and the number of needlestick injuries should be tracked because they represent a breakdown in IC procedures. For workers, the denominator is based on either the number of person-days or hours worked per month, quarter, or year. It is also important to distinguish between incident cases (new infections during a time period) and prevalence cases (all infections at a point in time or during a time period). Finally, it is important to only collect data that you intend to use.

Data Management: Importance and Uses

A serious weakness of any surveillance program is to not fully use the data gathered. To be effective, an IC program must develop a process for data management, implement this process, and monitor the process to assure that the approach is meeting the program's needs. The goal is to analyze data and compare it to a baseline or other benchmark. Data must then be interpreted to determine if there are any trends, and if warranted, some actions must be taken.

An Example of Data Management

Suppose there are four infections from a total of 58 C-sections performed in your hospital's obstetric unit during the months of July through December in 2007. The data management plan calls for quarterly monitoring of surgical site infections from Class 2 C-sections and comparing the results to the same time frame for the previous year. You determine that only two of the four infections and 25 of the 58 C-sections meet the definition of Class 2. The others would be considered higher risk procedures (Class 3 or 4). The surgical-site rate can be determined by dividing the two Class 2 infection cases by the 25 C-sections and multiplying by 100 for a quarterly rate of 8.0%. You would then compare this rate to the benchmark you have set for Class 2 C-sections. If this rate is significantly higher than average, then action is needed to reduce the rate.

Data Reporting

Once data have been analyzed, the next step is to prepare reports of the findings. The purpose of these reports is to lay the groundwork for improving outcomes (reducing the number of HAIs) or processes (improving performance for certain high-risk tasks). The level of detail of the reports varies with the size and type of facilities, but in most cases, simple descriptive statistics (percents and measures of central tendency) will suffice. The use of charts and graphs can be an important enhancement in the presentation of this information. This is especially true when current results are compared to historical trends. This allows committee members or other decision makers to see the significance of the results at a glance.

ASSESSMENT OF THE IC PROGRAM

As described earlier, the IC program should be data-driven, and the effectiveness of the program must be supported with objective evidence. Each year, the infection committee must set specific objectives for the year, and at least quarterly, progress on meeting these objectives should be measured. There are a variety of ways of evaluating the effectiveness of the program. However, the most important indicators of success would include a reduction in infections or development and implementation of an effective program to solve a problem.

Measuring Success

The reduction in HAI rates would provide strong evidence of an effective program. This reduction could be assessed in numerous ways. For example, the current year's total HAI rate per 1000 patient days could be compared to prior years' rates. Alternately, specific departmental infection rates could be compared to prior years' rates. Assessment of infection rates in the operating room should be stratified by surgery risk levels (see above under post-operative infection). One very useful assessment would be to look at the current year's infection rates for certain procedures that have an increased risk of infection. For example, infections due to central line-days or urinary catheter days could be compared to prior rates or to national data. If national data is to be used for comparison purposes, it is necessary to collect infection data using CDC protocols (CDC 2004b).

Measures of success could also include changes in process. The implementation of special studies or new initiatives provides evidence of a successful program. For example, suppose that an audit of the ICU found poor compliance with hospital's hand-hygiene policy. After an intensive educational campaign and periodic spot-checks, the unit is re-surveyed and a substantial improvement is noted. The challenge in this example would be to have built-in checks to assure that any improvement is long term. Other examples of successes would be documented learned skills or behavior changes by personnel, creation of or changes to policies and procedures, or changes in the employee health program or other key departments that may affect IC.

CONTROL PROGRAMS

IC activities must be driven by data that target supplies, equipment and people. The second part of the CDC definition for surveillance describes the importance of data in planning, implementing and evaluating a change in practice. For example, if it appears that this month's infection data for HAI bacteremia is significantly above expected levels, an investigation is launched to identify the cause, and once known, a program is developed to control it. Once the approach to control has been evaluated and found to be successful, then it behooves the IC professional to share this information with hospital staff and others in the IC discipline.

Selection of Supplies and Instruments

The IC program has an important role in the selection of certain types of supplies and equipment. The reason for this involvement is that the design of certain items, such as needles and syringes, may increase or decrease the potential for HAIs. In addition, the IC committee should approve the types of germicides used in the facility. While the IC program has an important role in the selection process, it is also important to remember that there must be involvement of users in the decision-making process. This means that there should be a field trial to determine efficacy, safety, and easy of use for several different versions of a product. Cost should not be the primary factor in selection.

Involvement in Construction and Renovation

Healthcare facilities frequently undergo new construction or major renovations. A significant concern is that these construction activities may have an effect on the IC program. This is especially important when the changes involve the hospital ventilation system or removal of walls or other natural barriers to the migration of contaminated air. Therefore, the American Institute of Architects (AIA) construction standards and CDC guidelines require the input of the IC program prior to the start and during all new construction and major renovations (AIA 2006; CDC 2003). Infection and safety hazards associated with new construction are covered in Chapter 13 of this book.

Patient Isolation

One of the most important means of controlling the spread of infection is prompt isolation of individuals who are suspected being infected with a communicable disease (CDC 2007a).

The CDC initially provided guidance in the establishment of isolation protocols in 1970 (*Isolation Techniques for Use in Hospitals*). This guidance was revised in 1975 with the provision of infection-category-specific precautions. A major revision occurred in 1983 when CDC published their *Guidelines for Isolation Precautions in Hospitals*. These guidelines were short-lived because of the concern for blood-borne diseases, especially HIV.

Universal Precautions

In 1985, CDC developed the concept of *universal precautions* (UP), the intent of which was to protect personnel from blood-borne infections. Most importantly, for the first time, these precautions were applied universally to all patients, regardless of presumed infection status. The primary focus of these precautions was the expanded use of gloves and other forms of PPE to protect skin and mucous membranes from contact with blood. There were some severe limitations to UP. The protocol only covered blood and body fluids containing visible blood; additional isolation precautions may be needed, since other fluids, excretions, and secretions not covered by UP may also present an infection risk.

Body Substance Isolation

In 1987, a group of IC professionals developed *body substance isolation* (BSI) to address the limitations of UP. BSI was applied to all moist and potentially infectious body substances, not just blood. Like UP, all patients were covered by the protocol, regardless of presumed infection status. A key feature of BSI was the use of "Stop Sign Alert" for patients suspected of having disease spread via the airborne route of transmission. There were limitations to BSI as well. A major concern was the increased cost of barrier equipment, especially gloves. Some felt that the routine protocol was difficult to maintain, and that there was uncertainty regarding the use of the "Stop Sign Alert." Finally, the protocol did not cover all isolation precautions to prevent transmission such as droplet spread.

Standard Precautions and Transmission-based Precautions

In the early 1990s, there was much confusion about isolation precautions. The requirements for compliance with UP and BSI were misunderstood. Some facilities stated that they followed UP in policy, but implemented BSI in practice (and vice-versa). The primary problem was a disconnection between policy, application and practice. It became clear that a new approach was needed, one that involved a two-tiered, patient isolation system.

In 1998, the CDC released their updated *Guideline for Infection Control in Health Care Personnel*, which included a two-tiered approach to patient isolation (Bolyard et al. 1998). The CDC's new two-tiered protocols were called *standard precautions* and *transmission-based precautions*. The two protocols were intended to be the primary strategy for the prevention and control of nosocomial infections. In 2007, CDC updated their guidelines for isolation precautions to address IC needs in other types of healthcare facilities besides acute-care hospitals, such as ambulatory and long-term care facilities (CDC 2007a). The revised guidelines were also intended to address growing concerns regarding emerging organisms, such as the causative agent of SARS and the increased prevalence of multi-drug-resistant strains of bacteria. Other concerns addressed in the 2007 *Guidelines* were the importance of environmental controls to protect severely immuno-compromised patients from fungal infections and the importance of staffing levels and composition as a means of preventing HAIs. The last concern points out the critical importance of having a proactive "culture of safety" in healthcare settings. See Chapter 5 for more information on safety culture.

Standard Precautions

Like the earlier UP and BSI, *standard precautions* (SP) applies to all patients regardless of their diagnosis or presumed infection status. All body fluids, secretions, and excretions, except sweat, are covered under SP, and it applies to non-intact skin and mucous membranes. The protocol follows basic rules of IC such as hand washing and the use of barrier protection (gloves, gowns, masks, and eye protection) when employees expect to come in contact with body fluids.

SP also requires compliance with the regulations of the Occupational Safety and Health Administration (OSHA) in the use of sharp devices. OSHA regulations require that a written plan be in place that will prevent injuries when staff is required to use hazardous devices such as needles and scalpels. Recapping of needles is only permitted with a one-hand technique or by using a mechanical device to hold the sharp. Used sharps should be placed in puncture-proof containers close to the point of care (OSHA 2006a).

Transmission-based Precautions

Transmission-based precautions (TBP) are used in addition to SP for specified patients known or suspected to be infected by pathogens spread by airborne, droplet, or contact modes of transmission. TBP is based on the method for transmission of the particular pathogen as described above.

Airborne Isolation. Airborne isolation is used for those diseases that are transmitted through the air by droplet nuclei, such as TB, measles (rubeola), chickenpox (varicella), and smallpox. Additional precautions for airborne isolation include the placement of such patients in a negative pressure isolation room. Anyone entering the isolation room must wear respirator that is an N-95, N-99, or N-100. Patients who leave the isolation room must wear a surgical mask when out of the room.

Droplet Isolation. This precaution protects against transmission of particles larger than five micrometers in diameter. According to the CDC, a surgical mask is only needed for this isolation and is only required within three feet of the infected patient. Some examples of diseases that require this type of isolation include pneumonic plague, pertussis, and influenza. The recommendation to use surgical masks in lieu of respirators is controversial and not supported by all public health authorities because these masks do not form a tight seal with the face. In addition to respiratory protection, persons entering these rooms must follow standard precautions.

Contact Isolation. Contact isolation is intended to prevent direct and indirect contact with a patient's infectious organisms; examples include a patient with a major draining abscess, a patient infected with *Clostridium difficile*, or a diapered infant with diarrhea. Such patients must be placed in a private room. All persons coming in contact with the patient must observe proper hand washing and use of gloves. Individuals in close contact with the patient are also required to use gowns.

ROLE OF IEHS IN IC

Some IEHS professionals work as IC practitioners, but in most cases, this role has been assumed by registered nurses or microbiologists. Nevertheless, there are important contributions that the IEHS professional can make to the IC program. First, it is important to remember that the control of certain occupational diseases caused by blood-borne or respiratory pathogens involves elements of safety and IC. Therefore, IC and safety programs must work together as one.

Assessing the Adequacy of Ventilation

The protection of healthcare workers from communicable diseases, such as TB or SARS, requires a hospital ventilation system that meets minimum standards (CDC 2007a). IEHS personnel, working with plant engineering staff, should monitor critical locations such as isolation rooms to assure that existing facilities achieve at least six ACH and new facilities achieve twelve ACH (AIA 2006). In addition, there may be a need for local exhaust ventilation systems or booths for such things as sputum induction or transportation of patients suspected of SARS infection (CDC 2007a). The CDC currently recommends that these ventilation booths achieve a minimum of twenty ACH. There are no design standards for portable isolation enclosures as of this writing.

Selection and Testing of Respirators

The selection and fit-testing of aerosol respirators is another important role for IEHS personnel. In most instances, properly fitted and tested N-95 disposable respirators provide an adequate measure of safety. However, under certain conditions, such as working with patients infected with multi-drug-resistant TB, a higher level of protection may be warranted. This would mean using N-100 respirators or even powered, air-purifying respirators (PAPRs). The OSHA standard on respiratory protection provides guidance on the selection and testing of these respirators (OSHA 2006b).

Selection of Germicides

In the past, the CDC provided guidance to hospitals on the selection and use of germicides. While the Association for Professionals in Infection Control & Epidemiology, Inc. (APIC) now provides this guidance, the selection of the appropriate germicide is complex because you must balance efficacy (whether it works) and safety of personnel and patients (Rutala 1996). Therefore, the decision-making process on the selection and use of sterilizing agents, disinfectants, and antiseptics should include the IEHS professional to assure that the germicide will be both effective and safe. See Chapter 4 for more details on germicides.

Applied Epidemiology

The IEHS professional should have at least basic training in epidemiology and data management. In addition, the IEHS professional should have expertise in anticipating and recognizing environmental or occupational hazards. This training and expertise makes the IEHS professional an important member of the hospital's hazard assessment team and IC committee. Some examples of specific tasks include organizing and interpreting data from routine surveillance or outbreak investigation, determining the appropriate study design (randomized trial, cohort, case-control or cross-sectional study) when assessing a particular problem, and monitoring the effectiveness of control strategies. The monitoring could take the form of measuring a process (ventilation rates) or by comparing outcome results (changes in infection rates after implementing the control). It is important to remember that the training of clinical staff is focused on protecting the individual. In comparison, the training of the IEHS professional is on protecting a community or group. This type of world view makes the IEHS professional an important member of the applied epidemiology team.

SUMMARY AND CONCLUSIONS

In this chapter, we reviewed the basic concepts of infection transmission, including a discussion of the chain of infection. By examining the components in the chain of infection, it is possible to select the optimal control strategy. Once you have controlled that element, the links in the chain of infection are broken and disease transmission is stopped. The IC concerns in selected hospital departments were reviewed. The risk of infection transmission varies greatly among different departments. Assessment is a critical component of any IC program at either the departmental or hospital-wide level. An effective program should be able to measure success in terms of either a reduction in infection rates or by process changes that reduce the risk of infections. We also described key personnel and key components in an effective IC program. Since the control of blood-borne or respiratory pathogens involves elements of both IC and safety, it is crucial that IEHS play an active role. The evolution of isolation techniques over the past 30 years was also described. The current approach is two-tiered, starting with SP to be applied to all patients regardless of their presumed infection status. The second tier is TBP for those patients who we suspect of having one type of disease, and we focus on controlling its method of spread. Finally, the role of the IEHS professional was described. Because of training in epidemiology and public health, the IEHS professional has an important contribution to the hospital IC program.

Review

1. Distinguish between healthcare-associated infections, nosocomial infections, and community-acquired infections.
2. The SENIC study found one type of infection to be most common, one type to be most costly, and one type to have the highest mortality. What were they?
3. What is a *sentinel event* as it relates to IC?
4. What is the *chain of infection*, and how is it used in IC programs?
5. What is the difference between droplet and airborne infections?
6. What is the difference between vector-borne and vehicle-borne infections?
7. What are the four classes of surgical procedures? Which one should have the lowest infection rate?
8. If there were twelve infections among women in the post-partum unit during the month of July and the average daily census for this unit was 50 women, what was the monthly infection rate?
9. What is the basic concept behind *Standard Precautions*?
10. What are *Transmission Based Precautions*?
11. List at least three roles that an institutional environmental health and safety professional can play in an IC program.

Additional Resources

Useful Guidelines in Infection Control: (at www.cdc.gov)

CDC Guidelines for Protecting Patients

- Preventing Healthcare-Associated Pneumonia, 2003
- Environmental Infection Control in Healthcare Facilities, 2003
- Hand Hygiene in Healthcare Settings, 2002
- Prevention of Intravascular Device-Related Infections, 2002
- Prevention of Surgical Site Infections, 1999
- Guideline for Isolation Precautions: Preventing Transmission of Infectious Agents in Healthcare Settings, 2007
- Prevention of Catheter Associated Urinary Tract Infections, 1981

CDC Guidelines for Protecting Healthcare Workers

- Management of Occupational Exposures to Hepatitis B, Hepatitis C, and HIV and Recommendations for Postexposure Prophylaxis - 2001
- Infection Control in Health Care Personnel - 1998

Other CDC Guidelines by Topic

- Guidelines for Preventing Opportunistic Infections Among Hematopoietic Stem Cell Transplant Recipients
- Guidelines & Recommendations for Ventilation, Construction, and Renovation of Hospitals
- Guidelines for Infection Control in Home Care Settings
- Infection Control Long-Term Care Facilities

Other Web Resources for IC

North Carolina Statewide Program for Infection Control and Epidemiology (SPICE) (http://www.unc.edu/depts/spice/)

Reference List

American Institute of Architects (AIA). 2006. *Guidelines for Design and Construction of Hospital and Health Care Facilities.* Washington, D.C.: American Institute of Architects.

Ayliffe, G. A. J., A. P. Fraise, A. M. Geddes, and K. Mitchell. 2000. *Control of Hospital Infection: A Practical Handbook.* 4th ed. London: Arnold.

Beam, J. W. and B. Buckley. 2006. "Community-Acquired Methicillin-Resistant Staphylococcus aureus: Prevalence and Risk Factors." *J.Athl.Train.* 41:337–340.

Berard, F. and J. Gandon. 1964. "Postoperative Wound Infections: The Influence of Ultraviolet Irradiation of the Operating Room and of Various Other Factors." *Ann.Surg.* 160:SUPPL 1:1–192.

Bolyard, E. A., O. C. Tablan, W. W. Williams, M. L. Pearson, C. N. Shapiro, and S. D. Deitchmann. 1998. "Guideline for Infection Control in Healthcare Personnel, 1998." *Infect.Control Hosp.Epidemiol.* 19:407–463.

Byrns, G. E. and L. A. Bland. 1980. "Environmental Health Impact in the Hospital Laundry." *Journal of Environmental Health* 42:258–262.

Centers for Disease Control and Prevention (CDC). 2005. *CDC Advisory Committee Offers Guidance to States on Developing Systems for Public Reporting of Healthcare-Associated Infections.* (retrieved August 11, 2008) (http://www.cdc.gov/od/oc/media/pressrel/r050228.htm)

———. 2006. "Conference Summary: Methicillin-resistant *Staphylococcus aureus* as a Community Pathogen." *Emerg.Infect.Dis.* 12:1–5.

———. 2007b. *Cover Your Cough Program* (retrieved August 11, 2008) (http://www.cdc.gov/flu/protext/covercough.htm).

———. 1998. "Guideline for Infection Control in Health Care Personnel, 1998." *Am.J.Infect.Control* 26:289–354.

———. 2007a. *Guideline for Isolation Precautions: Preventing Transmission of Infectious Agents in Healthcare Settings 2007.* (retrieved August 14, 2008) (http://www.cdc.gov/ncdod/dhqp/pdf/guidelines/Isolation2007.pdf)

————. 2003. "Guidelines for Environmental Infection Control in Health-Care Facilities: Recommendations of the CDC and the Healthcare Infection Control Practices Advisory Committee (HICPAC)." *MMWR* (No. RR-10) 52:1–42.

————. 2004a. "Guidelines for Preventing Health-care Associated Pneumonia, 2003." *MMWR* 53(RR-3):1–36.

————. 1997. "Immunization of Health-Care Workers: Recommendations of the Advisory Committee on Immunization Practices (ACIP) and the Hospital Infection Control Practices Advisory Committee (HICPAC)." *MMWR* (RR-18) 46:1–42

————. 2004b. "National Nosocomial Infections Surveillance (NNIS) System Report, data summary from January 1992 through June 2004." *Am.J.Infect.Control* 32:470–485.

————. 2002. "*Staphylococcus aureus* Resistant to Vancomycin - United States, 2002." *MMWR* 51:565–567.

————. 2001. "Updated Guidelines for Evaluating Public Health Surveillance Systems: Recommendations from the Guidelines Working Group." *MMWR* 50:1–35.

Centers for Disease Control and Prevention (CDC) and National Institutes of Health (NIH). 2007. *Biosafety in Microbiological and Biomedical Laboratories.* 5th ed. Washington, D.C.: U.S. Government Printing Office

Culver, D. H., T.C. Horan, R. P. Gaynes, W. J. Martone, W. R. Jarvis, and T. G. Emori. 1991. "Surgical Wound Infection Rates by Wound Class, Operative Procedure, and Patient Risk Index." *Am.J.Med., 91,* 152S–157S.

Food and Drug Administration (FDA) 2001. "HACCP: A State-of-the-Art Approach to Food Safety." Rep. # BG 01–4. Washington, D.C.: Food and Drug Administration.

Fichet, G., E. Comoy, C. Duval, K. Antloga, C. Dehen, and A. Charbonnierl. 2004. "Novel Methods for Disinfection of Prion-Contaminated Medical Devices." *Lancet.* 364:521–526.

Frain, J., D. Murphy, G. Dash, and M. Kassi. 2004. "Integrating Sentinel Event Analysis Into Your Infection Control Practice." *Position Statement of Association of Professionals in Infection Control and Epidemiology,* December 2004, 1–11.

Graves, N. 2004. "Economics and Preventing Hospital-Acquired Infection." *Emerg.Infect.Dis.* 10:561–566.

Haley, R. W., D. H. Culver, J. W. White, W. M. Morgan, T. G. Emori, and V. P. Munn. 1985. "The Efficacy of Infection Surveillance and Control Programs in Preventing Nosocomial Infections in U.S. Hospitals." *Am.J.Epidemiol,* 121:182–205.

Herwaldt, B. L. 2001. "Laboratory-Acquired Parasitic Infections from Accidental Exposures." *Clin.Microbiol.Rev.* 14:659–88.

Joint Commission on Accreditation of Healthcare Organizations (JCAHO). 2007. *Hospital Accreditation Standards.* Oakbrook Terrace, Illinois: Joint Commission Resources.

Kennamer, M. 2002. "The Disease Process." In *Basic Infection Control for Health Care Providers* (pp. 22–32). Albany, NY: Delmar.

Kuehnert, M. J., H. A. Hill, B. A. Kupronis, J. I. Tokars, S. L. Solomon, and D. B. Jernigan. 2005. "Methicillin-Resistant-*Staphylococcus aureus* Hospitalizations, United States." *Emerg.Infect.Dis.* 11:868–872.

Loutfy, M. R., T. Wallington, T. Rutledge, B. Mederski, K. Rose, and S. Kwolekl. 2004. "Hospital Preparedness and SARS." *Emerg.Infect.Dis.* 10:771–776.

McDonald, L. C., A. E. Simor, I. J. Su, S. Maloney, M. Ofner, and K. T. Chen. 2004. "SARS in Healthcare Facilities, Toronto and Taiwan." *Emerg. Infect.Dis.* 10:777-781.

Occupational Safety and Health Administration (OSHA). 2006a. 29 CFR 1910.1030, Bloodborne Pathogens (retrieved August 14, 2008) (http://www.osha.gov/pls/oshaweb/owadisp.show_document?p_table=STANDARD&p_id=10051).

———. 2006b. 29 CFR 1910.134, *Respiratory Protection* (retrieved August 14, 2008) (http://www.osha.gov/pls/oshaweb/owadisp.show_document?p_table=STANDARD&p_id=12716).

Rutala, W. A. 1996. "APIC Guideline for Selection and Use of Disinfectants, 1994, 1995, and 1996." *Am.J.Infect.Control* 24:313–342.

Stone, P. W., S. P. Clarke, J. Cimiotti, and R. Correa-de-Araujo. 2004. "Nurses' Working Conditions: Implications for Infectious Disease." *Emerg.Infect. Dis.* 10:1984-1989.

Tan, J. A., V. N. Naik, and L. Lingard. 2006. "Exploring Obstacles to Proper Timing of Prophylactic Antibiotics for Surgical Site Infections." *Qual.Saf Health Care.* 15:32–38.

Templeton, G. L., L. A. Illing, L. Young, D. Cave, W. W. Stead, and J. H. Bates. 1995. "The Risk for Transmission of Mycobacterium Tuberculosis at the Bedside and During Autopsy." *Ann.Intern.Med.* 122:922–925.

Thacker, S. B. and R. L. Berkelman. 1988. "Public Health Surveillance in the United States." *Epidemiol.Rev.* 10:164–90.

Thomas, M., M. D. Sanborn, and R. Couldry. 2005. "I.V. Admixture Contamination Rates: Traditional Practice Site Versus a Class 1000 Cleanroom." *Am.J.Health Syst.Pharm.* 62:2386–2392.

United States Pharmacopeia. 2008. *USP Pharmacists' Pharmacopeia.* Rockville, MD: United States Pharmacopeia Convention.

CLASSROOM ACTIVITIES

Data Collection and Recordkeeping

You will be assigned to a group to work on this project.

Scenario: The former infection control nurse at BroJoe Hospital recently retired, and her replacement is Sally Smith. Sally feels confident that she did a good job in gathering nosocomial infection data; however, she has no training in data analysis or epidemiology and is at a loss on how to evaluate her data. You are confident that you can help her. Attached is a copy of the infection data (Table R1). How do you proceed?

Your assignment is to review and discuss the data provided as a group, as well as individually, and type your answers to the six questions listed below. Be sure to include a table with your response.

1. The best place to start is to present an infection rate per 1000 patient days. Multiply the average census by the number of days in the month, e.g., 31. Present a total infection rate for the hospital, an infection rate by department, rates by type of microbe, and rates by class of surgery. If similarly sized hospitals had an average rate of less than 3 infections per 1000 patient days (typically around 2.5), how does this compare to the BroJoe Hospital rate?

2. If most hospitals of this size do not have a psychiatric unit; would this change your answer? In other words, is the situation at BroJoe better or worse than in the answer to #1 above? You need to calculate a new rate for total infections that ignores the psychiatric unit.

3. What three departments seem to have the most serious problem, based on the information presented? What additional information would confirm your choice? Is it possible that departments with lower rates could have a more serious problem? If yes, why?

4. Which two microbes seem to be causing the biggest problem? Again, what additional information would be useful to better answer these questions? Also, what is another way of presenting these data to identify trends? (In other words, is there another table that could be constructed that would help pinpoint problem areas?)

5. Which class of surgery seems to present the biggest problem?

6. If the average infection rate by class of surgeries was (see Table 1):

Table 1 Average Infection Rate by Surgery Class

Surgical Class	Example of Surgery	Typical infection rate
Class I	Bone marrow tranplant	2 or less per 100 procedures
Class II	Tonsillectomy	3–4 per 100 procedures
Class III	Bowel surgery	6–7 per 100 procedures
Class IV	Debridement of an infected wound	7–8 per 100 procedures

How would this information affect your answer? What additional information would be useful to determine if there was a problem in this department (see Table 2)?

Table 2 Breakdown of Nosocomial Infections by Hospital Unit for August 2006

Hospital Units	Rate per 1000 Patient Days	UTI*	Surgical Site	Lower Respiratory	Blood	Skin	Totals	Avg Daily Census	Total Patient Days
Medical/ Surgical	10	3**	0	1	1	15	200	
Orthpedics	4	2	0	0	0	6	50	
Psychiatric	1	0	0	0	0	1	100	
ICU	3	2	0	2	0	7	20	
OB/Gyn	1	1	0	0	2	4	50	
Pediatrics	2	1	4	0	0	7	100	
Nursery	0	0	1	0	3	4	30	
TOTAL	21	9	5	3	6	44	550	

*Urinary tract infection.
** One patient died.

Departments

Microbe:	Med/Surg	Ortho	Psych	ICU	OB/Gyn	Peds	Nursery	Totals	Rate
S. aureus	2	1	0	1	1	1	3***	9	
E. coli	7	3	0	3	2	1	0	16	
Klebsiella	1	1	0	0	0	4	1	7	
Enterobacter	2	1	0	1	1	1	0	6	
Pseudomonas	1	0	0	1	0	0	0	2	
Unknown	2	0	1	1	0	0	0	4	
TOTAL	15	6	1	7	4	7	4	44	

*** Two were MRSA.

Surgical site infection by class of surgery for the month of for August 2006

Class of Surgery	No. of infections	No. of Procedures	Rate
I (Clean)	3	75	
II (Clean-contaminated)	2	50	
III (Contaminated)	2	30	
IV (Infected)	2	25	
TOTAL	9	180	

Please note, there are three different surgeons and surgical teams at this hospital. Each team has performed all of the classes of surgery.

Class I means that the surgery involves normally sterile tissue.

Class II means that surgery will involve tissue that may contain some normal flora microorganisms.

Class III means that the surgery involves an area of the body that is highly contaminated with microorganisms.

Class IV surgery involves removal of tissues that are grossly infected with microorganisms.

Case Studies

Case Study 1: Response to an Outbreak

Scenario: You receive a referral from the Medical Surgical Head Nurse of an increase in *Staphylococcus* infections in post-operative patients on the Medical Surgical ward. She is concerned that there is an outbreak because at least one of her patients has been confirmed to have methicillin-resistant *Staphylococcus aureus* (MRSA). What is your first step?

You determine that only five cases were confirmed to be *Staphylococcus* according to the laboratory reports. Of those five, only four were *Staphylococcus aureus*. Of those four, only two were hospital–associated cases. Of those two, one was a sputum specimen, and the other was a blood specimen. Of those two specimens one was actually sensitive to methicillin and was not MRSA, but methicillin-sensitive *Staphylococcus aureus* (MSSA). The only one resistant was the initial case reported to you by the doctor. From this review, this is an outbreak, yes or no? What do you report to the medical staff?

Case Study 2: Developing a Surveillance Plan

Scenario: You work at Hospital A, which is a small, acute-care facility located in a rural area with a 50-bed inpatient capacity. Services provided include surgery, an intensive care unit (ICU), obstetrical services, outpatient dental services, a large ambulatory care clinic, and pediatric inpatient and outpatient services. The facility has a pharmacy, a laboratory, and radiology and physical therapy departments. It has three isolation rooms capable of negative air pressure: two in the inpatient and one in outpatient area. Three of the most frequently performed surgeries are cholecystectomies, appendectomies, and C-sections. One of the surgeons is also the local provider of health care for the community's school wrestling team. The community has a large diabetic population and a very active public health nursing program. The community hospital also provides healthcare services to the local jail system. A recent health problem noted in the community is an increase it the number of community-acquired MRSA cases. Also, there has been an increase in reported needle sticks in the inpatient area. Of note there is a reported increase of tuberculosis (TB) in the community. Three patients have been admitted to the facility for active pulmonary TB in the past year. The facility has five inpatient isolation rooms and three outpatient isolation rooms, including one in the emergency department. There is also a sputum induction booth in the Respiratory Therapy Department.

You are a new ICP for this hospital; your assignment is to begin development of a surveillance plan for the facility. Base your plan on either a patient or employee outcome or process. Determine what potential events you see that may need surveying, what data you will need to collect, and what measure you will use.

Exercises

Do these patients have hospital-acquired (nosocomial) infections? (Base your answers on the CDC definitions of nosocomial infections found at http://www.cdc.gov/ncidod/dhqp/pdf/nnis/NosInfDefinitions.pdf)

Scenario 1: A 65-year-old female from the Medical Surgical Unit has been hospitalized for five days and has had a urinary Foley catheter for four days since admission. She now complains of suprapubic tenderness with fever, and the urine dipstick is positive for nitrates.

Scenario #2: You receive a report from the Mental Health Day Treatment nurse that 20 of the 28 day-treatment patients are complaining of pain and redness of their eyes with yellow exudate (pus) from the eyes.

Scenario #3: You have 24 needlestick injuries reported during 2006. For 2007, 24 needlestick injuries were reported. The denominator you decide to use is the number of patient days. For 2006, the number is 25,000 patient days, and for 2007, the number is 26,000 patient days. Calculate the simple rate for each year and determine what additional information you may need to determine if you would need to change the current safety program for reduction of rate of needle stick injuries. Do you change current safety policies? Explain why or why not.

Scenario # 4: You see 600 employees during the months of November and December. You give 550 influenza vaccines to that group, but 50 decline the vaccine. The total employee population is 800. Calculate the rate of immunizations for the employees seen in the clinic. Calculate the rate of the influenza vaccinations given to the total employee population.

CHAPTER 4

Antisepsis, Disinfection, and Sterilization

George Byrns

Learning Objectives

1. **Define terms used in antisepsis, disinfection, and sterilization**

2. **Identify the major types of germicides used in health care.**

3. **Discuss the importance of hand hygiene and CDC's current recommendations**

4. **Identify types of sterilization methods used to reprocess medical equipment and supplies**

5. **Discuss the importance of matching the germicide with its intended use**

6. **Review the functions of central services, housekeeping, and linen and laundry**

In this chapter, we will describe uses and limitations of certain germicidal chemicals and processes. A key to the prevention of healthcare-acquired infections is appropriate disinfection and sterilization of instruments and equipment (Rutala 1996). However, in order to achieve our infection prevention objectives, there are some critical points to remember. First, there is no such thing as a perfect germicide. In the selection of a germicide, we must frequently balance efficacy (the ability to destroy microbes) with safety of people and products. If a germicide is capable of destroying bacteria spores, but in the process, an expensive instrument is damaged, the approach is obviously not acceptable. One approach to protecting heat-sensitive instruments was to use ethylene oxide as a sterilizing agent. However due to environmental and occupational hazards and long cycle times, some newer, low-temperature sterilization systems have been developed. Examples of these approaches include hydrogen peroxide vapor, chlorine dioxide gas, ozone gas, peracetic acid liquid, mixed chemical/gas-plasma, and hydrogen peroxide gas-plasma (Favero and Bond 2001). The second consideration is examining the application and intention of the germicide. It is not necessary or desirable to achieve sterility in all instances. While surgical implants must be sterile, most environmental surfaces, like floors, need only to be clean. Even surfaces that come in contact with mucus membranes do not need to be sterile; they need to be free of disease-causing microorganisms. The key is to match the desired task with the most appropriate type of germicide. A final point is that cleaning (the removal of all foreign materials) is a critical step in either disinfection or sterilization (Rutala 1996).

CLASSIFICATION OF GERMICIDES

There are two broad classifications of germicides: *antiseptics* and *disinfectants*. *Antiseptics* are used on living tissue, whereas *disinfectants* are used on inanimate objects. Another distinction is that disinfectants used on medical equipment are regulated by the Food and Drug Administration (FDA), whereas other disinfectants are considered pesticides and regulated by the Environmental Protection Agency (EPA). Certain chemicals, such as alcohol, tincture of iodine (a mixture of alcohol and iodine), and iodophor (a chemical solution of iodine and a solubilizing agent), may be both antiseptics and disinfectants, depending on the concentration. The potential confusion from overlapping jurisdictions led the two agencies to sign a Memorandum of Understanding in which the FDA took responsibility for regulation of liquid chemicals used for high-level disinfection or sterilization, and the EPA took responsibility to regulate general purpose disinfectants. The Centers for Disease Control and Prevention (CDC) is not a regulatory body, but it does provide some guidance on the use of germicides in the prevention of nosocomial infections (CDC 2003).

Types of Disinfection

With the exception of prions (a transmissible form of an abnormal protein), bacterial spores are most difficult to kill, and vegetative bacteria and lipid viruses are easiest to kill. E.H. Spaulding proposed three levels of germicidal action: high, intermediate, and low (Favero and Bond 2001). High-level disinfectants are expected to kill vegetative bacteria, *Mycobacterium tuberculosis* (TB), some spores, fungi, and viruses. Intermediate-level agents kill vegetative bacteria, TB, fungi, viruses, but are not expected to kill bacterial spores. Low-level agents kill most vegetative bacteria, fungi, and lipid viruses. They will not destroy spores or non-lipid viruses, and they are sometimes less active against TB or gram negative rods such as *Pseudomonas sp.*

Examples of Disinfectants by Germicidal Activity

High-level disinfection is the minimum level recommended by the CDC for reprocessing semicritical instruments (CDC 2003). See the classification of devices below.

Some examples of high-level germicides are:

- 8% formaldehyde
- 2% glutaraldehyde
- 100% ethylene oxide gas (EtO)
- 10–20% stabilized hydrogen peroxide
- 58% hydrogen peroxide plasma
- 0.55% ortho-phthalaldehyde (OPA)

Some examples of intermediate-level germicides are:

- 70–90% alcohol
- 0.1–0.5% chlorine
- phenolic
- 0.01–0.007% iodophor

An example of a low-level is quaternary ammonium compounds (quats).

Classification of Devices

Critical devices have a substantial risk of causing an infection because they are used in procedures that enter sterile tissue or the vascular system (Favero and Bond 2001). Some examples of critical devices are surgical implants, heart-lung oxygenerators, needles, scalpels and other surgical instruments. Semicritical devices do not ordinarily penetrate body tissues but may come in contact with mucous membranes. Some examples of semicritical devices are flexible endoscopes, laryngoscopes, endotracheal tubes, other similar instruments. Noncritical devices or surfaces are expected to only touch intact skin. These devices may be subcategorized into medical equipment surfaces with routine patient contact and housekeeping surfaces with little to no patient contact. Some examples of noncritical devices or surfaces are stethoscopes, tabletops, bed railings, floors, walls, and ceilings.

Matching Devices to Processes

All evidence suggests that the most important issue in destroying potentially pathogenic microorganisms in instruments such as endoscopes is cleanliness and not the level of germicidal activity (Favero and Bond 2001). Thorough decontamination and cleaning must precede either sterilization or disinfection for any process to be considered reliable. The reason that cleaning is most important is that residual biofilm or other organic matter can shield microbes from the germicide. Also, the mechanical action of cleaning can remove a large number of microbial contaminants.

Critical Items. These devices present a high risk of infection; usually, steam sterilization is the most efficacious means of reprocessing critical instruments.

While steam is the cheapest and most effective means of achieving sterility, certain heat-labile equipment must be reprocessed using other means. The minimum level of treatment for heat-labile critical instruments is high-level disinfection, and preferably sterilization (Favero and Bond 2001). Chemical germicides that are sporicidal take much longer time to achieve sterility than steam sterilizers, in some cases, as long as 24 hours.

Semicritical Instruments. For heat-stable semicritical instruments, steam sterilization may be the most cost-effective means of reprocessing (Favero and Bond 2001). On the other hand, heat-labile semicritical instruments typically do not enter sterile tissue, so sterility is not required. If the instrument can not withstand long contact with a chemical germicide, high-level disinfection is sufficient. It should be noted that the primary difference between sterilization and high-level disinfection when using chemical germicides is the amount of contact time.

Noncritical Items. Since noncritical items offer little risk of infection, the main issue is cleanliness and not disinfection. Medical equipment surfaces may frequently become contaminated during patient procedures, so it is prudent to use low- to intermediate-level germicide on these surfaces. Housekeeping surfaces would not be expected to play a role in nosocomial infections. Some authorities suggest that to be on the safe side, even housekeeping surfaces should be disinfected (Rutala and Weber 2001b). This issue is controversial, and others believe that detergents or low-level disinfectants are appropriate (Favero and Bond 2001). The major exception is laboratory culture or blood spills. These require special precautions. The following steps are recommended to handle these types of spills:

1. Don a pair of disposable gloves
2. Remove excess fluids using absorbent materials such as paper towels
3. Dispose of the absorbent materials in a red bag
4. Use any germicide labeled as a "hospital disinfectant" to clean the area

Characteristics of a Good Germicide

As previously stated, there is no such thing as the perfect germicide. When selecting a germicide, consider the following issues:

- **Biocidal properties:** Will the germicide kill those organisms of concern?
- **Applicable to intended use:** Will the germicide be efficacious without harming people or the objects being disinfected?
- **Contact time:** How long does it take for the germicide to do the intended job?
- **Employee acceptance:** Will the employees find the germicide easy and safe to use, and are there any unpleasant odors or staining problems associated with its use?

■ **Chemical characteristics:** Review the germicide's label for the following properties:

1. Toxicity
2. Corrosiveness
3. Flammability
4. Compatibility with other materials
5. Stability (Will the product degrade over time?)

■ **Environmental factors:** Review the label for environmental factors:

1. pH (Will the product be neutralized by water or the contaminant's pH?)
2. Hardness (Will the product function in hard water?)
3. Temperature (Will the product work in lower temperatures? Temperature can have a major effect on the speed of microbial destruction.)
4. Organic load (Will the product work in the presence of a heavy organic load?)
5. Soap or detergent residues (Will the product leave a residue? For certain types of medical equipment such as infant transport units or incubators, it is important to be able to visualize skin tones. A residue may obscure the ability to see if an infant's skin is becoming jaundiced.)
6. Environmental harm and persistence (Will the product degrade in the environment or will it harm aquatic or other species)

■ **Service from the vendor:** Will the vendor provide free of charge certain critical services such as:

1. Training in the use of the product
2. Routine consultations on the product
3. Material Safety Data Sheets (MSDS) for the product. Please note that this is *not* negotiable. The vendor must provide an MSDS when requested by the user.

■ **Personal protective equipment (PPE) issues:** It is critical to review the MSDS for a product to determine potential exposure routes. Most germicides are irritating to the skin and some are also sensitizers (for example: glutaraldehyde and ortho-phthalaldehyde). Therefore at a minimum, goggles and heavy gloves must be worn when working with the concentrate. It is important to determine if the chemical can be absorbed through the skin (see below under phenolic germicides) or have a high enough vapor pressure to be an inhalation hazard (see below under glutaraldehyde). All personnel using the germicide must be monitored to assure that they follow the minimum PPE for the product.

■ **Cost:** The cost of the germicide must be calculated based on use dilution concentrations.

Characteristics of Selected Germicides

The following section provides a brief overview of the uses and limitations of the major types of germicides used in an institution. The germicides include:

- Alcohol
- Chlorhexidine glucconate
- Chlorine
- Formaldehyde
- Glutaraldehyde
- Hexachlorophene
- Hydrogen peroxide
- Iodine
- Ortho-phthaladehyde (OPA)
- Para-chloro-meta-xylenol (PCMX)
- Peracetic acid
- Phenolic compounds
- Quaternary ammonium compounds (quats)
- Triclosan

Alcohol

Ethyl and isopropyl alcohol are intermediate-level germicides and skin antiseptics. They are effective against TB but have no effect on spores. Ethyl alcohol is more effective against viruses than isopropyl, which only inactivates lipid viruses. Alcohols have some disadvantages in that they evaporate quickly, leave no antimicrobial residual, are flammable, may cause plastic tubing to swell, and are irritating to skin (Rutala 1996).

Chlorhexidine Glucconate

Chlorhexidine is a type of chemical called a biguanide that was originally synthesized in 1950 (Denton 2001). It is used in a 4% solution as a skin-wound cleanser, patient preoperative skin preparation, skin antiseptic, surgical hand scrub, and as an ingredient in antimicrobial hand soap (FDA 1994). In normal use, chlorhexidine does not appear to cause skin irritation, and there is no evidence of carcinogenicity (Denton 2001). Since it has been shown to be ototoxic, it should never be placed in the ears. It has a relatively broad spectrum activity against bacteria and most viruses, and due to its lower toxicity, chlorhexidine has replaced hexachlorophene as a skin antiseptic (Favero and Bond 2001).

Chlorine

Inorganic chlorine has long been recognized as one of the most cost-effective and fastest acting intermediate-level germicides available (Rutala and Weber 1997). Chlorine shows sporicidal activity, is tuberculocidal, and will inactivate viruses (Favero and Bond 2001). Household bleach is an effective means for decontaminating blood spills. If the surface to be cleaned is porous, use a 1-to-10 dilution of bleach and water (Rutala 1996). For hard surfaces, 1-to-100 dilution of bleach and water is effective. Chlorine has long been used to disinfect water systems; however to destroy *Legionella pneumophilia*, hyperchlorination (greater than 50 ppm concentrations) is needed. Chlorine solutions have limited use for disinfection of medical devices because they are corrosive and may damage metal or other surfaces. They are also skin irritants, so gloves should be worn when using this type of germicide.

Formaldehyde

Formalin (a mixture of formaldehyde gas and water or alcohol) is considered an intermediate- to high-level germicide, depending on the concentration. In the past, it has been used to disinfect hemodialysis systems. Currently, formalin's use as a disinfectant has diminished because of its severely irritating properties and the fact that it is considered a potential human carcinogen.

Glutaraldehyde

Glutaraldehyde formulations have been used for many years as a high-level disinfectant or cold sterilizing agent, depending on contact time. Some formulations require the addition of an activator to achieve full potency. Glutaraldehyde used for disinfection purposes usually comes in a 2% solution. This solution loses potency over time and especially with repeated use. Glutaraldehyde is considered to be highly toxic to humans via inhalation, ingestion, or skin contact and allergic sensitization can occur. For this reason, the American Conference of Governmental Industrial Hygienists (ACGIH) lowered the threshold limit value (TLV) to 0.05 ppm as a ceiling level (ACGIH 2008). In order to achieve this ceiling level, solutions must be tightly covered at all times or used in an area with dedicated local exhaust to capture any vapor release (Rutala 1996). Dedicated local exhaust is preferred but may not be feasible in all locations, for example, in soaking ultrasound probes. The use of glutaraldehyde in automatic disinfecting units significantly reduces but does not eliminate exposures. There have been recent efforts to replace this product with safer alternatives because of exposure concerns.

Hexachlorophene

Hexachlorophene is a bisphenol (two phenol compounds linked together) that in the past was used extensively as a skin antiseptic. In the 1970s, hexachlorophene was found to be absorbed in the brains of infants and is no longer available except by prescription (Crabtree et al. 2001; FDA 1994). There are recent concerns that bisphenols are endocrine disrupters and therefore a danger to downstream water quality.

Hydrogen Peroxide

Unstable, low concentrations of hydrogen peroxide were used in the past as a skin antiseptic (Favero and Bond 2001). More recently, hydrogen peroxide is finding favor as an instrument disinfectant. A system called Sterrad™ uses

50% hydrogen peroxide in a low-temperature gas plasma as its sterilizing agent. It is approved for use on medical devices, including endoscopes. Among the advantages of this system over EtO is a much shorter cycle time (less than one hour), less potential for operator exposure, no toxic residues remaining on the medical device, and the end-products are non-hazardous. Some instrument manufacturers have recently noted undesirable materials compatibility with the Sterrad™ process, and the technology is limited in the diameter and the length of lumened instruments it can sterilize.

Iodine

Tincture of iodine and iodophors have been used for many years as low- to intermediate-level disinfectants and as skin antiseptics. Iodophors have been used for disinfection of medical equipment, although corrosion may occur with repeated use and the product tends to stain everything a golden brown color. The chemistry of iodophors is complex and failure to follow the manufacturer's mixing requirements by making the solution either too dilute or too concentrated will significantly decrease germicidal activity (Favero and Bond 2001).

Ortho-phthaladehyde (OPA)

OPA is a relatively new germicide that was cleared in 1999 by the FDA for use as an instrument disinfectant (Rutala and Weber 2001a). It is similar in action to glutaraldehyde but has several advantages over glutaraldehyde. It requires no activation, and it is more stable than glutaraldehyde. It also has a lower vapor pressure, so it is less likely to be volatilized. One major disadvantage is that it will stain unprotected skin a gray color. It appears to be a potent skin sensitizer. OPA was believed to be the cause of four patients developing anaphylactic shock following a cystoscopy (Sokol 2004). OPA is also much more toxic to aquatic life than glutaraldehyde. In some states it is characterized as a toxic waste unless neutralized with glycine prior to disposal. Another disadvantage is the newness of the product means that little is known about long-term health effects and, as of this writing, there is no validated NIOSH or OSHA analytical method to measure exposures.

Para-chloro-meta-xylenol (PCMX)

PCMX is a phenol derivative used in concentrations of 0.5 to 4.0% as a skin antiseptic (Crabtree et al. 2001). It is considered a low-level germicide and has been added to such products as shampoos and deodorants (Goddard & McCue 2001).

Peracetic Acid

Peracetic acid is also known as peroxyacetic acid. Peracetic acid in low concentrations (0.001 to 0.2%) is an effective broad-spectrum germicide that is capable of destroying spores (Rutala 1996; Favero and Bond 2001). It has been used to disinfect endoscopes and hemodialyzers. However, due to the chemical's extremely irritating properties, it should only be use in closed systems.

Steris$^{(TM)}$ is a closed system using 0.2% peracetic acid in a 30-minute cycle. It is an alternative to glutaraldehyde for endoscope reprocessing. Steris introduced the P6000 system, which uses a mixture of 35% peroxyacetic acid in equilibrium with acetic acid and hydrogen peroxide, which is mixed in a closed system after the cycle is started. The concentrate mixture poses several hazards as defined by the NFPA, the most limiting of which is its classification as a highly toxic material, as well as a Class II organic peroxide, a Class II unstable (reactive) material, and a Class II combustible. It should not be stored with flammables, and in addition, the design of the concentrated, "cup-of-noodles" packaging is intended to allow the contents to "burp off," thus posing the problem of accumulated vapors if the concentrate is stored in closed cabinets without ventilation. The fire code allows up to six cases to be stored in a sprinklered, one-hour-rated fire enclosure, but quantities over that should be stored in a ventilated acid cabinet. Some equipment manufacturers (such as Olympus) prohibit preprocessing with the Steris P6000 system for their flexible endoscopes because of significant material incompatibility. They will not honor new equipment warranties if gastrointestinal and some other types of scopes are reprocessed in the P6000. As of this writing, high-level disinfection systems using peracetic acid were no longer available for purchase.

Phenolic Compounds

Phenol and phenolic compounds are among the oldest known germicides and are considered low- to intermediate-level disinfectants (Favero and Bond 2001; Goddard and McCue 2001). Phenolic germicides should never used on medical devices because they are difficult to rinse, and they are toxic to the skin. As discussed in Chapter 2, phenolic compounds are readily absorbed through intact skin, permanently destroying skin pigment and are also toxic when inhaled. Infants exposed to phenolic germicides may develop a life-threatening condition called *hyperbilirubinemia* (CDC 1996). The condition is the result of the inability of the liver to process billirubin, a yellowish/orange pigment released during the destruction of red blood cells. Untreated, the condition can cause brain damage and death. The CDC recommends that phenolics should not be used to disinfect infant incubators or bassinets (CDC 2003). Phenolic germicides also have not been approved for use on food contact surfaces. It is important for anyone using these products to obtain and wear the proper PPE to protect mucous membranes and the skin from exposure. Phenolic germicides have been largely replaced with quaternary ammonium compounds for low-level disinfection because of these toxic properties.

Quaternary Ammonium Compounds (Quats)

Quats are less toxic than many other compounds and are considered low-level germicides. Since they are less effective against gram negative bacteria and are not tuberculocidal, they should not be used for the disinfection of medical instruments (Favero and Bond 2001). However, they are excellent for use as a general-purpose, housekeeping-surface cleaner. It is important to remember that using a disinfectant labeled as tuberculocidal will not prevent transmission of TB. It is simply a benchmark by which to measure germicidal potency.

Triclosan

Triclosan is structurally similar to a bisphenol but without the apparent toxicity of hexachlorophene (Goddard and McCue 2001). However, in terms of its action, triclosan is considered more of a bacteriostat than a germicide. As a result, it is used primarily as an additive to antimicrobial soaps and deodorants. One manufacturer recently added this product to toothpaste.

New Disinfection and Sterilization Methods

The field of microbial disinfection and sterilization continues to evolve. Antimicrobial coatings and superoxidized water are two examples of relatively recent changes in technology. It is important to be aware that new technology may have benefits but also unforeseen hazards. For example, OPA (described above) was developed as a safer substitute for the more toxic glutaraldehyde. It now appears that OPA may be less toxic via inhalation, but may be more toxic via skin exposure than glutaraldehyde (Rideout et al. 2005).

Antimicrobial Coatings

Recently, there has been much interest in the use antimicrobial coatings containing silver halide, which may be applied to either animate or inanimate surfaces (Rutala and Weber 2001a). According to one manufacturer, the coating is inert, non-toxic to human cells, and can withstand repeated washing. As of this writing, it had not been FDA-approved for medical device disinfection.

Superoxidized Water (SW)

Superoxidized water (SW) is created by electrolyzing sodium chloride saline solution; the main active component of the mixture is hypochlorous acid. It is considered an intermediate- to high-level disinfectant, and a commercial application of SW is marketed in the United Kingdom (UK) and received FDA approval for medical device disinfection in 2002. It has been recommended as a method of flushing dental lines and other lumens. In addition, it has been used in the UK for the disinfection of endoscopes, but as of this writing is not approved for this application in the U.S. It is not recommended for use with metal objects because it contains no rust inhibitor. The actual mode of germicidal action is not known but early studies show that it is fast-acting (Rutala and Weber 2001a). Recently, the manufacturer has recommended its use as a room-fogging agent. Currently, the CDC does not recommend the practice of room fogging in patient-care areas (CDC 2003). Generating SW requires large quantities of water and a large work space. Healthcare organizations that have limited space or are concerned about resource conservation may not find this an attractive option.

HAND HYGIENE

For many years, with the exception of vaccine-preventable diseases, hand washing was considered to be the single most effective means of preventing the spread of infection. Unfortunately, hand-washing compliance by healthcare providers continued to be a problem. The CDC reported adherence rates for required hand-washing that ranged from 29–48%. The CDC promoted using alcohol-based hand rubs for routine decontamination of skin (CDC 2002). Alcohol has long been recognized as an excellent skin antiseptic; however, prolonged use was associated with skin irritation and drying. Chapped and cracked skin increased the chance of acquiring a skin infection. Newer, alcohol-based skin rubs incorporate emollients and moisturizers that have eliminated the problem. According to the CDC, either isopropanol or ethanol solutions containing 60%–95% alcohol are most effective in destroying bacteria on the skin. The ratings by the CDC for various antiseptic formulations are found in Table 4.1.

Alcohol was rated as the most effective skin antiseptic because of its fast action and broad-spectrum activity. A final issue was the use of gloves in the prevention of infection transmission. The CDC recommends the use of gloves to prevent transmission of infections; however, glove use is no guarantee of safety since breaks and tears in gloves occur (CDC 2002). They also reported that vinyl gloves had higher leakage rates than latex or nitrile gloves. Therefore, compliance with hand washing following the use of gloves must still be emphasized. Also, there is the issue of latex allergies in workers, discussed in Chapter 2.

INFECTION CONTROL IN FLEXIBLE ENDOSCOPY

Flexible fiber-optic endoscopes were originally designed to give surgeons and gastroenterologists an important tool in the diagnosis and treatment of a wide range of conditions. Increasingly, they have become useful in other fields of medicine, such as urology, obstetrics and gynecology, cardiology, and head and neck surgery (Alvarado and Reichelderfer 2000). However their potential as a source of nosocomial infection transmission became apparent shortly after their introduction. Such infections may be caused by endogenous or exogenous microorganisms. *Endogenous infections* occur when normal flora gain access to the bloodstream during endoscopic procedures. Prevention of infections from endogenous organisms is extremely challenging and often requires the use of prophylactic antibiotics. *Exogenous infections* result from inadequately disinfected scopes. This type of infection underscores the importance of thorough cleaning and decontamination of endoscopes between patient uses. There are two reasons that these scopes present such a high risk of infection. First, they are expensive and relatively fragile, so they cannot be sterilized with steam under pressure or with certain types of chemicals. The high heat of steam will delaminate the glues used to bind the plastic materials

Table 4.1 Antimicrobial Spectrum and Characteristics of Hand-hygiene Antiseptic Agents (Source: CDC 2002)

Group	Gram-positive Bacteria	Gram-negative Bacteria	Mycobacteria	Fungi	Viruses	Speed of Action	Comments
Alcohols	+++	+++	+++	+++	+++	Fast	Optimum concentration 60%–95%; no persistent activity
Chlorhexidine (2% and 4% aqueous)	+++	++	+	+	+++	Intermediate	Persistent activity; rare allergic reactions
Iodine compounds	+++	+++	+++	++	+++	Intermediate	Causes skin burns; usually too irritating for hand hygiene
Iodophors	+++	+++	+	++	++	Intermediate	Less irritating than iodine; acceptance varies
Phenol derivatives	+++	+	+	+	+	Intermediate	Activity neutralized by nonionic surfactants
Tricolsan	+++	++	+	—	+++	Intermediate	Acceptability on hands varies
Quaternary ammonium compounds	+	++	—	—	+	Slow	Used only in combination with alcohols; ecologic concerns

Note: +++ = excellent; ++ = good, but does not include the entire bacterial spectrum; + = fair; — = no activity or not sufficient.
* Hexachlorophene is not included because it is no longer an accepted ingredient of hand disinfectants.

that make up the body and sheath of the scopes. The second issue is that they have long, narrow lumens that may accumulate biofilms; these biofilms insulate and protect microorganisms from exposure to disinfecting agents. Therefore, the first step in reprocessing these scopes must be mechanical cleaning, which may involve small brushes or enzymatic cleaning agents to break down the biofilms, followed by disinfection, thorough rinsing, and finally forced air-drying (Alvarado and Reichelderfer 2000). The water used for rinsing should be sterile to avoid re-contaminating the scopes. Automatic endoscope reprocessing machines have been developed to minimize employee exposure to toxic germicides such as glutaraldehyde, OPA, hydrogen peroxide, or peracetic acid. However, even with these machines, the endoscopes must undergo the manual cleaning step before reprocessing. After disinfection, scopes should be hung vertically to aid in drying and stored in a manner to prevent contamination.

HYDROTHERAPY TANKS AND POOLS

These tanks and pools may become heavily contaminated, especially when they are used for wound debridement. The CDC recommends that they be thoroughly cleaned and disinfected between patient uses with an EPA-registered hospital disinfectant in accordance with the manufacturer's instructions (CDC 2003). There is some debate whether it is appropriate to use an antiseptic chemical such as chloramine-T in the water during hydrotherapy treatments.

PRIONS AND CREUTZFELDT-JAKOB DISEASE (CJD)

Reprocessing instruments used on patients suspected of having CJD requires special consideration, since it has been demonstrated that prions are resistant to heat and chemical germicides (Favero and Bond 2001). Also, the fact that CJD infection is invariably fatal requires additional preventive measures. Unfortunately, there is relatively little scientific evidence currently available to provide guidance in reprocessing instruments that may have been contaminated with prions. Some authorities recommend disposing and incinerating instruments used on CJD patients. Favero recommends a less drastic approach. First, the type of tissue on which the instrument was used should be determined; second, the cleanability of the instrument should be considered. If the instrument was used on high-risk tissue like brain matter and the instrument will not withstand rigorous cleaning and sterilization, then the instrument should be discarded. However, if the tissue was not considered to be high risk and the instrument can be cleaned and sterilized, the instrument should be reprocessed. Some of the approaches recommended to destroy prions and CJD include extended autoclaving (121°C for 1–2 hours), soaking in 1 N NaOH for 30–60 minutes, or soaking in 2.5–5.25% chlorine bleach for 30–60 minutes.

ENVIRONMENTAL SAMPLING

In the past, the effectiveness of disinfection of environmental surfaces was monitored using replicate organism detection and counting (RODAC) plates, swabs and streak plates. RODACs are petri dishes with the agar surface filled above the edges of the dish. The RODAC or streak plates were then incubated and enumerated. Plate counts above a certain level were considered evidence of a disinfection failure. The current recommendation is to only perform environmental monitoring in outbreak investigations where there appears to be a link between an environmental surface or object and an infectious agent (Favero and Bond 2001; CDC 2003). Another example of environmental sampling, a *settling plate*, is an uncovered agar plate intended to measure dust accumulations on surfaces. This approach is of limited value, and the CDC does not recommend the use of environmental monitoring for routine housekeeping surveillance. The reasons against this practice are that it is costly and usually does not correlate with the presence of healthcare-associated infections. There are exceptions to this recommendation. The CDC recommends monitoring the water supply used in hemodialysis fluids and spore testing of sterilization cycles (described in more detail later). They also do not recommend environmental monitoring of endoscopes. Muscarella believes that the risk of endoscope-related infection from *Pseudomonas aeruginosa* and other gram negative bacteria in rinse water used in reprocessing endoscopes is significant and warrants routine environmental monitoring (Muscarella 2002). At least once a month, he recommends sampling the rinse water used during endoscope reprocessing, whether the rinse water is unprocessed and from a tap or filtered through a bacterial filter membrane.

METHODS OF STERILIZATION

The primary method of dealing with heat-stable critical items is sterilization, and there are several methods: steam; gas; and low-temperature steam formaldehyde.

Steam Sterilizers

The most cost-effective way of sterilizing reusable equipment is steam under pressure (Perkins 1969). These steam sterilizers are operated as either gravity displacement or high-vacuum units. The high-vacuum units can achieve higher temperatures and sterilize in shorter times because they are more effective in displacing air and removing cold spots. Gravity units typically operate at 121° C for 30 minutes, but flash or high-vacuum units operate at 140° C for 10 to 15 minutes. Flash sterilization is only appropriate for dropped sterile instruments when there is not another terminally sterilized replacement available. The instruments must be used immediately and so this process is termed *just-in-time* sterilization. Dry heat is seldom used for sterilization because it requires higher temperatures and much longer processing times to achieve sterilization (Joslyn 2001b), as well as possibly damaging materials.

Gas Sterilization

Ethylene Oxide (EtO). In the past, most EtO sterilizers used a mixture of 88% freon and 12% EtO. However, concerns about freon damaging the ozone layer resulted in the elimination of this type of sterilizer. For a short while, there was an attempt to replace the freon with carbon dioxide, but there was a serious problem with this approach because the mixture tended to separate into layers. Since 100% EtO is explosive, this presented a serious safety risk. The only type of EtO sterilizer currently available uses 100% EtO in small, single-use canisters. Overall, EtO sterilization has been decreasing because of its acute and chronic toxicity and its explosiveness. See Chapter 2 for more details on the hazards of EtO. One way of reducing the environmental risks associated with EtO is by installing exhaust catalytic converters on the units. These converters change EtO into water and carbon dioxide. The catalytic converter must be continuously monitored to detect the possibility of explosive vapors in the exhaust flue.

Ozone Sterilizers. Ozone has long been recognized as an effective means of disinfecting water supplies. Recently it has been proposed as a low-temperature sterilizing method. See Figure 4.1 for the process for generating ozone and converting it back to water and oxygen.

The duration of a cycle is about 4.5 hours, and it has FDA clearance for use as a sterilizing method on stainless steel instruments, hinged instruments and instruments with rigid stainless steel lumens. Its use for other types of medical devices is currently under investigation, but as of this writing, it has not been approved for use on endoscopes.

Low-Temperature Steam Formaldehyde. Low-temperature steam using formalin (typically a mixture of 37% formaldehyde in water with 8–15% methanol) has been used in parts of Europe (Joslyn, 2001a). Concerns about the acute and chronic toxicity of formaldehyde have limited its use in the U.S. One exception is a formaldehyde sterilizer that has been used in dental applications, primarily for the sterilization of heat-labile hand pieces.

Monitoring Performance of Sterilizers

There are many ways to monitor the performance of sterilizers:

- Biological indicators
- Rapid readout devices
- Physical and chemical indicators
- Shelf life

These are discussed in greater length below.

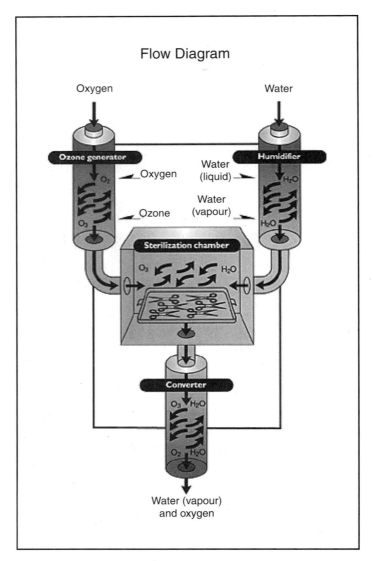

Figure 4.1 Design of the TSO3(TM) sterilizer. (Used with permission of TSO3)

Biological Indicators (BIs)

Biological indicators (BIs) are special preparations of resistant microorganisms that are placed in a test pack (Joslyn, 2001b) to monitor the ability of a particular system to achieve sterility. In each case, the most resistant type of organism is selected. For example, *Geobacillus stearothermophilus* spores are used as a test challenge for gravity displacement steam sterilizers. EtO sterilizers are challenged using another spore, *Bacillus atrophaeus*. In the past, spore test strips were incubated for seven days, but newer spore test preparations provide results in 24 hours.

The basic approach in biological monitoring is once per week, and two BIs are used. One is placed in a test pack to be sterilized, and the other is a control that is not sterilized. Both BIs are immediately placed in an incubator. After 24 hours of incubation, the BI used in the test pack should be negative for bacterial growth, and the control BI should be positive. The purpose of the control is to assure that the spores used for monitoring are viable and that the process is truly sterilizing the items. One exception to the weekly monitoring requirement is sterilization of surgical implants. These should have a BI test pack in each load, and the results should be verified before the implants are used on a patient.

Rapid Readout Devices. Even with a 24-hour turn-around time, there have been situations where a surgical device was used before the monitoring results were available. In the event of a sterilization failure, this presents a serious liability issue for the healthcare institution. The most recent advance in biological monitoring has been the development of a rapid readout system for both EtO and steam sterilizers. After the test pack is sterilized, the rapid readout BI for the gravity steam unit is incubated for one hour, and the BI for the EtO sterilizer is incubated for four hours. After the allotted time has pasted, the test BIs and their controls are placed in a fluorescent reader. A positive test detects acid metabolites from *G. stearothermophilus* or *B. atrophaeus*. The rapid readout devices have been accepted by the Joint Commission on Accreditation of Healthcare Organizations (Joint Commission or JCAHO) in lieu of conventional spore strip tests.

Physical and Chemical Indicators. Other indicators are often utilized with each pack that is undergoing sterilization (Joslyn 2001b). The most common type is a tape that changes color. These indicators only tell you that a temperature was reached, not that the items in the pack have achieved sterility. Nevertheless, these devices do provide a quick visual indication that the pack has been processed, and some chemical indicators are available that also measure time. These provide greater assurance of sterilization but are still not considered to be a substitute for biological monitoring.

Shelf Life. In the past, sterile packs were wrapped in sheets of muslin. Since this was a porous material, there was concern about microbial penetration and contamination of the packs. As a result, double-wrapped packs were assigned a shelf-life of one month. Products placed in dust covers were often assigned a shelf-life of six months. At the end of the shelf-life, packs were collected, disassembled and reprocessed, at a considerable expense. Now other products, such as non-woven wraps and plastic materials, are routinely used to wrap instruments. These newer materials offer significant barriers to microbial contamination; the assumption is that undamaged sterile packs remain sterile for indefinite periods of time. The new trend is to observe an *event-related* shelf–life; in other words, packs do not get reprocessed unless some event jeopardizes their sterility, such as getting wet, ripped, or visibly soiled. In a recent study, researchers found that even the older style muslin wraps offered significant protection (Webster et al. 2005). However, it is unlikely that most facilities will revert to the muslin wraps because they become more porous over time and require additional monitoring of their integrity (Leonas 1998).

CENTRAL SERVICES (CS)

Central Services (CS), also called Sterile Processing Department, is responsible for providing an adequate supply of sterile products to those who require them. A key issue is the prevention of cross-contamination between soiled items and those that are clean or sterile. The design of the CS department should be such that there is physical separation between three areas (AIA 2006):

- soiled receiving and decontamination
- clean assembly, packaging, and sterilizing
- sterile storage

It is desirable to have a cart-washing room located between the decontamination and clean assembly areas. It is also important that individuals assigned to these areas do not cross over into other areas without changing their apparel. Persons assigned to the decontamination area should wear PPE that includes, at a minimum, face shields or goggles and a face mask, heavy gloves, and gowns that are resistant to the penetration of liquids.

Staff must be thoroughly trained in reprocessing the instruments and assessed regularly on their competency. This is especially important in areas like the operating room, ambulatory surgical centers, and medical offices where nurses or medical assistants often take on the responsibility for reprocessing instruments in addition to their clinical duties. A major concern is the adequacy of their training and the oversight of their ability to clean and sterilize the instruments properly. Some healthcare organizations focus on having consolidated reprocessing of instruments, especially flexible endoscopes, so enough volume of instrumentation justifies having a certified sterile processing technician on staff and a room that is adequately designed and equipped to do the job properly.

HOUSEKEEPING

The housekeeping department provides an important service in keeping the healthcare environment clean. While there may be some debate over the risk of dirty housekeeping surfaces as a cause of infections, there is no doubt about the negative psychological impact on patients when these surfaces are visibly soiled. The CDC recommends that all housekeeping surfaces in patient-care areas be cleaned using a hospital-grade detergent or disinfectant (CDC 2003), Nonpatient-care areas may be cleaned with just detergent and water. Cleaning agents in use throughout the facility must be evaluated and approved annually by the hospital IC committee. This review should include cleaning schedules and techniques, training, policies, and products.

LAUNDRY AND LINEN

Linen may be provided and processed either in-house or by contract with a vendor. A key issue is maintaining the separation of soiled and clean linen during storage, transport, and processing. If a vendor is providing linen service, the contract's scope of work must be monitored by site visits to the laundry. It is also important that in-house laundry operations be monitored.

SUMMARY AND CONCLUSIONS

In this chapter, we reviewed basic approaches used for antisepsis, disinfection, and sterilization. One of the most important considerations is balancing germicidal efficacy with patient and product safety. Since there is no such thing as a perfect germicide, it is important to match the germicidal approach with the intended use of the object under consideration. No matter what process is used, the first step should be to clean the object. Failure to do so can interfere with the microbiocidal action of the germicide.

Review

1. Compare the terms antiseptic and disinfectant.
2. What are the three levels of disinfectants?
3. What are the three classifications of medical devices?
4. Compare the advantages and disadvantages of phenolic versus quaternary ammonia germicides for use on environmental surfaces.
5. Explain the significance of a germicide being labeled as tuberculocidal.
6. According to the CDC, one approach to hand hygiene was the best. What was the approach they recommended and why did they recommend it?
7. Compare the uses of biological monitors to chemical indicators as tests of sterility.

Reference List

American Conference of Government Industrial Hygienists (ACGIH). 2008. *Threshold Limit Values and Biological Exposure Indices.* Cincinnati, OH: American Conference of Government Industrial Hygienists.

American Institute of Architects (AIA). 2006. *Guidelines for Design and Construction of Hospital and Health Care Facilities.* Washington, D.C.: The American Institute of Architects.

Alvarado, C. J. and M. Reichelderfer. 2000. "APIC Guideline for Infection Prevention and Control in Flexible Endoscopy." *Am.J.Infect.Control.* 28:138–155.

Centers for Disease Control and Prevention (CDC). 2002. "Guideline for Hand Hygiene in Health-Care Settings: Recommendations of the Healthcare Infection Control Practices Advisory Committee and the HICPAC/SHEA/APIC/IDSA Hand Hygiene Task Force." *MMWR* (RR-16) 51:1–44.

———. 2003. "Guidelines for Environmental Infection Control in Health-Care Facilities: Recommendations of the CDC and the Healthcare Infection Control Practices Advisory Committee (HICPAC)." *MMWR* (RR-10) 52: 1–42

———. 1996. "Pentachlorophenol Poisoning in Newborn Infants—St. Louis, Missouri, April-August 1967." *MMWR* 45:545–549.

Crabtree, T. D., S. J. Pelletier, and T. L. Pruett. 2001. "Surgical Antisepsis." In S. S. Block , ed. *Disinfection, Sterilization, and Preservation*, 5th ed., pp. 919–934. Philadelphia: Lippincott Williams & Wilkins.

Denton, G. W. (2001). "Chlorhexidine." In S. S. Block, ed. *Disinfection, Sterilization, and Preservation*, 5th ed., pp. 321–336. Philadelphia: Lippincott Williams & Wilkins.

Favero, M. S. and W. W. Bond. 2001."Chemical Disinfection of Medical and Surgical Materials." In S. S. Block, ed., *Disinfection, Sterilization, and Preservation*, 5th ed., pp. 881–917. Philadelphia: Lippincott Williams & Wilkins.

Food and Drug Administration (FDA). 1994. "Tentative final monograph for healthcare antiseptic drug products; proposed rule." *Federal Register* 59:31402–31452.

Goddard, P. A. and K. A. McCue. 2001. "Phenolic Compounds." In S. S. Block, ed. *Disinfection, Sterilization, and Preservation*. 5th ed., pp. 255–281. Philadelphia: Lippincott Williams & Wilkins.

Joslyn, L. J. 2001a. "Gaseous Chemical Sterilization." In S. S. Block, ed. *Disinfection, Sterilization, and Preservation*, 5th ed., pp. 337–359. Philadelphia: Lippincott Williams & Wilkins.

Joslyn, L. J. 2001b. "Sterilization by Heat." In S. S. Block, ed. *Disinfection, Sterilization, and Preservation*, 5th ed., pp. 695–728. Philadelphia: Lippincott Williams & Wilkins.

Leonas, K. K. 1998. "Effect of Laundering on the Barrier Properties of Reusable Surgical Gown Fabrics." *Am.J.Infect.Control.* 26:495–501.

Muscarella, L. F. 2002. "Application of environmental sampling to flexible endoscope reprocessing: the importance of monitoring the rinse water." *Infect.Control Hosp.Epidemiol.* 23:285–289.

Perkins, J. J. 1969. *Principles and Methods of Sterilization in Health Sciences.* 2nd ed. Springfield, IL: Charles C. Thomas Publisher, Ltd.

Rideout, K., K. Teschke, H. mich-Ward, and S. M. Kennedy. 2005. "Considering Risks to Healthcare Workers from Glutaraldehyde Alternatives in High-Level Disinfection." *J Hosp.Infect.* 59:4–11.

Rutala, W. A. 1996. "APIC guideline for selection and use of disinfectants." *Am.J.Infect.Control,* 24:313–342.

Rutala, W. A. and D. J. Weber. 1997. "Uses of Inorganic Hypochlorite (Bleach) in Health-Care Facilities." *Clin.Microbiol.Rev.* 10:597–610.

Rutala, W. A. and D. J. Weber. 2001a. "New Disinfection and Sterilization Methods." *Emerg.Infect.Dis.* 7:348–353.

Rutala, W. A. and D. J. Weber. 2001b. "Surface Disinfection: Should We Do It?" *J.Hosp.Infect.* 48 Suppl A:S64–S68.

Sokol, W. N. 2004. "Nine Episodes of Anaphylaxis Following Cystoscopy Caused by Cidex OPA (Ortho-phthalaldehyde) High-Level Disinfectant in 4 Patients after Cytoscopy. " *J.Allergy Clin.Immunol.* 114:392–397.

Webster, J., E. Radke, N. George, J. Faoagali, and M. Harris. 2005. "Barrier Properties and Cost Implications of a Single Versus a Double Wrap for Storing Sterile Instrument Packs." *Am.J.Infect.Control.* 33:348–352.

CLASSROOM ACTIVITY

Salmonella Infections in a Hospital

Scenario: You are the environmental health and safety manager for a 400-bed, acute care hospital, and you have just been informed by Ms. Smith, the infection control nurse, that there were two cases of salmonella infection in the last three days. The infections were in two adult patients on one of the medical-surgical units. (While the patients were located in the same unit, they did not share the same room.) She suspects a problem in the dietary department and is asking you to investigate. You agree to do the investigation but are skeptical.

Why should you be skeptical?

Results of the Kitchen Investigation. None of the dietary department staff reported being sick in the last week, and no problems in kitchen sanitation were noted.

Medical Histories. Patient A is a 55-year-old male who was recently diagnosed with colon cancer. Patient B is a 62-year-old male who is being evaluated for severe rectal bleeding. Both patients are under the care of Dr. Jones, a recently hired gastroenterologist, and both patients had colonoscopies. (A colonoscopy is a procedure that involves the insertion of a flexible, fiber-optic endoscope into the rectum and the colon. This procedure is frequently used to diagnose colon cancer.)

Disinfection Procedures. Because of a need for rapid turn-around time, the Gastroenterology Service decided to do endoscope reprocessing in the soiled utility room on the medical-surgical unit. The current practice is to soak the scopes in an enzymatic detergent for 15 minutes, followed by a thorough rinse with tap water, and then a 30-minute soak in a solution of 0.55% ortho-phthalaldehyde (OPA). After soaking, the scopes are rinsed in sterile water and then allowed to air-dry. The OPA solution is changed whenever there is an observed change in color. This occurs approximately monthly.

Your assignment is to identify the most likely cause of this outbreak. In your answer, identify potential problems with the current approach to reprocessing these endoscopes.

CHAPTER 5

Healthcare Safety

George Byrns, George Stevens, Greg Heck, Christopher Janicak, Joyce Hood, Angel Boyce, and Denise Knoblauch

Learning Objectives

1. Explain why there is a need for a healthcare safety program.

2. Describe the major elements of a healthcare safety program.

3. Describe the role of the Joint Commission in safety management.

4. Discuss safety culture in healthcare facilities.

5. Discuss safety management strategies.

6. Describe an effective workers' compensation case management system.

The healthcare industry has a poor record in protecting both patients and employees from injuries and illnesses (DiBenedetto 1995; Dunbar et al. 2007; Foley 2004; Foley et al. 2001; Lundstrom et al. 2002). There has been considerable effort in the last few years to address the problem of patient safety, particularly as it relates to medical errors (Lundstrom et al. 2002; Rozovsky 2005). This effort has been motivated in large part to avoid malpractice claims. Injuries to healthcare workers continue to exceed the general industry average, and the most common cause of injuries is strains or sprains (BLS 2006):

Lost time rates per 10^5 workers

- Total industry = 127.8 (strain and sprains = 51.1)
- Hospitals = 175.9 (strain and sprains = 97.0)
- Nursing homes = 264.3 (strain and sprains = 135.9)

Workplace violence to healthcare workers is also a growing problem. See Chapter 12 for more information on the prevention of workplace violence. The actual number of healthcare worker deaths due to injuries or assaults is unknown. The best estimates for healthcare occupational death rate range from 17 to 57 per 10^6 workers (Sepkowitz and Eisenberg 2005). However, this death rate also includes deaths from infectious diseases. While the number of healthcare workers killed on the job is unknown, there is a clearly a need to better protect them from injuries and fatalities.

One reason why the healthcare occupational injury rate has been higher than other industries is that traditionally, hospital workers think first about the safety and welfare of their patients and second about themselves. This culture of concern for the patient rather than the employee continues today in many instances. (The issue of safety climate and culture is discussed later in this chapter.) It is important to remember that there are linkages between patient safety and employee safety (Foley 2004; Foley et al. 2001; Ramsay et al. 2006; Lundstrom et al. 2002). For example, if a patient falls, a healthcare provider may be injured while attempting to catch the patient or attempting to lift the fallen patient. Other reasons for the high injury rate in hospitals are that the work can be unpredictable and involve awkward postures. In the previous example, it is difficult to predict when a patient will lose balance or muscle control and fall, and moving or lifting patients often results in awkward postures for the healthcare provider. Fortunately, the same basic safety management approaches can be applied to either patients or employees; in preventing patient injury, employee injury may also be prevented.

There are some differences in managing employee and patient safety programs. Injuries to employees may be discussed openly in occupational safety committee meetings, but patient incidents can only be discussed in ways that do not disclose patient identifiers due to privacy and malpractice concerns. Even though the names of patients who are injured are never discussed in open meetings, researchers have found that open disclosure with the patient or the patient's family about the specifics of the incident tends to reduce the number of malpractice lawsuits (Popp 2005). As with employee injuries, there is value in identifying patient injury trends in order to identify effective solutions. The focus of this book is primarily on prevention of occupational injuries and illnesses, and prevention strategies are presented below.

PURPOSE OF HEALTHCARE SAFETY PROGRAM

Safety programs in hospitals and other healthcare institutions are similar to those in other industries with some important exceptions. As previously discussed, healthcare safety programs must protect non-occupationally exposed individuals (patients and visitors) as well as employees. Obviously, safety programs must protect property and obey the law by complying with regulations. In addition, healthcare operations must maintain accreditation through the Joint

Commission on Accreditation of Healthcare Organizations (Joint Commission or JCAHO) or other organizations. Therefore, the four purposes of a healthcare safety program should be to:

- Prevent injuries and illnesses
- Contain costs
- Comply with Occupational Safety and Health Administration (OSHA) or other regulations
- Meet accreditation requirements

Each of these purposes is essential in the establishment of a culture of safety, which is described later in this chapter.

Prevention of Injuries and Illnesses

A safety program that fails to prevent occupational injuries and illnesses to its employees or injuries to patients is an ineffective one. In Chapter 1, the importance of anticipating, recognizing, evaluating, and controlling hazards was examined, and a method was described to sort through potential options to prevent or control the hazard using Haddon's Matrix (Robertson 1992; AIHA 2003). Whether the concern is patient safety or employee safety, the most successful program is one that anticipates a potential hazard and eliminates it before anyone is injured. One approach to anticipating a problem is to review prior years' injury and illness data to look for patterns where injuries are more likely to occur. For instance, if there is a high back-injury incident rate in one nursing unit, an investigation may reveal design, equipment, training, or personnel problems. If prior records are not revealing or are not available, another approach is to maintain frequent and open communications with employees or colleagues at similar institutions. If any employee believes there are design, equipment, training, or staffing issues that may cause a future incident, it is critical that this information be communicated to the health and safety program manager. Lastly, it is important to stay current with the relevant health and safety literature. If there are published reports about a new problem in another institution, what is the likelihood that it will occur in your institution?

If we fail to anticipate the problem, then we must recognize hazards through a safety surveillance system (described below). Figure 5.1 is a simplified schematic of a safety surveillance system.

In surveillance system below, a problem is recognized as the result of referrals from a hospital department, another committee or from the insurance carrier, from routine safety surveys, from an employee complaint, or from other sources. Once the problem is recognized, it must be tracked in the hospital safety surveillance system. This generally involves assigning the problem a code number. For example, 08-001 could be the first entry into the system for fiscal or calendar year 2008. It is important to maintain a tracking system because some problems may require capital improvements that could take

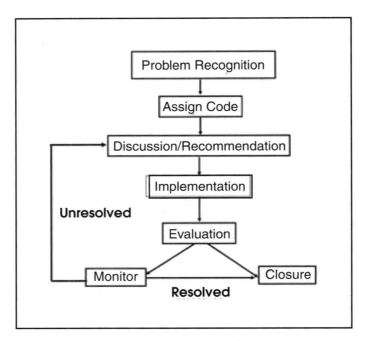

Figure 5.1 Safety surveillance system schematic.

several years to resolve, and the system must assure that these issues will not be forgotten. Safety surveys will be discussed later in this chapter. Also, see Chapter 10 for more information on surveillance and surveys.

The next step is to refer the problem to a committee. In most cases, this will be the hospital safety committee. Needlestick prevention may either be referred to the infection control committee (ICC) or it may involve coordination between both committees. After the issue is referred to a committee, it is discussed and an intervention plan is formulated. This intervention plan is assigned to an individual or program for implementation, and after the strategy is implemented, an evaluation of effectiveness must take place. If the implementation is deemed successful because the hazard is eliminated, then the incident can be considered closed. However, if there is uncertainty as to whether the hazard has been eliminated, the situation should be monitored for a period of time. After a sufficient time has elapsed and no new problems have been uncovered, the matter may be considered closed. On the other hand, if the intervention strategy was unsuccessful, the incident should be referred back to the committee for additional discussion and development of another, hopefully successful, plan. The point is that steps must be in place to assure that safety hazards are known and have either been corrected or are under investigation by the system and awaiting a solution. It is also essential that the root cause of the problem be identified and corrected, and that the root cause and action plans be communicated to employees who have the same job functions.

Example of Hazard Surveillance

You recently accepted a position as the institutional environmental health and safety manager for a hospital in Anchorage, AK. A review of the occupational injury log for last year reveals that back injuries are the most frequent nature of injury. Your initial assumption is that patient handling by nursing personnel is the probable cause for most of these injuries. Upon further review, you notice two things: the injury rates are similar by department, and the most frequent cause was trips, slips or falls. Your next step is to report your findings to the hospital safety committee and request assistance in conducting an investigation. The committee assigns you and the employee health nursing supervisor the responsibility to interview fall victims, identify root causes, and report back to the committee. Your investigation reveals that most of the injured worked during the first shift, and there were two primary injury locations, the employee parking lot and the employee entrance stairway. In your report to the health and safety committee, you state the two major findings:

- The contractor responsible for ice and snow removal routinely arrives after the first shift starts work.
- The stairs become very slick when wet.

Since the contractor will not guarantee an early arrival, the committee recommends to the hospital CEO that a snowplow/sanding truck be purchased for the plant engineering department and that all stairways near outside entrances be provided with a slip-resistant surface. The final steps in this process include monitoring the plant engineering department for their efficiency in ice and snow removal and the effectiveness of the new stair surfacing. Since it is December and there are only three more months of winter, you continue to track this problem for an additional year before the case is considered to be closed.

Cost of Workplace Injuries

One primary motivator for healthcare managers to support safety programs should be the cost of failure to prevent injuries or property damage. Both direct and indirect costs are associated with occupational injuries and illnesses. Direct costs are easily measured; examples of direct costs include salaries, medical fees, treatment costs, and the cost for overtime pay or for temporary hires. Other examples of direct costs are employment-related litigation, environmental impairment claims, property damage claims, civil penalties, loss of accreditation, and criminal actions (West 2007). In 2005, the cost for workers' compensation in the U.S. was $55.3 billion (NASI 2007).

Indirect costs are much less easily measured but, by some estimates, indirect costs far exceed those of direct costs to an organization (Leigh et al. 1997). Examples of indirect costs include lower employee morale and reduced worker productivity. Workers who see their colleagues injured and disabled may perceive the organization's safety climate as less than optimal, causing an adverse effect on morale. Also, workers who are pressured into working longer hours to cover for missing staff may be less productive than the persons that they are replacing. This reduced productivity could also result from the use of temporary hires and the time it takes to train them. Another indirect cost of failure to provide a safe environment may result from fines due to regulatory violations. A list of some of OSHA violations is set out in the section below. Perhaps the most significant cost of failure of a hospital's safety program would be loss of accreditation from the Joint Commission. This accreditation allows an organization to submit Medicare/Medicaid charges for reimbursement. These reimbursements can represent a major portion of an organization's operating budget; and loss of these funds may result in bankruptcy. Accreditation requirements are discussed later in the chapter.

Regulatory Compliance

OSHA has jurisdiction in healthcare facilities, a fact that is often forgotten. Hospitals, nursing homes, and similar health services operations are included in Standard Industrial Classification (SIC) 8000. During fiscal year 2006, the most frequently cited violations of Title 29 of the Code of Federal Regulations (CFR) were, in order:

- 1910.1030, Bloodborne pathogens
- 1910.1200, Hazard communication
- 1904.29, Forms (recordkeeping forms and recording criteria)
- 1910.132, General requirements (personal protective equipment)
- 1910.147, The control of hazardous energy (lockout/tagout)
- 1910.305, Wiring methods, components, and equipment for general use
- 1910.37, Maintenance, safeguards, and operational features for exit routes
- 1910.151, Medical services and first aid
- 1910.303, General requirements (electrical)
- 1904.32, Annual summary (other OSHA injury and illness recordkeeping requirements)

OSHA inspectors generally do not visit hospitals unless there has been a fatality, serious injury or an employee complaint. However, since nursing homes are included in OSHA's special emphasis program because of the high rate of occupational injuries in these facilities, they are inspected more often (OSHA 2002a). See Chapter 14 for more information on safety in nursing homes.

An important aspect when ensuring compliance is to keep in mind the intent of OSHA regulations is to maintain a safe and healthy environment. Safety programs that are focused on ensuring compliance with low-risk items do not meet the intent of OSHA's rules. A good example is compliance with the *Hazard Communication Standard* (OSHA 1996). If the emphasis of the program is placed on labeling secondary containers or collecting MSDSs, it may fail to identify who is working with the most dangerous chemicals. It is most important to determine if workers fully understand the hazards of these chemicals and are following appropriate procedures to protect themselves and their fellow workers from serious injury or illness. The emphasis should be on identifying what is wrong with the management system and fixing the root causes of the problems.

Standards and Violations

There are the two types of safety standards, specification and performance standards. *Specification-based standards* provide the exact method of compliance. For example, OSHA's *Ventilation Standard* (OSHA 2007) provides detailed information on the use of ventilation to control airborne contaminants. *Performance-based standards* describe only the expected outcome. For example, the *Bloodborne Pathogen Standard* (OSHA 2006a) provides general guidance on meeting the requirement. With a performance standard there is considerable flexibility in how a program might meet the objective of preventing occupational exposure to blood-borne pathogens. Most standards are of the performance type because it may not be feasible to specify the most effective method of controlling a hazard when a newer, advanced technology may render the current method obsolete.

Failure to comply with OSHA standards may result in one or more violations. The terms used for types of violations are:

- **Other-than-serious:** This is a situation that has a minor injury potential.
- **Serious:** This situation may result in a substantial, serious injury if left uncorrected.
- **Willful violation:** Evidence suggests that the employer knew the situation was in violation of standards.
- **Repeated violation:** Employers that continue to violate a standard may face increased fines.
- **Failure to abate:** Employers who fail to correct a violation during the prescribed abatement period could face a penalty for each day the violation continues.
- *De minimis*: This is a trivial violation that may not result in a fine.

De minimis and other-than-serious violations generally would not result in a return visit by an OSHA inspector. Situations judged serious may be immediately life-threatening and have the highest priority for OSHA abatement. These situations involve a return visit and, in some cases, an inspector would expect the hazard to be controlled immediately.

There are other federal or state agencies with enforcement authority that affect worker safety issues, such as the use of radioactive substances by the Nuclear Regulatory Commission (NRC). The NRC has stringent regulations under Title 10 for licensure of radioisotopes. The Food and Drug Administration (FDA) has enforcement authority over the pharmacy under Title 21. One example of an FDA pharmaceutical safety concern is trans-filling oxygen cylinders (filling a smaller empty gas cylinder from a larger one). This procedure was being done in some extremely remote hospitals because of the high cost of shipping empty cylinders. Trans-filling can be extremely dangerous without proper controls. In addition, the FDA's Center for Devices and Radiological Health regulates all medical equipment and instruments, including radiation-producing equipment such as x-ray units and ultrasound machines. In most cases, state agencies enforce these regulations rather than federal inspectors. Another federal agency that enforces safety requirements is the Department of Transportation (DOT). The DOT standards cover safe packaging of hazardous materials during transport and spill response procedures. At the state and local level, fire marshals have the right to inspect healthcare facilities to determine the status of fire protection. The Environmental Protection Agency (EPA) has many standards that are relevant to healthcare organizations. See Chapter 6 for more information.

Accreditation

Accreditation of health care is the oldest method of standardizing the delivery of care in the U.S. Accreditation existed prior to healthcare-specific fire codes, national insurance plans, or governmental regulations. Accreditation is a voluntary process that an organization chooses to participate in to reduce its risks, compare itself to competition, and receive deemed status with the Centers for Medicare and Medicaid Services (CMS), and other insurance programs. There is a fee for this process, which covers the cost of the service.

Accreditation Providers. Table 5.1 below lists the current providers of accreditation safety standards and the settings that they cover.

The requirements of the Joint Commission are the most comprehensive of all accrediting bodies, so we will focus primarily on their accreditation standards in this chapter.

THE JOINT COMMISSION ON ACCREDITATION OF HEALTH CARE ORGANIZATIONS (THE JOINT COMMISSION)

The stated mission of the Joint Commission is to continually improve the safety and quality of the care provided to the public through healthcare accreditation and related services that support performance improvement in healthcare organizations.

Joint Commission accreditation includes a set of standards that cover a wide range of safety concerns. From building materials to the number of medical gas outlets, from leadership to human resources, and from medication management to physician credentialing, they cover all the bases. It should come as no surprise then that safety in all of its forms is addressed in the standards. Because of the limitation of this textbook, we will address only those standards concerned with occupational safety and health management.

Table 5.1 Providers of Healthcare Accreditation

Organization	Acute Hospital[1]	Ambulatory[2]	Nursing Homes[3]	Psychiatric Residential[4]	Office Practice[5]	Laboratory[6]
Association of American Ambulatory Health Care (Currently accrediting over 2,700 organizations) (aaahc, 2007)		X			X	
College of American Pathologists (6,000 labs) (CAP, 2007)						X
Commission on Accreditation for Rehabilitation Facilities (5,000 locations) (CARF, 2007)			X	X		
Centers for Medicare and Medicaid Services	X	X	X	X	X	
The Joint Commission (15,000 organizations) (JCAHO, 2007)	X	X	X	X	X	X

1. Acute Hospital: 4 or more patients incapable of self evacuation due to general anesthesia or medical procedure, housed for 24 hours or longer.
2. Ambulatory: same as Acute, but not housed for 24 hours.
3. Nursing Homes: 4 or more patients mostly incapable of self evacuation due to age or infirmity.
4. Psychiatric Residential: group housing for clients recovering from metal illness, addiction, or other related
5. Office Practice: primary care up to and including minor local surgery.
6. Laboratory: Facility that provides diagnostic and testing results to health care providers.

History of the Joint Commission

The Joint Commission traces its roots back to a visionary surgeon, Dr. Ernest Amory Codman of Boston, Massachusetts. In the early 1900s, Codman formulated the *end results idea,* which states that surgical outcomes should be closely monitored and openly documented. At the same time, healthcare standardization also began under the purview of the American College of Surgeons (ACS). The ACS secured a grant from the Carnegie Foundation in the amount of $30,000 to underwrite the beginning of an actual hospital standardization program. In 1917, 300 ACS fellows met in Chicago to discuss conditions in hospitals and the kinds of improvements that would be necessary to ensure proper care and treatment of patients. This conference established the principle that knowledgeable healthcare professionals should assess hospital conditions and endeavor to achieve consensus among themselves on standards that would have the greatest effect on improving patient care. This principle would become fundamental to hospital standardization and later to hospital accreditation. The ACS developed the first American healthcare standards in 1918, and continued to expand them for the next 33 years.

The American Hospital Association (AHA), the American Medical Association (AMA), and the American College of Physicians (ACP) had all begun their own efforts to develop and control healthcare standards. Each group fought to push their system of standards at the expense of the others. Finally at an impasse, in 1950, the four major medical societies (ACS, AHA, AMA, and ACP) formulated a "joint commission" to draw information from all participants, and to develop standardization that would be acceptable to all. Originally called the Joint Commission of Hospital Standardization, the name was changed that next spring to the Joint Commission on Accreditation of Hospitals.

Over the years, additional membership to the Joint Commission was granted to first the Canadian Medical Association (which later left the Commission), and then the American Dental Association. As the name implies, the first standards were written for only hospital services. They have since been expanded to include:

- Hospital accreditation programs
- Long-term care programs
- Ambulatory healthcare programs
- Office-based surgery programs
- Laboratory programs
- Homecare programs
- Critical access hospital programs
- Assisted living programs
- Behavioral healthcare programs
- Managed care programs

The name of the body thus changed to the Joint Commission on Accreditation of Healthcare Organizations (JCAHO), to be all inclusive (Brauer 2001). This name was normally pronounced "jayco," by those in the healthcare field and is still used today. However, in 2007, the name changed once again in an effort to re-brand; it is now called simply the Joint Commission.

Purpose of the Joint Commission

The Joint Commission evaluates the quality and safety of care for nearly 15,000 healthcare organizations in the United States. Although it has competition in

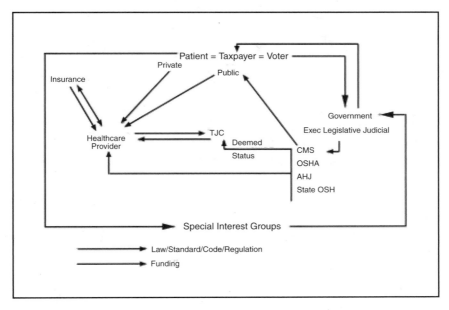

Figure 5.2 Relationships among accreditation, payers, insurance and regulatory agencies.

every program listed above, it is by far the dominant healthcare accrediting body operating in the U.S. No competitor offers the full range of programs that the Joint Commission can deliver. To earn and maintain accreditation, organizations must have an extensive onsite review by a team of Joint Commission healthcare professionals at least once every three years. The purpose of the review is to evaluate the organization's performance in areas that affect patient care and safety. Accreditation may then be awarded based on how well the organization meets the standards.

The relationship between the Joint Commission, private insurance, the authorities having jurisdiction (AHJ) and publicly funded health care is complex. Figure 5.2 illustrates the flow of accreditation, regulation and funding within the U.S. healthcare system.

Basic Content of Joint Commission Standards

The *Hospital Accreditation Manual* for 2009 is organized into the following chapters. The ordering of the chapters places safety related issues first, emphasizing the Joint Commission's mission. Please note that at the time of this writing, the following are pre-publication and subject to revision by the Joint Commission.

- *Environment of Care* examines the safety of the physical environment of the healthcare facilities for the protection of patients, staff and visitors.
- *Emergency Management* delineates the steps taken to mitigate, prepare, respond, and recover from a disaster.

- *Management of Human Resources* evaluates how well the healthcare organization plans for and provides an adequate number of competent staff, as well as how well it provides education and training for all personnel, including orienting, training and educating staff, assessing competence, and defining the qualifications and duties of each job.

- *Infection Prevention and Control* evaluates whether there is a comprehensive, healthcare organization-wide program for the surveillance, prevention and control of infection.

- *Information Management* addresses the extent to which the right information is provided to the right people at the right time, including how effectively the healthcare organization provides for information management planning that ensures accuracy.

- *Leadership* assesses the degree to which the healthcare organization's leaders provide a framework for healthcare services that are responsive to patient needs.

- *Life Safety* requires compliance with the 2000 edition of the NFPA's *Life Safety Code*, a subcategory of safety addressing the provision of a built environment that reasonably protects people from fire and similar emergencies.

- *Medication Management* are pharmaceutical standards to safeguard the procurement, storage, distribution, and dispensing of drugs and other therapeutics.

- *Medical Staff* addresses the organization of the medical staff and how well the organization evaluates the qualifications and competency of physicians and other licensed independent practitioners who provide patient care in the healthcare organization.

- *Nursing* focuses on the nurse executive's oversight of nursing care and services.

- *Provision of Care, Treatment, and Services* addresses how patients are assessed to determine what kind of care is required to meet a patient's initial needs, as well as his or her needs as they change in response to care.

- *Improving Organization Performance* examines the degree to which ongoing processes are in place to improve care and patient health outcomes.

- *Record of Care, Treatment, and Services* requires that all activities are documented accurately, safely stored and confidentially used over the period of coverage for each patient.

- *Rights and Responsibilities of the Individual* addresses the healthcare organization's conduct related to the protection of the rights of patients: whether patients are treated with dignity and respect, whether patients are encouraged to be actively involved in decisions about their care, and whether specific information about patients is given appropriate confidentiality protection.

- *Transplant Safety* requires a protocol for the donation and recovery of organs and tissues to assure ethical treatment and respect throughout the process. The safety and efficacy of the gifted product is monitored to benefit the recipient.

- *Waived Testing* is laboratory work that is done by the provider or other staff using simplified processes. Controls are in place to assure that this testing is valid and accurate (JCAHO 2009).

Steps to Joint Commission Accreditation in Health Care

Accreditation is not a single activity; it is a series of steps:

1. The organization must define and document its processes and daily activities while addressing each of the requirements of the standard.
2. Once defined, the organization then implements their documented system.
3. A survey is then scheduled during or after the implementation stage.
4. The survey team of a doctor, nurse, and administrator carries out an assessment of standard compliance in all areas.
5. If the survey team finds the organization to be in compliance, the Joint Commission issues a certificate of accreditation that is recognized nationally.

The accreditation process is made up of three primary activities; the first is a document review, which assesses whether all of the requirements of the standards have been addressed. This is followed by the onsite survey that determines whether all of the processes have been implemented. Following the survey, the organization performs a self assessment at the eighteen-month point, and shares its findings with Joint Commission. Surveys are normally conducted once every three years, although random, unannounced (additional) surveys may occur at any time.

The International Organization for Standardization (ISO) is the world's leading developer of international standards. Although ISO 9000 was developed for occupational health and safety management systems, the two approaches provide a close fit for healthcare standards.

Additional Areas of Joint Commission Accreditation Benefit

Accredited organizations report adverse outcomes to Joint Commission on a confidential basis. These data are aggregated and trended to identify emerging patient safety concerns. Once high-risk practices are identified, these issues become National Patient Safety Goals. The goals are promulgated nationally at the beginning of each year. Compliance with the goals is strictly enforced by the Joint Commission, and failure to do so will jeopardize accreditation status.

Joint Commission accreditation is required by many insurance providers prior to liability coverage. Accreditation status is also a function of the premium cost charged annually.

The Joint Commission has been audited by the CMS, a federal agency, which judged the standards to be as at least as severe as its own. CMS therefore granted the Joint Commission *deemed status*. This status allows the organization to bill CMS for reimbursement, as if CMS had performed the certification itself. The Joint Commission is the only accreditor to have deemed status across the healthcare industry. It thus has a quasi-governmental or regulatory aspect, an enviable position compared to its competitors.

Within the Joint Commission, there is a department that continuously scans the healthcare field for adverse outcomes. Input is collected from disgruntled employees, news articles, internet information, governmental inspections, and other confidential sources. This information is used to drive the random, unannounced, resurvey process. Although not seen as a benefit by the accredited organization, it is a tremendous benefit to the paying public.

Management of the Environment of Care Standards

The Joint Commissions requirements that apply to safety management are described in the Management of the Environment of Care (EC) standards. They are divided into six management sections of concern, but they all share the major needs of planning, implementing, and testing.

The proposed 2009 JCAHO Standards within the Environment of Care are (JCAHO 2009):

EC.01.01.01. The organization is expected to write plans designed to minimized risks caused by both safety and security concerns.

Each accredited healthcare organization is required to establish a safety management program. Policies and procedures should be based on experience, compliance with applicable laws and regulations, and accepted practices.

As part of this safety management program, a qualified individual, often called a safety officer or health and safety manager, is to be appointed by the chief executive officer and charged with responsibility to develop, implement, and monitor it. The duties of a health and safety manager are described later in this chapter. The health and safety officer is required to work with appropriate staff to implement these recommendations and monitor their effectiveness.

EC.02.01.01. The elements of performance in this JCAHO standard concern managing safety and security risks affecting all individuals: patients, visitors and all those who work in the organization.

Risk identification and reduction activities are required that will achieve the lowest potential for adverse impact on safety and security. Security procedures also must specifically be established to address:

- Identification of patients, staff and visitors entering the facility,
- Control over access to sensitive areas, such as pharmacies, laboratories, and operating rooms, and
- Actions taken in the event of a security incident or failure, including an infant or pediatric abduction.

The standards also address response to product safety notices and recalls and responses by appropriate healthcare organization staff.

EC.02.01.03. This standard, found under the umbrella of the safety plan, prohibits tobacco smoking. This prohibition extends to all staff, visitors, and patients. In certain cases if a physician has deemed it necessary, an adult inpatient may be permitted to smoke, but only based on specific medical criteria developed by the medical staff. Examples might be terminal cases or nicotine withdrawal interference with narcotic withdrawal. If this permission is granted, smoking must be limited to environmentally separate areas. The intent of this policy is to reduce the likelihood of fire and secondhand smoke exposure.

EC.02.02.01. This standard specifically addresses performance requirements for managing hazardous materials.

The hazardous materials and waste management plan (which must also be written) must establish how the organization will effectively manage its risks concerning such hazardous products. The intent is for the organization to identify all materials used that need special handling and implement processes to minimize the risks of their unsafe use and improper disposal.

From this plan, an inventory is created to catalog what products it stores, uses, and generates. This inventory is to be correlated to the requirements of OSHA's *Hazard Communication Standard* (OSHA 1996) and the *Resource Conservation and Recovery Act* (RCRA 1976).

All of the following specific materials are part of the plan, including selecting, handling, storing, transporting, using, and disposing of hazardous materials from receipt or generation through use and final disposition. Some examples of these items are:

- Chemicals (laboratory, maintenance or pharmacy)
- Chemotherapeutic (some of the most toxic substances known, a/k/a cytotoxic)
- Radioactive (used in imaging and cancer treatment)
- Regulated medical waste, including sharps

All of these materials require appropriate space and equipment to safely store and handle them, including separation distances, exhaust hoods, or other protective devices, such as explosive or fire-proof enclosures. The plan must detail the personal protective equipment (PPE) that must be worn when staff is required to work with these substances.

The plan must address the release of harmful gases and vapors, which would otherwise contaminate the breathing air for staff or patients, or create explosive situations. This standard is all-encompassing, from oxygen-deficient atmospheres, to waste gases exhaled by patients undergoing general anesthesia, to corrosives or laser plumes with viral contaminates. In developing the plan, it is important to cite OSHA's *Hazardous Waste Operations and Emergency Response Standard,* which covers employee exposure or the reasonable possibility for employee exposure to safety or health hazards involving clean-up operations due to a spill (OSHA 2006b).

In the event of a plan failure, the staff using the hazardous materials must have knowledge of what to do to contain the incident, and how to clean up the contamination. Failure planning is a theme that is repeated throughout the EC standards.

To comply with OSHA and EPA regulations, the facility must maintain appropriate records, including permits, transfers, manifests, licenses, or other documentation required by law or regulation. Chapter 6 describes the environmental requirements in greater detail. Also see Chapter 9 for more information on hazardous waste management.

EC.02.03.01. The elements of performance for this standard address managing fire risks.

Life Safety is a specialized subdivision of general safety, specifically for protection from fire, smoke, and heat. Fire historically was a mass killer of hospitalized patients who, because of their infirmities, were unable to escape by themselves. As recently as 1980 to 1983, 325 patients died on average each year. This danger was magnified in years prior to this due to unregulated smoking, the use of flammable anesthetics (ether), and the use of open flames for heating and sterilization. All of these dangers are now well-controlled, and the number of hospital fire deaths from 1999 to 2002 was one on average, an incredible decrease (Ahrens 2006).

The life safety management plan must include provisions for staff orientation and education on life safety issues, program performance monitoring provisions, and periodic plan review. In addition, the plan must establish emergency procedures that address: facility-wide and area-specific fire-response needs, fire evacuation routes, and specific roles and responsibilities of personnel at and away from a fire's point of origin, as well as preparations for building evacuation.

EC.02.03.03. This standard's elements of performance concern requirements for conducting fire drills and evaluating fire safety equipment, fire safety building features, and staff response to fire.

Fire drills must be completed once per quarter every year, on each shift, ensuring that every employee has a chance to participate in the drill. The drill must simulate an actual fire emergency, so staff must take the actions assigned to them as though a fire was actually occurring. Each drill is monitored and critiqued, and the plan modified where necessary. At least half of the drills must be unannounced simulations, but actual fire responses may be counted for the remainder.

EC.02.03.05. The elements of performance concern fire safety equipment and fire safety building features. Requirements for testing specific equipment and features are to be performed in accordance with specific NFPA standards.

Testing is required of all protective systems in the facility. The list is lengthy and covers all automatic smoke or fire separation equipment, smoke detection, audio-visual alarms, initiating devices, suppression systems, portable suppression devices, and off-premises communication equipment.

EC.02.04.01. This standard specifies performance requirements for the management of medical equipment risks.

The medical equipment management program describes how the organization will establish and maintain a plan to promote safe and effective use of medical equipment. *Medical equipment* is defined as permanent electrical or mechanical devices used for diagnosing, monitoring, or treating patients. The medical equipment plan should cover processes for selection and acquisition of medical equipment. It also should establish criteria for identifying, evaluating, and taking inventory of equipment to be included in the program before the equipment is used, as well as for reporting medical equipment incidents to the FDA under the Safe Medical Devices Act of 1990 (SMDA 1990), which was been revised as a part of the FDA's Modernization Act of 1997 (FDA 1998).

After equipment is identified as requiring testing and maintenance, it is further categorized as life support and non-life support. According to EC standards, life support equipment testing and maintenance must be completed at a 100% rate. Life support equipment takes the place of a required bodily function, without which the patient would die. Equipment in this category is rare, including heart-lung bypass machines or ventilators. Non-life support equipment, such as an X-ray machine, may also cause harm to a patient if it were out of calibration. Non-life support equipment requires a rate of 90% maintenance. There are no specific requirements for other types of low-maintenance equipment, such as an otoscope used to peer inside of ear canals. The primary concern with these types of equipment is that they be disinfected and stored properly. The medical equipment management plan also should provide for an orientation and education program, program performance monitoring provisions, emergency procedures if critical equipment fails unexpectedly, and procedures for plan review.

EC.02.04.03. The elements of performance for this standard concern inspection, testing and maintenance of medical equipment.

Biomedical equipment is tested prior to initial use for safety, then placed in service. The ranking from above dictates the subsequent frequency of ongoing maintenance, which must be documented. Two specialty areas are highlighted in the standard: the maintenance and testing of sterilizers used to process durable instruments, and the water quality used in renal hemodialysis treatments.

EC.02.05.01. This standard addresses the management of risks associated with an organization's utility systems.

A utility systems management program is required to promote a safe, controlled, comfortable environment of care, assess and minimize risks of utility failures, and ensure operational reliability of utility systems.

As with medical equipment above, utilities are divided into life support and non-life support critical equipment. Life support utilities would result in patient death if they fail, as would be the case with compressed oxygen distribution. Non-life support but critical utilities would affect the provision of patient care, such as the domestic water system. Utilities that are not covered may include items such as drinking fountains, since there is minimal risk of harm if a drinking fountain fails to function. All other requirements are similar to those for medical equipment described above.

The utility management plan also should establish an orientation and education program, program performance monitoring provisions, emergency procedures for system disruptions or failures, and provisions for periodic plan review.

EC.02.05.03. The elements of performance for this standard concern emergency electrical power for specific equipment, lighting, and systems within a facility.

Emergency power is required for Life Safety, and critical functions. Life safety emergency power backs up the building fire alarm, exiting illumination, fire stair lighting, at least one elevator, and exit signs. Critical power backs up blood, bone and tissue storage, intensive care units, medical air compressors, medical and surgical vacuums, and any area with electrical life support equipment.

EC.02.05.05. This standard specifies performance requirements for inspecting, testing, and maintenance of utility systems.

Prior to initial use, all utility equipment in inventory is tested. As before, 100% of life support and 90% of non-life support utilities must be maintained as planned. Infection control utility systems are maintained appropriately, whatever the source of the sterilant used. Noncritical equipment is maintained as determined to be necessary by the organization without a required minimum.

EC.02.05.07. Performance elements for inspection, testing, and maintenance of emergency power systems are specified in this standard.

All of these requirements are taken directly from the applicable NFPA code, covering battery and generator systems.

EC.02.05.09. This standard's elements of performance concern the inspection, testing and maintenance of medical gas and vacuum systems.

These systems supply some of the most critical utilities within the hospital. Because of their criticality, these systems have many controls and alarms that must be maintained appropriately. Any malfunction of the system or notification devices could easily result in patient or staff death or serious injury. When ever these systems are breached, purity, correct gas and proper pressure must be verified and documented. Because of the potential for fire acceleration with piped medical gasses and vacuums, shut-off controls must also be clearly labeled and accessible.

EC.02.06.01. This standard addresses the performance requirements necessary for an organization to establish and maintain a safe, functional environment. Elements include: space for recreation and social interaction; storage space; lighting; ventilation; control of odors; emergency access, and furnishing and equipment.

Appropriate Environment. This standard serves as a repository for those standards that do not fit in the *Patient Rights, Nursing,* or other chapters. Very little of this section is safety-related, but instead lists such items as: appropriate space that is clean and well-furnished; preservation of patient's dignity and privacy; space to store personal belongings; access to a telephone; and support for patient personal growth for those staying longer than 30 days. Even the readily apparent mistakes of placing a bariatric chair in a pediatric area or not providing ventilation to remove objectionable odors are covered here.

The standards under this section require establishment of an environment that supports the hospital's basic mission and services. The environment should support the care process and the needs of the population served by the organization. The standards cover the following categories:

- **Space:** Appropriate space is provided to support patient services.
- **Furnishings:** These are safe, in good repair, and appropriate for the patient's level of need and ability.
- **Outside access:** For patients housed for longer than 30 days, a suitable, safe, and healthy environment to experience the outdoors is provided.
- **Areas:** All areas are safe, clean, functional, and comfortable.
- **Lighting:** Lighting is suitable for care, treatment, services, and the specific needs of patients.
- **Ventilation:** There is sufficient ventilation to remove odors, with acceptable temperature and humidity.
- **Locks:** Locks are suitable for privacy, but accessible by staff when emergencies necessitate entrance.

EC.02.06.05. This standard specifies performance requirements for managing a hospital environment during demolition, renovation, or new construction to reduce risk to those in the organization.

The requirement for new construction or major renovation to conform to laws and regulation is also found in this section, as well as the *Guidelines for Design and Construction of Hospitals and Healthcare Facilities* (or similar design standards) (AIA 2006). Prior to starting this type of work, the organization must complete a risk assessment, detailing how the work will interfere with the provision of care due to the creation of new hazards. Such hazards may include vibration, noise, offensive or hazardous fumes, reduced fire protection, and most importantly, infection control issues. Hospital-acquired infections (HAI) have been traced directly to construction projects that result in the disturbance of fungal, viral, or bacterial colonies. See Chapter 13 for more information on design and construction.

EC.03.01.01. The standard's requirements address the roles and responsibilities of staff and licensed independent practitioners relative to the environment of care.

Under the EC standards, the safety management plan must describe how the organization will provide a physical environment that is free of hazards and manage staff activities to reduce the risk of injury to anyone within the facility. In addition, the safety management plan must establish a staff orientation and education program that addresses safety issues, program performance, monitoring provisions, and provisions for periodic review.

The outcome of this effort is gauged by staff demonstration of how to eliminate hazards, react to an incident, or to report a risk area.

EC.04.01.01. The elements of performance in this standard specify requirements for the collection of information and monitoring of conditions in the hospital environment.

The implementation of the safety plan is discovered in the day–to-day practices and operation of staff and equipment, maintenance of walkways, and fixing trip hazards. It is also formally assessed by inspection, once every six months in patient care areas and once each year in non-patient areas. These inspections are commonly called *hazard surveillance rounds.*

EC.04.01.03. The standard specifies how a hospital shall analyze and identify environment of care issues.

A health and safety committee, which includes representatives from administration, clinical services, and support services departments, as well as other departments if necessary, is to be established to analyze identified EC management risks and develop recommendations for resolving them. This activity is critical in monitoring safety performance.

EC.04.01.05. This standard addresses performance requirements for the improvement of care in a hospital environment.

This may be the most important area of the *Accreditation Manual for Hospitals,* in that it addresses the defining mission of the Joint Commission. The safety management plan states what the organization will do. The implementation and testing section puts the plan into action; mistakes and imperfections are found by monitoring and bringing those issues to light for correction of the plan. This area describes the roles and responsibilities of a health and safety officer and the health and safety committee in collecting, assessing, and correcting mistakes or imperfections that are discovered. Each plan must be assessed annually for its scope, objectives, performance and effectiveness. Improvements are made to the plan; the next year, this iterative (or looped sequence) process starts again (JCAHO 2009).

Plans

The EC sections are subdivided into numerous elements of performance that may have as many as 38 requirements. Each one of these elements of performance is individually cited if not accomplished correctly by the organization. The plans requirement is to simplify the surveyor's task, in that the organization states in writing how it intends to fulfill the requirements of the standard. In other words, the standards say, "You will...," and the plans say, "We do... in the following way."

Another useful aspect of the written plan is for new employee orientation and training. Both the surveyor and the employees are looking for a business plan or an executive summary of the important safety concerns that are present in this hazardous workplace. Common elements are: who is responsible for the sections, how risk assessments are performed, what actions are taken when risks are identified to achieve the safest environment, and how the ongoing maintenance of safety for the section is to be ensured.

Implementation and Testing

This common element describes actions to take in response to healthcare industry known (high-probability) risks. For instance, if there is a fire, staff should react automatically to contain it and reduce the possible harm it would have caused to patients or themselves. Surveyors judge this by asking staff to demonstrate how they have been trained to respond (as specified by the plan) by simulating what they would do in the event of an actual unsafe condition. Large or facility-wide responses also require group activities that test every aspect of the plan, such as facility fire drills, emergency management drills, and infant abduction drills. Due to the size of such responses, these functions are not simulated by the surveyor, but by the organization in advance of the survey, and the results provided to the surveyor.

The Joint Commission standards cover seven major elements. While the specific wording for these standards changes from year to year, the basic intent remains the same; that is, to protect people and resources.

PROGRAM MANAGEMENT

A *management system* has been described as "the way an organization operates, the way it carries out its business, the way things are. Its purpose is to enable the organization to accomplish its mission, its purpose, its goals and its objectives" (Hoyle 2005). Management systems in occupational health, safety and the environment provide us with the components needed to meet and exceed our goals and objectives.

In 2005, the American National Standards Institute, Inc. (ANSI) approved AIHA/ANSI Z-10-2005, *Occupational Health and Safety Management Systems (OHSMS)* (Manuele 2006; ANSI/AIHA 2005). The purpose of this standard was "to provide organizations an effective tool for continual improvement of their occupational health and safety performance" (ANSI/AIHA 2005). It further stated that, "An OHSMS implemented in conformance with this standard can help organizations minimize workplace risks and reduce the occurrence and cost of occupational injuries, illnesses and fatalities" (ANSI/AIHA 2005). The emphasis for the OHSMS is on "continual improvement and systematically eliminating the underlying or root causes of deficiencies" (ANSI/AIHA 2005). It was noted that this voluntary consensus standard used recognized management system principles found in such standards as the ISO 9000 and ISO 14000 series. The ISO 9000 family of standards was designed to assist organizations in operating effective quality management systems (Hoyle 2005). According to Hoyle, ISO 9000 is a set of criteria that will help organizations develop the capability to create and retain satisfied customers. It utilizes many of the best principles of leadership, management and business in developing a quality management system. The ISO 14000 family of standards covers a wide range of subjects under the term environmental management. The ISO 14001 standard spells out the requirements of an effective environmental management system. It lists minimum policy requirements of management and the checks and balances needed to conform to that policy. Continual improvement is an important part of the system requirements. Information on this standard can be found on the ISO Web site; also see Chapter 6 for more information on ISO 14000.

One common element to both the ISO 14001 standard and the ANSI Z-10 standard is the use of the methodology known as Plan-Do-Check-Act (PDCA) (ANSI/AIHA 2005). This methodology helps ensure continual improvement in the system.

The continual improvement model used in the OHSMS cycle includes five key components. These components are part of the PDCA cycle and include:

- policy, management leadership and employee participation
- planning
- implementation and operation
- checking and corrective action
- management review

To comply with ANSI Z-10, the findings from the hazard surveillance program must be assessed for their impact on health and safety. Then priorities are established based on:

- potential for OHSMS improvements;
- health and safety standards and regulations; and
- consequences of the risk from a business perspective.

See Chapter 11 for more information on risk assessment and management.

Safety Climate and Safety Culture

The most important determinant of a successful health and safety program is assurance that safety is a part of every organizational element (Brauer 2006a). While many feel that support for the program by the departmental supervisor is the key to success, this is not likely to happen unless top managers (the governing board and the hospital's chief executive officer) demonstrate their support. Top management sets the safety climate or culture for the organization (Lundstrom et al. 2002).

Most safety efforts have been reactive instead of proactive, and there has been growing concern in aviation and other high-risk industries, including health care, for the need to establish a culture of safety (Pronovost et al. 2003; Wiegmann et al. 2002). This means that all employees perceive the workplace to be a safe one and that all actively contribute to the prevention of injuries, illnesses or other adverse outcomes.

There are a variety of definitions for an organization's safety climate or safety culture. One definition of *safety climate* is "a psychological phenomenon, encompassing the perceptions of the state of safety at a particular time"

(Wiegmann et al. 2002). Safety climate is tied to intangible issues such as situational and environmental factors, and it is a temporal phenomenon that is relatively unstable and subject to change. *Safety culture* is defined as "the enduring value and priority placed on worker and public safety by everyone in every group at every level of an organization" (Wiegmann et al., 2002). It is the extent to which employees are personally committed to safety.

In Costa Rica, researchers found that hospitals with a combination of poor safety climate and poor safety practices increased the likelihood of injuries (Gimeno et al. 2005). In the U.S., there is evidence that the safety culture of healthcare facilities is poor. In a study by the American Nurses Association (ANA), 88% of respondents expressed concern about the safety of their workplace, and 60% feared that they would receive a disabling back injury (ANA 2001). One study comparing safety culture in aviation to that of health care found that airline cockpit crews scored higher in safety culture than did healthcare workers (Sexton et al. 2000). Another study found low rates of problems in safety climate in naval aviators and high rates of problems in healthcare workers for most questions (Gaba et al. 2003). In some cases, these responses differed by a factor or three or more. A study at the Johns Hopkins Hospital found that the staff perceived their direct supervisors to be more committed to safety than top management; this was especially true of nurses (Pronovost et al. 2003). They also found that physicians were less aware of the safety program than nurses. The major conclusions of the Johns Hopkins study were that senior leaders needed to be more visible in their support of the safety program, and that greater effort was necessary to educate physicians regarding safety.

One solution to the problem of poor safety culture in health care could be a *top-down strategy*, where managers visit front-line workers and watch them as they perform their jobs (Gaba et al. 2003). Researchers found that routine rounds by hospital executives on nursing units improved nurses' perceptions of the organization's safety climate (Thomas et al. 2005). Another approach is a *bottom-up strategy* (Gaba et al. 2003). In this approach, new hires would be carefully trained and their performance monitored to verify that they were complying with hospital policy. Thus, these new workers will perceive that the organization cares about their safety. However, given the perceptions of nurses that top management lacks a commitment to safety, the *top-down* approach must be a part of the solution. The importance of management's involvement is described in Figure 5.3, where the conclusion was that companies with outstanding safety cultures scored high in the following critical characteristics (Stewart 2002).

Outstanding companies also scored 1000 times better than the worst companies and 100 times better than average companies (Stewart 2002). Based on the survey from the ANA, it is likely that safety performance in most healthcare organizations would fall in the "worst companies" category (ANA 2001). Some might argue that the reason healthcare safety performance is so poor is the hazardous nature of the work. However, Stewart found that the presence of a hazardous work environment was less important than the condition of the safety culture. He found hazardous industries with good safety cultures had

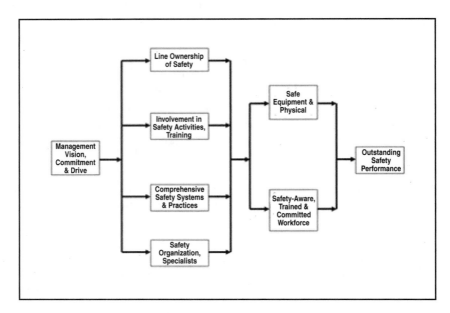

Figure 5.3 The model of managing for outstanding safety.
(Source: Stewart 2002. Used with permission)

better safety records than companies with poor safety cultures in office environments. What was most important to having a strong safety culture was management's open communication on the importance of safety, direct involvement in safety, and empowering employees to take an active role in safety (Stewart 2002).

Statement of Authority

Any organization must establish policies that emphasize the importance of safety for employees, visitors, customers, and the community (Brauer 2006b). In a healthcare organization, such policies are generally stated in bylaws that are approved by the governing board and signed by the chief executive officer. These bylaws establish the need for a safety program and delegate authority for implementing the program. An important component of the policy statement is defining responsibility and establishing accountability. At each level in the organization, specific responsibilities, along with the corresponding authority and resources to meet those responsibilities, need to be in place. The appendices in the ANSI Z-10 standard provide an example of responsibilities at different levels in the organization (ANSI/AIHA 2005). However, it is vital that responsibilities come with the authority to take action when needed. Requiring accountability for compliance with the safety program by department heads and supervisors is the key to success (Brauer 2006a). In addition, providing staffing and funding resources are also critical to the success of the safety program.

Employee Involvement

Another important element of safety program management is allowing for and encouraging employee involvement at all levels in the organization. A good leader ensures employee participation in the safety process and listens to employees' concerns. There should be no barriers in communication. If there are multiple layers of bureaucracy between employees and management, very often vital information is filtered out. Leaders who listen to employee concerns and respond to those concerns build trust and achieve employee buy-in. This approach is also important for health and safety managers to build trust with employees. Once this trust is established, real progress can be made in developing a successful safety culture.

Employees also need to be involved in the planning, implementation and evaluation processes. Some examples where employees can be involved include: conducting job hazard analysis on a process; participating in incident investigations to help identify root causes; providing training activities in their areas of expertise; reviewing and pilot testing new products and chemicals. They should also be involved in renovation planning to ensure they can service equipment planned by engineering. It is not uncommon to find new facilities built and equipment installed without input from those who service the equipment, resulting in additional risks. For example, if maintenance personnel are not involved in the installation process, a technician may work on a compressor in a dangerous or awkward position and risk a musculoskeletal injury. Also, since more time may be required to perform basic service, the cost is increased.

Health and safety managers should work with supervisors and teach them the basic skills needed in this process, including job hazard analysis and improved communications. The National Institute for Occupational Safety and Health (NIOSH) offers information on training supervisors using coaching techniques (NIOSH 2005). This guidance document assists the health and safety manager with strategies to lead and facilitate training meetings.

Safety Manual

Although there is no requirement to have a healthcare facility safety manual, it is a useful way to organize required policies, procedures and supporting materials in one place.

The manual should start with a *statement of purpose* or a mission statement to provide an overall framework for the healthcare safety program. An example of this would be:

> It is the mission of the _____ Hospital Safety Program to prevent injuries and illnesses to employees, patients and visitors and to prevent property damage at this facility. It is also the mission of this program to comply with all relevant regulations and accreditation requirements.

Each year, a set of specific objectives should be identified by the healthcare safety committee. These objectives may be based on expected outcomes or processes. They should be measurable tasks that are selected for their importance in assuring that the safety program meets its statement of purpose. Some examples of possible objectives might be to reduce the number of back pain cases from the baseline average of twenty per year to five per year. Another example might be to review all departmental safety policies by the end of the year. It is useful to assess progress in meeting these objectives on a quarterly basis, and the results of these assessments should be reported to the safety committee. At the end of the year, progress in meeting the annual objectives should be included in an annual report, which is discussed below.

Policies and Procedures

Policy has been defined as, "any statement made by management at any level that is designed to constrain the actions and decisions of those it affects" (Hoyle 2005). According to ANSI Z-10, policy should be committed to four things:

1. Protection and continual improvement of employee health and safety;
2. Effective employee participation;
3. Conformance with the organization's health and safety requirements; and
4. Compliance with applicable laws and regulations (ANSI/AIHA 2005).

One important policy statement is a requirement to conform actions of staff to the organization's health and safety policies. For example, a healthcare institution's policy may define what is expected of the facility's department heads. They may be required to conduct periodic audits, assess new equipment and processes, train employees on certain safety procedures and follow up on incident investigations or survey findings within a specified time frame.

The final area that the policy should address is compliance with applicable laws and regulations. This aspect is very straightforward. One caution: a program focused only on compliance will not guarantee a safe workplace. According to the American Society of Safety Engineers (ASSE), it was reported that the "standards-setting process is broken and needs to be fixed" (Cecich 2007). Many standards have not been updated to meet current needs in safety management.

Organization of the Safety Manual

The main reason for assembling a safety manual is to organize copies of facility-wide and department-specific safety policies and procedures in one convenient place. Policies are implemented using written procedures which describe in detail the means of accomplishing an activity or function.

The following list provides some examples of subject matter that are addressed in facility-wide policies:

- Incident reporting
- General employee safety
- Patient and visitor safety

■ Hazardous materials and hazard communication

■ Laboratory safety and chemical hygiene plan

■ Hazard surveys

■ Safety education

■ Smoking

■ Internal and external emergency planning

■ Personal protective equipment (PPE)

Department-specific safety policies should not be written solely by the health and safety manager because it is essential that the department employees consider these policies to be their own. However, it may be necessary to assist the department manager in preparing or revising these policies to be sure that they meet the intent of the safety program's statement of purpose.

Health and Safety Committee

There are a number of important reasons for having a health and safety committee. Some of the more important functions are to:

■ set policy and monitor performance

■ establish and maintain communication

■ manage injury and cost data

■ direct educational activities

■ investigate and abate hazards

■ meet accreditation requirements

An effective committee is not too large. Some key individuals that should be included on the committee are the facility's chief executive or a representative, the director of nursing, the health and safety manager, the plant engineer, and an employee representative. Some hospitals use focused subcommittees. Examples of these subcommittees might include:

■ Safety education

■ Equipment and utilities management

■ Emergency preparedness

■ Patient and visitor safety

■ Employee and property safety

■ Hazardous materials and waste management

Hospitals using this approach typically have each of these subcommittees reporting to an executive health and safety committee. It is optimal, but not required, to have the executive committee chaired by the chief executive officer or other senior leader.

Recordkeeping and Reports

You may have heard the expression, "The job's not done until the paperwork is finished." This is especially true of a healthcare safety program. As far as OSHA inspectors or Joint Commission surveyors are concerned, if there are no records, the job was never done, and the organization is in violation of the standard or regulation. Records are also important to protect the legal rights of employers and employees (Brauer 2006c). If there were no injury or incident report records, there would be no way for an employee to support a workers' compensation claim. Also, if there were no industrial hygiene exposure monitoring reports, it would be difficult to refute a claim by an employee that his/her disease was the result of working at that facility.

There are certain records that must be maintained (OSHA 2001a; OSHA 2003). For example, employee work-related injuries or illnesses must be reported on an incident report, such as OSHA Form 301 or equivalent. Information from these incident reports then may be entered into OSHA Form 300 (OSHA 300 Logs) if it meets one of the recordable criteria, such as required medical treatment beyond simple first aid or which resulted in time away from work. A summary of the total number of work-related injuries and illnesses for the previous year must be posted each February 1st until April 30th of the following year. OSHA 300 Logs must be retained for a period of five years, plus the current year. Not all employers are required to maintain OSHA Logs. Those employers with ten or fewer employees and those employers whose industries are classified as *exempt* (lower risk for injury) are not required to maintain OSHA 300 logs, but all industries, regardless of size and hazard risk, are required to report work-related fatalities and incidents involving in-patient hospitalization of three or more employees. All employers are also required to provide accident reports if OSHA requests them in writing and must reply to requests from the Bureau of Labor Statistics (BLS) to complete the *Survey of Occupational Injuries and Illnesses* (OSHA 2001b). Employers covered under the OSH Act have to record every fatality, injury, or illness that:

- Is work-related,
- Is a new case,
- Meets at least one of the general criteria for recordability (Klamert 2002).

Definitions

What does OSHA mean by an injury or illness being work-related? The occupational injury and illness reporting requirements state that a case is *work-related* if an event or exposure at work is the cause of an injury or illness, or if a preexisting condition has been significantly aggravated by a work event or exposure and none of the rule's nine exceptions to work relatedness apply (OSHA 2001c). The requirement defines *work environment* as "the establishment and any other locations where one or more employees are working or present as a condition of employment" (OSHA 2003). It is important to remember that these rules are specifically for the purpose of OSHA log recordability and are independent of determining eligibility for compensation under worker's compensation systems. (Workers' compensation is covered later in this chapter.) A *preexisting condition* is an injury or illness that has been the result of a non-work-related event or exposure, such as diabetes. The final rule states that "an aggravation is significant if, the contribution of the aggravation at work is such that it results in tangible consequences that go beyond those that the worker would have experienced as a result of the preexisting injury or illness alone, absent the aggravating effects of the workplace" (OSHA 2001b). While it may be difficult at times to determine whether a preexisting condition was significantly aggravated, one can sort through these issues by considering whether the event would have happened regardless of the place it happened (such as a heart attack or stroke).

Recordability Criteria

General recordability criteria include the following: death, missed work days due to the injury/illness, modified or restricted work duty, loss of consciousness, significant injury diagnosed by a physician or other licensed medical practitioner, and/or an injury/illness that requires medical treatment beyond first aid. Most of these criteria are self-explanatory, but defining what is or is not first aid can be a little more difficult. There are fourteen treatments defined in OSHA regulations (OSHA 2003; OSHA 2006c) that are not considered to be first aid. Some examples include:

- applying wound dressings such as bandages or butterfly closures (but the use of items such as sutures or staples are medical treatment);
- using any type of immobility devices while transporting the injured worker (examples are back boards or neck collars);
- applying hot and cold therapy;
- administering fluids for heat-related illness;
- employing massage therapy for treatment other than that prescribed for physical therapy or by chiropractors;
- cleaning or irrigation of surface wounds;
- giving tetanus boosters;
- using over-the-counter medications in non-prescription dosages (but asking workers to take them in larger doses constitutes medical care);
- using supportive devices such as elastic bandages (but use of rigid items for immobilization is considered medical care);
- removing splinters or foreign bodies other than from the eye; and
- using finger guards and eye patches.

Recordability Criteria Specific to Healthcare Workers

The determination of whether an incident is recordable may be straightforward in some instances; however, in others it may require consultation with the local or area OSHA office. The following sections include some concrete examples of incidents that may occur in a healthcare setting, as well as discussion on whether each example is a recordable event or not.

Blood-borne Pathogen Exposures. The Needlestick Safety and Prevention Act amended the *Bloodborne Pathogens Standard* (OSHA 2006a) to include additional requirements, such as the requirement for employers to make and maintain a sharps injury log. The sharps injury log can be kept as part of the OSHA 300 Log, but injuries from contaminated sharps must be easily separated from other injuries. These entries should be recorded as "privacy case" and contain information about the department or work area where the injury occurred, how the injury occurred, and the type and brand of device involved in the exposure. The sharps injury log must protect the confidentiality of the individuals involved. The information in the sharps injury log serves as a valuable tool to identify departments, procedures or devices involved for future improvement efforts (OSHA 2001d).

Example:

> A surgical services employee is stuck with a suture needle during an operative procedure. The patient is HIV positive. Immediate evaluation and initiation of post exposure prophylaxis (PEP) ensues, along with baseline laboratory testing and appropriate emotional care. Subsequent follow-up testing shows that the employee did not seroconvert.

The example above would be recordable on the sharps injury log. If the employee had seroconverted, s/he would have additionally had to have been recorded as an occupational illness.

Tuberculosis. "If an employee is occupationally exposed to anyone with an active case of TB and subsequently develops a TB infection, as evidenced by a positive skin test or diagnosis by a physician or licensed health care professional (PHLCP), the employer must record the case" (OSHA 2001e)

Example:

> During their annual health screen, several staff members from the patient care unit exhibit a positive tuberculin skin test, but were negative the previous year. Additionally, each individual reports providing care to the same patient with active TB several weeks ago. Upon investigation, maintenance reports that the negative pressure ventilation system was not functioning properly over the last several weeks. One staff member has a cough and fever; the chest x-ray shows the possibility of active tuberculosis and the staff member is furloughed and referred to the public health department for evaluation and treatment.

In the example above involving TB exposure, all cases would be entered on the OSHA 300 log. If it had been determined, through medical investigation, that the employee was exposed to someone outside of the work environment, the entry can be crossed off and thus removed from the OSHA 300 Log.

Musculoskeletal Disorders. Due to the burden of moving and lifting patients, musculoskeletal disorders (MSDs) are among the most common injury for hospital workers. While the OSHA ergonomics standard, including recordkeeping requirements, was rescinded, MSD injuries are still covered by OSHA (OSHA 2003; OSHA 2006c). In addition, many states have adopted standards for the prevention of prevention of MSDs. These regulations are state-specific and vary in the content and requirements. In comparison to the previous log, the OSHA 300 Log includes the ability for privacy and limitations on the duration of a lost work time case.

Example:

> An environmental services staff member slips on a recently mopped floor. In an attempt to brace himself and minimize the fall, he incurred a groin injury which subsequently required seven months out of work. He expresses concerns about privacy.

In the above example, the recorder could identify the individual name as a private case and also list the time away from work as 180 days with the cap that is allowed by OSHA (tracking cases that result in more than six months away from the job is not required by OSHA).

Hearing Loss. Many healthcare facilities have areas where hearing protection must be used due to noise exposure at or above the hearing conservation criterion of 85 dB for an eight-hour, time weighted average (TWA). Employees who work in these areas should have baseline audiometry and annual testing done as part of the hearing conservation program. If, during the course of annual testing, a standard threshold shift (STS) in hearing loss averaging 10 decibels is noted, it must be recorded on the OSHA 300 log (OSHA 2002b).

Example:

> During annual testing, a plant operations worker has a standard threshold shift. Upon retest, the hearing loss is determined to be a possible recordable shift. The information is entered on the OSHA 300 Log while the question as to whether the loss is work related is determined.

One scenario that is quite common in the healthcare setting is post-exposure prophylaxis to infectious diseases, such as pertussis or meningococcal meningitis. These would generally not be OSHA recordable unless the exposed individual actually contracts the illness. The rationale is that this incident should be viewed as preventative treatment and is not considered an injury or illness. However, this issue has been interpreted differently in some OSHA jurisdictions. Until there is national agreement on the recordability of post-exposure prophylaxis, healthcare organizations should consult with their local OSHA representatives for guidance.

Other Recordkeeping Criteria. Some other examples of required reports are emergency preparedness and fire safety records, training records, occupational exposure monitoring, and certain medical surveillance and immunization records. Recordkeeping requirements for these other activities are varied and complex. For example, recordkeeping for emergency preparedness and fire safety is extensive and beyond the scope of this book. (See Chapter 7 for more information on this topic.) In general, training records must be kept for at least three years; however, even this is standard-specific. For example, the *Bloodborne Pathogens Standard* (OSHA 2006a) has specific language for annual training and three-year record retention, whereas maintenance of training records under *Hazard Communication Standard* (OSHA 1996) is non-specific. In any event, it is prudent to maintain these records for longer periods to provide documentation in the event of a dispute. Worker exposure monitoring records are covered under OSHA regulations (OSHA 2006d). These records are not required to be included in the employee's medical record file; however, they must be accessible to the employee and maintained for the duration of employment plus 30 years.

Monitoring Program Performance

One of the most important reasons for maintaining records is to monitor program performance. Hazard surveys, injury and illness incident reports, or property damage reports should be compiled to establish baselines. These baselines allow the health and safety manager to compare current injury, illness, or property damage experience to past experience. One major limitation of these records in monitoring improvements to the safety program is employee under-reporting. By some estimates, under-reporting is a high as several hundred percent (Azaroff et al. 2002). There are many reasons for this problem, including employers who warn employees about reporting incidents or illnesses because it will raise the workers' compensation insurance rates. This approach is counter-productive because it interferes with the identification of injury risk factors. It should also be avoided because it is a serious violation of OSHA's recordkeeping requirement. See Chapter 10 for more information on the use of the hazard surveys and data collection results.

The annual safety program evaluation report is perhaps the most important of all safety reports. As discussed earlier in the chapter, it is an opportunity to assess progress on meeting key program objectives. It is also an important method of communicating to the chief executive officer and the governing board of the importance of the health facility safety program. If at all possible, it is important to describe any economic benefits of the program. For example, lowering the number of workers' compensation claims reduced the hospital's insurance rates. The health and safety program should be viewed as a cost-savings resource, not simply administrative overhead.

Recordkeeping requirements differ for federal facilities (OSHA 2004) and facilities under OSHA state plans (OSHA 2006c). Complete coverage of OSHA recordkeeping requirements is beyond the scope of this book.

Key Staff

Three key staff members must work closely together to achieve the mission of the health and safety program: the health and safety manager, the employee health coordinator, and the workers' compensation case manager.

Health and Safety Manager

The person delegated the responsibility for managing the program might be called the health and safety manager, the hospital safety director or safety officer. Whatever the title, this individual should have clear authority to take action in an emergency. Some of the responsibilities of this position include:

- Providing advice and guidance to the health and safety committee
- Performing safety consultations for managers and employees
- Conducting surveys and collecting and tabulating data
- Managing the hazardous materials and wastes program
- Developing or assisting in developing policies and procedures
- Conducting or arranging for training
- Reviewing construction, renovation or demolition plans and specifications

Employee Health Coordinator

This individual could be either a nurse or a physician who has the responsibility of providing medical or clinical guidance for the health and safety program. Some of the responsibilities of this position include:

- Monitoring the medical care for employees receiving workers' compensation
- Providing or monitoring the initial evaluation and treatment of an injured worker
- Recommending medical review of questionable claims
- Managing the employee medical files
- Monitoring light-duty employees
- Conducting or monitoring pre-assignment evaluation such as obtaining complete history and baseline testing or screening
- Providing or monitoring employee vaccinations
- Participating in hazard surveys

Workers' Compensation Case Manager

The third member of this group usually works in human resources or personnel. This person has been trained in the rules and requirements governing the workers' compensation program. Some of the responsibilities of this position include:

- Managing paperwork for claims
- Providing a liaison between local team and compensation carrier
- Providing guidance on workers' compensation to the team

Training of Health and Safety Staff

In the past, a hospital maintenance worker with little or no training may have been assigned the responsibility of hospital safety officer. In today's climate of complex health and safety regulations, accreditation requirements, and the need to run a cost-efficient operation, it is essential that the person who is assigned the responsibility as the facility's health and safety manager be qualified to do the job. Some of the more important training courses for the health and safety manager include:

- **Basic Epidemiology:** This course is important because of the need to analyze injury and illness data to identify trends.
- **Environment of Care (EC):** The Joint Commission and the American Society of Healthcare Engineering (ASHE) provide training in understanding and complying with the Joint Commission EC standard.
- **Collateral Duty Course:** OSHA provides a special course for individuals for whom safety is an additional duty.

The NFPA also provides a number of courses on fire safety, healthcare hazards and other topics.

Workers' Compensation

During the 1800s, employers demanded that workers produce a great quantity but usually paid nothing to workers who were injured on the job (Harger 2007). Also, even the minimum elements of a safety program were non-existent in most of these jobs. The growth of the legal profession in the late 1800s enabled injured workers to take their employers to court for workplace injuries. By 1908, workers were winning approximately 15% of these cases. Federal Employer's Liability Act of 1908 was passed in response to the high numbers of injuries and deaths to railroad workers, and provided the first federal workers' compensation program. While this law was limited in scope, it ultimately spawned similar laws passed by state governments. Wisconsin was the first state to establish a workers' compensation program in 1911, and by 1948, all U.S. states had some type of workers' compensation requirements. The fact that there is no national workers' compensation program, and that each state's program may differ presents major challenges in the ability to study and understand the status of workers' compensation in the U.S. (NASI 2007). This lack of uniformity also means that determination of coverage varies from state to state. The workers' compensation program for federal workers significantly differs from state programs, and it, as well as certain states such as California, tends to be more liberal in determining whether a worker's condition is work-related. This is particularly true in cases such as psychological stress and cumulative trauma disorders (CTDs).

Certain federal workers, such as active duty military personnel, are not covered by workers' compensation. They are considered fit for duty, on temporary sick leave, or unfit, receiving a medical disability discharge.

Benefits and Compensation

Workers' compensation benefits include payments for medical treatment for work-related injuries and illnesses and partial wage replacement. The cost of workplace injuries and illnesses is staggering. In 2005, the total cost in workers' compensation benefits was $55.3 billion ($26.2 billion for medical care and $29.1 billion for wage replacement) (NASI 2007).

Income

For those employees who are eligible, sick leave typically pays 100 percent of wages until workers' compensation payments begin. State workers' compensation programs pay temporary total disability (TTD) benefits when the worker recuperates away from work while under active medical care. TTD continues until the worker has reached the "maximum medical improvement." TTD usually pays about 2/3 of a worker's weekly wage and may last up to two years.

About 30% of employees in the private sector receive long-term disability insurance that is provided by the employer (NASI 2007). Long-term disability insurance generally begins after three to six months and is designed to replace 60% of a worker's wages. It is reduced if the worker receives workers' compensation or Social Security disability benefits. If a condition has long-term consequences, the worker may be eligible for permanent disability benefits under workers' compensation. This also generally pays two-thirds of a worker's weekly wage. In some states, there is a maximum payment cap. If the work-related incident resulted in a fatality, the worker's dependents receive survivor benefits, including funeral expenses. Approximately 64% of claims are listed as temporary disability, but these account for only about 20% of costs (NASI 2007). The remaining 80% of benefits are paid as the result of a fatality or permanent disability.

Managed Care

Because the costs of workers' compensation and medical care have increased at an accelerated rate, some states are pursuing managed care for medical claims. However, certain historical and legal aspects of workers' compensation legislation make this approach challenging. Studies found that medical costs are lower for managed care claims than for matched non-managed care claims (Cheadle et al. 1999; Baldwin et al. 2002).

Independent Medical Evaluations (IMEs)

When there are questions of the validity of a claim, an employer may request an independent medical evaluation (IME) from a qualified medical provider. The number of IMEs that an employer may request varies from state to state (Nakamura 2007). The main issues that an IME should resolve are the appropriateness of the:

- length of disability determined by the treating physician;
- physical restrictions or limitations imposed by the treating physician; and
- medical care plan developed by the treating physician.

IMEs, when used appropriately, can significant reduce the costs of workers' compensation and assist in the early return of the employee to work.

Rehabilitation

An important part of an effective return-to-work (RTW) program is early and effective rehabilitation of injured workers. Recommendations for six weeks of total bed rest for a worker with a back injury should no longer be acceptable because this type of approach may lead to a permanent disability. For workers who have been medically cleared to return to work, but who are still unable to do so, vocational rehabilitation may be necessary (ICF Consulting 2004). This may enable the worker to return to meaningful work in another type of job.

Compensability Determination

The key issue for determining compensation is whether an injury or illness arose from, or in the course of, performance of work (Nakamura 2007). Determination of work-relatedness can be challenging and will vary from state to state. For example, a worker who is injured during a company softball game may be covered under workers' compensation if participation in the event was mandatory. Injuries or illnesses during business travel may also be covered unless the employee is engaged in an activity unrelated to the performance of the job. Another complex issue is whether a preexisting condition is worsened by an exposure on the job. For example, an asthma sufferer who is exposed to glutaraldehyde on the job may experience an asthmatic attack, which may be compensable even if the exposure is at levels below the occupational exposure limit. On the other hand, an individual with a heart condition who suffers a stroke on the job would generally not be covered under workers' compensation. In general, it is easier to determine whether a condition is compensable if it results in an injury as opposed to a one that results from a health condition.

Appeals

The complexity of compensation laws means that there will be times when a condition that is labeled as "work-related" may not be, and conversely, an employee may be denied compensation for a claim that truly is work-related. One of the first steps in the appeal process is to ask for a second opinion from a medical provider. This can be particularly important if the initial provider is related in some way to the employee.

Management Strategies

The importance of management support for the occupational health and safety program has already been discussed in this chapter. This support is particularly important in workers' compensation because a failed program can harm the worker and add significant cost to the organization (Nakamura 2007).

Cost Reduction

Costs associated with the workers' compensation program can be reduced by preventing the initial claim and by case management of existing claims (ICF Consulting 2004). The most effective workers' compensation program is proactive as opposed to reactive. This means that employee health personnel screen workers for potential risk factors such as immunization status or fitness for duty, and health and safety staff identify and eliminate potential sources of injury and illness. The best long-term strategy for reducing costs is identifying and eliminating hazards so there is no compensation claim. In the event that an injury or illness results in a claim, the second strategy is to manage the case with the goal of returning the worker to the job as soon as possible. Effective workers' compensation case management at the local level involves collaboration and cooperation between employee health personnel, the worker's treating physician, the human resources representative, and the health and safety manager. Elements of case management are described below.

Case Management

One of the first and most effective methods of case management is by placing a weekly telephone call to workers who have a lost-time injury or illness. The purpose of the call is not to harass but to reassure workers that people are concerned for their welfare and wish them a speedy recovery. Workers who are away from the workplace with a temporary or permanent disability may experience a sense of disconnection that may lead to depression and substance abuse. Frequent contact with the worker can help dispel these concerns. The major goals of case management are as follows (ICF Consulting 2004):

- Ensuring that people with disabilities have equal opportunities in the workplace;
- Improving employment prospects for persons with disabilities by facilitating recruitment, return to work, job retention, and opportunities for advancement;
- Promoting a safe, accessible, and healthy workplace;
- Assuring that employer costs associated with disability among employees are minimized, including healthcare and insurance payments, in some instances; and
- Maximizing the contribution which workers with disabilities can make to the enterprise.

Return-to-Work (RTW) Program

Establishing and implementing an effective return-to-work (RTW) program can significantly reduce the cost of workers' compensation and improve employee morale (Nakamura 2007). Once again, top management must visibly support the workers' compensation management team in establishing RTW positions. Some managers consider these positions to be a burden. These jobs are often referred to as *light* or *restricted* duty because worker's assignments must comply with restrictions established by the medical provider. This can be accomplished by either reducing the number of hours of work or by changing the job assignment. The challenge is to develop meaningful work while avoiding further injury to the employee. Another challenge is the need to routinely monitor employees on light duty and to modify the tasks to fit the worker's capabilities. RTW programs can both be a positive experience for the employee and aid in their recovery.

Evidence-based Guidelines

One of the major concerns in diagnosing work-related injuries and illnesses is the practice of *doctor shopping* where workers seek the services of medical providers who they hope will strengthen their disability claims (NASI 2007). The best means of addressing this problem is by having objective methods of rating permanent disability. The American College of Occupational and Environmental Medicine (ACOEM) and the Work Loss Data Institute provide these evidence-based guidelines.

SUMMARY AND CONCLUSIONS

The healthcare industry traditionally had a poor record in protecting its employees. Therefore, an important question is, "What are the most effective management strategies improve this record?" First, and most important, it must be clear that top management supports and promotes a proactive safety culture. In addition, there needs to be an effective team of key players to organize a workers' compensation management plan. The three most important members of this team are the health and safety manager, the employee health coordinator, and the workers' compensation case manager. This team needs to manage existing cases by assuring that disabled worker receives rehabilitation, retraining, and return-to-duty as soon as possible. It is also essential to prevent additional injuries and illnesses. In order to determine which employees are at risk, the team should use principles of epidemiology to target *who* is at risk, *what* the hazards are, *when* is the risk greatest, and *how* to best control the risk. Using this comprehensive strategy will allow the team to implement cost-effective solutions and monitor program effectiveness.

Review

1. Discuss why the culture of safety in health care is so poor.
2. What are some of the linkages between patient safety and employee safety?
3. What are some of the differences between patient safety and employee safety programs?
4. What are the four major purposes of a hospital safety program?
5. What were the top four most frequently cited OSHA violations in 2006?
6. Why is it so important for hospitals to maintain their accreditation through the Joint Commission?
7. Describe an approach to improve the culture of safety in hospitals.
8. Why is recordkeeping so important to a hospital safety committee?
9. Who are the three key staff members in implementing an effective safety management program?

10. Why is training in epidemiology so important for a hospital safety manager?
11. Describe the process in establishing an employee return-to-work program.

Reference List

Ahrens, M. 2006. *Healthcare Facilities, Excluding Nursing Homes* Quincy, MA: National Fire Protection Association.

American Industrial Hygiene Association (AIHA). 2003. *The Occupational Environment: Its Evaluation, Control, and Management.* 2nd ed. Fairfax, VA: American Industrial Hygiene Association.

American Institute of Architects (AIA). 2001. *Guidelines for Design and Construction of Hospital and Health Care Facilities.* Washington, D.C.: The American Institute of Architects.

American National Standards Institute/American Industrial Hygiene Association (ANSI/AIHA). 2005. ANSI/AIHA Z10-2005, *Occupational Health and Safety Management Systems.* New York: American National Standards Institute.

American Nurses Association (ANA) (2001). *Health & Safety Survey* (retrieved 09/16/08) (http://www.nursingworld.org/MainMenuCategories/OccupationalandEnvironmental/occupationalhealth/HealthSafety-Survey.aspx).

Azaroff, L. S., C. Levenstein, and D. H. Wegman. 2002. "Occupational Injury and Illness Surveillance: Conceptual Filters Explain Underreporting." *Am.J.Public Health.* 92:1421–1429.

Baldwin, M. L., W. G. Johnson, and S. C. Marcus. 2002. "Effects of Provider Networks on Health Care Costs for Workers with Short-Term Injuries." *Med.Care.* 40:686–695.

Brauer, C. M. 2001. *Champions of Quality in Health Care.* Lyme, Connecticut: Greenwich Publishing Group, Inc.

Brauer, R. L. 2006a. "Fundamentals of Safety Management." In *Safety and Health for Engineers* (2d ed., pp. 629–644). Tolono, IL: Wiley-Interscience.

Brauer, R. L. 2006b. "Procedures, Rules and Training." In *Safety and Health for Engineers* (2d ed., pp. 579–591). Tolono, IL: Wiley-Interscience.

Brauer, R. L. 2006c. "Record Keeping and Reporting." In *Safety and Health for Engineers* (2d ed., pp. 79–92). Tolono, IL: Wiley-Interscience.

Bureau of Labor Statistics (BLS). 2006. *Incidence rates of nonfatal occupational injuries and illnesses involving days away from work by selected worker and case characteristics and industry, All U.S., private industry, 2006* (retrieved August 11, 2008) (http://www.bls.gov/iif/home.htm).

Cecich, Thomas. 2007. "American Society of Safety Engineers' Member Testifies on Benefits of OSHA Competitive Program" (retrieved September 19, 2008) (http://www.asse.org/search.php?VarSearch=cecich).

Cheadle, A., T. M. Wickizer, G. Franklin, K. Cain, J. Joesch, and K. Kyes, K. 1999. "Evaluation of the Washington State Workers' Compensation Managed Care Pilot Project II: Medical and Disability Costs. *Med.Care.* 37:982–993.

DiBenedetto, D. V. 1995. "Occupational Hazards of the Health Care Industry: Protecting Health Care Workers." *AAOHN.J.* 43:131–137.

Dunbar, J. A., P. Reddy, B. Beresford, W. P. Ramsey, and R. S. Lord. 2007. "In the Wake of Hospital Inquiries: Impact on Staff and Safety." *Med.J.Aust.* 186:80–83.

Environmental Protection Agency (EPA). 2006. "EPCRA Overview" (retrieved 09/16/08). (http://www.epa.gov/osw/inforesources/pubs/orientat).

Foley, M. 2004. "Caring for Those Who Care: A Tribute to Nurses and Their Safety." *Online.J.Issues Nurs.* 9:2.

Foley, M. E., D. Keepnews, and K. Worthington. 2001. "Identifying and Using Tools for Reducing Risks to Patients and Health Care Workers: A Nursing Perspective." *Jt.Comm J.Qual.Improv.* 27:494–499.

Food and Drug Administration (FDA). 1998. *Guidance for Industry and FDA Staff: SMDA to FDAMA: Guidance on FDA's Transition Plan for Existing Postmarket Surveillance Protocols* (retrieved 09/17/08) (http://www.fda.gov/cdrh/modact/smdatran.html).

Gaba, D. M., S. J. Singer, A. D. Sinaiko, J. D. Bowen, and A. P. Ciavarelli. 2003. "Differences in Safety Climate between Hospital Personnel and Naval Aviators." *Hum.Factors.* 45:173–185.

Gimeno, D., S. Felknor, K. D. Burau, and G. L. Delclos. 2005. "Organisational and Occupational Risk Factors Associated with Work Related Injuries among Public Hospital Employees in Costa Rica." *Occupational and Environmental Medicine* 62:337–343.

Harger, L. 2007. "Workers' Compensation, A Brief History." (retrieved 09/17/08) (http://www.fldfs.com/WC/history.html).

Hoyle, D. 2005. *ISO 9000 Quality Systems Handbook.* 5th ed. Burlington, MA: Butterworth-Heinemann.

ICF Consulting. 2004. *Federal Employees Compensation Act (FECA) Program Effectiveness Study* (Rep. No. GS-23F-8182H). Washington, D.C.: Office of Workers' Compensation Programs (OWCP), U. S. Department of Labor.

Joint Commission on Accreditation of Healthcare Organizations (JCAHO). 2009. *Hospital Accreditation Standards* Oakbrook Terrace, Illinois: Joint Commission Resources.

Klamert, P. C. 2002. "Complying with Changes in OSHA's Recordkeeping Requirements: An Overview." *AAOHN.J.* 50:324–333.

Leigh, J. P., S .B. Markowitz, M. Fahs, S. Chonggak, and P. J. Landrigan. 1997. "Occupational Injury and Illness in the United States: Estimates of Costs, Morbidity, and Mortality." *Archives of Internal Medicine* 157:1557–1568.

Lundstrom, T., G. Pugliese, J. Bartley, J. Cox, J., and C. Guither. 2002. "Organizational and Environmental Factors that Affect Worker Health and Safety and Patient Outcomes." *Am.J.Infect.Control.* 30:93–106.

Manuele, F. A. 2006. "ANSI/AIHA Z-10: The New Benchmark for Safety Management Systems." *Professional Safety* (February) 25–33.

Nakamura, P. 2007. "Workers' Compensation Programs in Health Care Organizations." In G.T.Troyer ed. *Business Risk: Legal, Regulatory and Technological Issues* 5th ed., pp. 79–116. San Francisco, CA: Jossey-Bass.

National Academy of Social Insurance (NASI). 2007. *Workers' Compensation: Benefits, Coverage, and Costs, 2005*. Washington, DC: National Academy of Social Insurance.

National Institute of Occupational Safety and Health (NIOSH). 2005. *Coaching Skills for On-the-Job Trainers* (Publication No. 2005-146) (retrieved September 16, 2008) (http://www.cdc.gov/niosh/mining/pubs/pdfs/2005–146.pdf)

Occupational Safety and Health Administration (OSHA). 2006d. 29 CFR 1910.1020, *Access to Employee Exposure and Medical Records* (retrieved September 17, 2008) (http://www.osha.gov/pls/oshaweb/owadisp.show_document?p_table=NEWS_RELEASES&p_id=10027).

———. 2006c. 29 CFR 1952, *Approved State Plan for Enforcement of State Standards* (retrieved September 17, 2008) (http://www.osha.gov/pls/oshaweb/owadisp.show_document?p_table=standards&p_id=10975).

———. 2004. 29 CFR 1910.1960, *Basic Program Elements for Federal Employees OSHA* (retrieved September 17, 2008) (http://www.osha.gov/pls/oshaweb/owadisp.show_document?p_table=standards&p_id=11262).

———. 2006a. 29 CFR 1910.1030, *Bloodborne Pathogens* (retrieved September 16, 2008) (http://www.osha.gov/pls/oshaweb/owadisp.show_document?p_table=standards&p_id=10051).

———. 2001c. 29 CFR 1904.5, *Determination of Work-relatedness* (retrieved September 19, 2008) (http://www.osha.gov/pls/oshaweb/owadisp.show_document?p_table=standards&p_id=9636).

———.1996. 29 CFR 1910, 1200, *Hazard Communication* (retrieved September 16, 2008) (http://www.osha.gov/pls/oshaweb/owadisp.show_document?p_table=standards&p_id=10099).

———. 2006b. 29 CFR 1910.120, *Hazardous Waste Operations and Emergency Response* (retrieved September 17, 2008) (http://www.osha.gov/pls/oshaweb/owadisp.show_document?p_table=standards&p_id=9765).

———. 2001a. 29 CFR 1952.4, *Injury and Illness Recording and Reporting Requirements* (retrieved September 17, 2008) (http://www.osha.gov/pls/oshaweb/owadisp.show_document?p_table=standards&p_id=10979)

———. 2002a. "National Emphasis Program for Nursing and Personal Care Facilities" (retrieved September 17, 2008) (http://www.osha.gov/pls/oshaweb/owadisp.show_document?p_table=NEWS_RELEASES&p_id=1311).

———. 2001b. "Occupational Injury and Illness Recording and Reporting Requirements: Final Rule." (retrieved September 17, 2008) (http://www.osha.gov/pls/oshaweb/owadisp.show_document?p_table=FEDERAL_REGISTER&p_id=16312).

———. 2003. 29 CFR 1904, *Recording and Reporting Occupational Injuries and Illness* (retrieved September 13, 2008) (http://www.osha.gov/pls/oshaweb/owadisp.show_document?p_table=STANDARDS&p_id=9631)

———. 2001d. 29 CFR 1904.8, *Recording Criteria for Needlestick and Sharps Injuries* (retrieved September 17, 2008) (http://www.osha.gov/pls/oshaweb/owadisp.show_document?p_table=standards&p_id=9639)

————. 2001e. 29 CFR 1904.11, *Recording Criteria for Work-related Tuberculosis Cases* (retrieved September 17, 2008) (http://www.osha.gov/pls/oshaweb/owadisp.show_document?p_table=standards&p_id=9642)

————. 2002b. 29 CFR 1904.10, *Recording Criteria for Cases Involving Occupational Hearing Loss* (retrieved September 17, 2008) (http://www.osha.gov/pls/oshaweb/owadisp.show_document?p_table=standards&p_id=9641)

————. 2007. 29 CFR 1910.94, *Ventilation* (retrieved September 17, 2008) (http://www.osha.gov/pls/oshaweb/owadisp.show_document?p_table=standards&p_id=9734)

Popp, P. P. 2005. "Claims Management Risks in Patient Safety Events." In F.A.Rozovsky AND J. R. Woods, eds. *The Handbook of Patient Safety Compliance: A Practical Guide for Health Care Organizations*, pp. 124–139. San Francisco, CA: Jossey-Bass.

Pronovost, P. J., B. Weast, C. G. Holzmueller, B. J. Rosenstein, R. P. Kidwell, K. B. Haller. 2003. "Evaluation of the Culture of Safety: Survey of Clinicians and Managers in an Academic Medical Center." *Qual.Saf Health Care.* 12:405–410.

Ramsay, J., F. Denny, K. Szirotnyak, J. Thomas, E. Corneliuson, and K. L. Paxton. 2006. "Identifying Nursing Hazards in the Emergency Department: A New Approach to Nursing Job Hazard Analysis." *Journal of Safety Research* 37:63–74.

Resource Conservation and Recovery Act. 1976. 42 USC 6901 et seq. (retrieved September 17, 2008) (http://www.access.gpo.gov/uscode/title42/chapter82_.html).

Robertson, L. S. 1992. "The Problem, History, and Concepts." In *Injury Epidemiology*, pp. 3–22. New York: Oxford University Press.

Rozovsky, F. A. 2005. "Patient Safety: Crossing the Chasm from Legal and Regulatory Compliance." In F. A. Rozovsky and J. R. Woods, eds. *The Handbook of Patient Safety Compliance: A Practical Guide for Health Care Organizations*, pp. 1–15. San Francisco, CA: Jossey-Bass.

Safe Medical Devices Act (SMDA). 1990. 21 CFR 629, P.L. 101–629 (retrieved September 23, 2008) (http://edocket/access.gpo/gov/cfr_2008/aprqtr/pdf/21cfr80792.pdf).

Sepkowitz, K. A. and L. Eisenberg. 2005. "Occupational Deaths among Healthcare Workers." *Emerg.Infect.Dis.* 11:1003-1008.

Sexton, J. B., E. J. Thomas, and R. L. Helmreich. 2000. "Error, Stress, and Teamwork in Medicine and Aviation: Cross Sectional Surveys." *BMJ* 320:745–749.

Stewart, J. M. 2002. *Managing for World Class Safety.* New York: John Wiley & Sons, Inc.

Thomas, E. J., J. B. Sexton, T. B. Neilands, A. Frankel, and R. L. Helmreich. 2005. "The Effect of Executive Walk Rounds on Nurse Safety Climate Attitudes: A Randomized Trial of Clinical Units." *BMC.Health Serv.Res,* 5:28.

West, J. C. 2007. "Occupational and Environmental risk Exposure for Health Care Facilities." In G. T. Toyer, ed. *Business Risk: Legal, Regulatory, & Technology Issues,* 5th ed., pp. 117–166. San Francisco: Jossey-Bass.

Wiegmann, D. A., Z. Hui, T. von Thaden, G. Sharma, and A. Mitchell. 2002. *A Synthesis of Safety Culture and Safety Climate Research* (Technical Report ARL-02-3/FAA-02-2) (retrieved September 17, 2008) (http://www. humanfactors.uiuc.edu/Reports&PapersPDFs/TechReport/02-03.pdf).

CLASSROOM ACTIVITY

Data Collection and Recordkeeping Assignment

Purpose: One of the most important functions of an institutional environmental health and safety professional is data collection. However, collecting the data is only the first step. The information must be assembled into appropriate tables and graphs and analyzed. Hazard evaluation is much more important than data collection. This assignment is designed to test the ability to use data to help identify problem areas.

Scenario: You were recently hired as the new Environmental Health and Safety Manager for BroJoe Memorial Hospital. Your first job is to prepare an Annual Safety Report for the Board of Directors. Searching through your desk, you find information on employees who were injured last year. How can this date be used to prepare a report?

1. The best place to start is to present an injury rate per 100 employees. Refer to the table entitled "Breakdown of Injuries by Department" at the end of this activity. Present a total injury rate for the hospital, an injury rate by department, rates by nature of injury and rates by cause of injury. If hospitals of similar size had total injury rates of 3 to 4 per 100 employees, how does this compare to the BroJoe Memorial Rate?

2. Which three departments seem to have the most serious problem, based on the information presented? What additional information would be important to have to confirm this choice?

3. What three types of injuries (nature) seem to be causing the biggest problem? What three causes seem to be the biggest concerns? What additional information would be useful to better answer these questions? (In other words, is it possible that departments with lower rates could have a more serious problem? If yes, why? Also, what other table would help to pinpoint the most serious problem in the hospital.)

4. What kinds of interventions might be appropriate to reduce the incidence of back injuries? List at least three of the most appropriate types of interventions.

5. Why might there be a cluster of upper extremity injuries in the administrative department, which includes billing and patient registration?

Prepare a report for the Hospital Board of Directors that addresses the above issues. Be sure to include the appropriate tables.

Table Breakdown of Injuries by Department

Nature of Injury:	Nursing	Supply	Physicians	Engineers	Janitors	Lab/X-ray	Dietary	Admin.	Other	Totals	Injury Rates
Back	22	9	1	8	7	2	7	3	2	61	—
Upper Extremity	1	2	0	1	0	1	2	10	0	17	—
Lower Extremity	1	1	0	1	1	0	0	0	0	4	—
Head	1	1	0	2	2	0	0	0	0	6	—
Other	1	1	1	3	2	2	3	0	0	13	—
Total	**26**	**14**	**2**	**15**	**12**	**5**	**12**	**13**	**2**	**101**	—
Rate/100 workers	—	—	—	—	—	—	—	—	—	—	
Cause of Injury:											
Falls	4	2	0	2	2	1	2	3	2	18	—
Lifting	10	7	0	6	5	2	5	1	0	36	—
Struck by/against	1	2	0	2	1	0	0	1	0	8	—
Violence	6	0	0	0	0	0	0	2	0	8	—
Cut/puncture	4	1	1	1	2	2	2	0	0	13	—
Chemicals	1	1	0	1	2	2	3	0	0	10	—
Other	0	1	1	3	0	0	0	6	0	11	—
Total	**26**	**14**	**2**	**15**	**12**	**5**	**12**	**13**	**2**	**101**	—

Departments

	Nursing	Supply	Physicians	Engineers	Housekeeping	Lab/X-ray	Dietary	Admin.	Other
Number of Employees	700	50	200	150	100	35	65	200	100

Total staff in 2007: 1600

CHAPTER **6**

Environmental Management

George Byrns and Lee Shands

> ## Learning Objectives
>
> 1. Explain why healthcare programs must address environmental management issues.
> 2. Review the basics of applicable environmental laws that affect healthcare facilities.
> 3. Discuss the process involved in an environmental audit.
> 4. Identify the most frequently cited Environmental Protection Agency (EPA) violations.
> 5. Explain the EPA's Environmental Management Pyramid.
> 6. Describe environmental management systems that have been used in healthcare facilities.

Why should healthcare organizations care about environmental management? The first and most obvious reason is that there are numerous laws, regulations, and presidential executive orders that require that these institutions meet the minimum requirements for managing the environment. Executive orders cover federally operated healthcare organizations like the U.S. Department of Veterans Affairs (formerly known as the Veterans Administration). Failure to meet these minimum requirements can result in substantial administrative costs, fines, or even imprisonment. There are other reasons that we must care for the environment. Providing healthcare services is very resource-intensive. (See Chapter 9 for more information on waste reduction.) Healthcare organizations consume significant amounts of natural and man-made resources in order to provide patient care. Therefore, *stewardship* (a moral and ethical responsibility to use resources wisely) is another good reason to care about the environment. Later in the chapter we will discuss the importance of pollution prevention and sustainability. Finally, as a purely practical matter, it is good public relations to demonstrate that an organization cares for the environment (Wilson et al. 2000; Environmental Science Center with Bristol-Myers Squibb Company 2007).

ENVIRONMENTAL LAWS

The healthcare industry is highly regulated. Compliance with environmental laws and their associated regulations is mandatory and time-consuming, but noncompliance can lead to serious consequences. A partial list of environmental laws involved includes:

- Clean Air Act (CAA)
- Comprehensive Environmental Response, Compensation and Liability Act (CERCLA)
- Clean Water Act (CWA)
- Emergency Planning and Community Right-to-Know Act (EPCRA)
- Federal Insecticide, Fungicide and Rodenticide Act (FIFRA)
- Resource Conservation and Recovery Act (RCRA)
- Safe Drinking Water Act (SDWA)
- Toxic Substance Control Act (TSCA)
- Oil Pollution Act (OPA)

Laws, regulations, and policies are always changing; new ones may be added and old ones amended or revised. There can also be differences in how regulations are applied by various regulatory agency regions. The healthcare staff needs to continually monitor regulatory requirements to insure they are meeting the current regulations. An effective way to do so is to set up an environmental management system and conduct periodic environmental audits, which will be discussed in greater detail later in this chapter. The EPA Office of Enforcement and Compliance Assurance (OECA) developed thirteen multi-media audit protocols to assist and encourage organizations to perform audits and disclose violations. The protocols provide checklists for the regulations and can be customized. Audit protocols are set out below under the specific Act.

Clean Air Act (CAA)

The Clean Air Act (CAA 1970) is the comprehensive federal law that regulates air emissions from stationary and mobile air pollution sources. After RCRA, it is the most commonly violated environmental law by healthcare facilities. While CAA has many elements, in this chapter we will focus on the issue of air emissions because it is most relevant to healthcare facilities. The primary CAA regulations that apply to healthcare facilities are emissions

from air conditioning and refrigeration units, boilers, medical waste incinerators, and other sources, such as spray paint booths and degreasing tanks.
Hospitals have also been cited for release of asbestos fibers during
renovations or demolitions and for failure to have the necessary air permits.
Those facilities requiring air permits must have risk management plans in
place that describe their plans to monitor and control the release of
asbestos, oxides of nitrogen, ozone, particulate matter ($PM_{2.5}$ and PM_{10}),
sulfur dioxide, and other regulated air toxic chemicals. Additionally, some
states have requirements that restrict or prohibit the release of chemicals, such
as ethylene oxide or formaldehyde.

Comprehensive Environmental Response, Compensation and Liability Act (CERCLA)

The Comprehensive Environmental Response, Compensation and Liability
Act (CERCLA 1980) or, as it is more commonly known, the Superfund Act,
was passed by Congress to address the problem of identifying, containing,
and cleaning hazardous waste sites. This law can affect a healthcare organization in several ways. First, if the site for the facility contains sufficient quantities of hazardous materials, it can be included as one of the EPA's National
Priorities List sites. If the original owner of the hazardous materials is other
than the healthcare organization, the EPA can pursue that owner for clean-
up costs. If the healthcare facility is deemed liable, it will be required to pay
for the clean-up. Additionally, generating facilities are responsible for the
proper disposal of all hazardous materials. Whenever a hazardous waste is
transferred to a disposal site, the generating facility needs to insure that
proper disposal methods are followed. If the disposal company is later found
to have disposed of materials improperly, the healthcare facility that generated the waste can be held liable for clean-up costs. Care needs to be exercised when choosing a disposal facility or firm because the majority of
Superfund sites that are currently being cleaned up were originally operating
within regulatory requirements.

The second issue involves facility operations. If the facility emits, releases,
spills, or discharges regulated quantities of a hazardous material, it may be
found to be in violation of CERCLA (EPA 1998).

Clean Water Act (CWA)

The Clean Water Act (CWA 1972) was passed in response to the nation's concern over the state of our surface waters, including rivers and lakes. One of the
most-publicized events was the burning of the Cuyahoga River in 1969. At the
time, highly industrialized cities, such as Cleveland, routinely dumped solvents
and other toxic substances directly into surface water systems. CWA protects
the physical, chemical and biological conditions of these rivers and lakes. One
of the provisions of this Act that may affect healthcare facilities is the need to
obtain a permit for discharges to the sanitary sewer. The need for a permit

depends on the quantities and types of substances released. Permitted facilities need to monitor and, in some cases, pre-treat these discharges before they are released to the community sewage system. For example, some states require that ortho-phthaladehyde be neutralized with glycerin prior to discharge because of its aquatic toxicity. As a part of the CWA, the National Pollutant Discharge Elimination System (NPDES) program controls water pollution by regulating point sources that discharge pollutants into waters of the U.S. *Point sources* include pipes or man-made ditches, and facilities must obtain permits if they discharge directly into surface waters.

Another major issue is the need to control stormwater from roofs, parking lots and other hard surfaces, as well as during construction activities. Stormwater may also require pre-treatment if it contains solvents or any other toxic substances. A healthcare facility may also be required to obtain a NPDES stormwater permit for stormwater discharges. NPDES stormwater permits may be required for construction sites that disturb one or more acres of land, or smaller sites if they are part of a larger development (EPA 2008a). Stormwater discharges from new construction areas may be regulated by NPDES requirements.

States are authorized to implement the EPA's stormwater management plan. Information on implementation may be found under "Authorization Status for EPA's Stormwater Construction and Industrial Programs" on the EPA's Web site. See Chapter 13 for a discussion of "green" uses of stormwater discharges. In April of 2007, the EPA formed a partnership with a number of other groups (called Partnership for Green Infrastructure); in 2008, they issued an action strategy (EPA 2008b). Further information on NPDES green infrastructure can also be found on the EPA Web Site.

If the healthcare facility uses an onsite wastewater treatment system such as a septic tank, there are additional monitoring provisions that must be met in EPA's "Underground Injection Control Program;" see "Additional Resources" at the end of this chapter.

Emergency Planning and Community Right-to-Know Act (EPCRA)

The Emergency Planning and Community Right-to-Know Act (EPCRA 1986), also known as SARA Title III, was established in 1986 under the Superfund Amendments and Reauthorization Act (SARA). This law was passed in response to the chemical disaster in Bhopal, India, that claimed the lives of thousands of people, and the fear that a similar disaster could occur in the U.S. The goals of EPCRA are to:

- Prevent injury or property damage associated with a major chemical release.
- Inform communities and proper authorities about chemicals in the community.
- Provide the public with information about toxic chemicals in the community.

This law is far-reaching, covering federal agencies, state and local governments, tribal nations, and industries and institutions. The four major provisions of EPCRA are:

- Emergency planning (Sections 301–303),
- Emergency release notification (Section 304),
- Hazardous chemical storage reporting requirements (Sections 311–312), and
- Toxic chemical release inventory (Section 313).

Emergency Planning for Chemical Accidents

Response to a chemical release would be coordinated by a community's emergency preparedness organization. Chapter 7 describes the major steps to be taken when planning for and organizing the community's response to a disaster, including a chemical release. An important part of this plan is the need for proper notification of a spill or other release of hazardous chemicals. The plan should specify who is notified, how quickly the notification should occur, and the types of information that should be provided.

Hazardous Chemical Inventory

Each industry in the community, including healthcare facilities, must prepare an inventory of hazardous chemicals, as required by OSHA's *Hazard Communications Standard* (OSHA 1996). SARA Title III requires that facilities inventory reportable quantities of any of the 300+ extremely hazardous substances listed as part EPCRA. A copy of this inventory of hazardous chemicals, including where they are stored, must be provided to the community's first responders, which is generally the local fire department. In addition, copies of chemical material safety data sheets (MSDSs) and their storage locations must also be provided for all chemicals that have MSDSs. Local agencies and emergency responders may require labeling of extremely hazardous substances storage areas.

Emergency Release Notification

Facilities must provide an emergency notification and a written follow-up notice to the local emergency planning committee (LEPC) and the state emergency response commission (SERC) if there is a release into the environment of a hazardous substance that exceeds the minimum reportable quantity for any area likely to be affected by the release. There are two types of chemicals that require this type of reporting: (1) extremely hazardous substances (EHSs); and (2) CERCLA hazardous substances (EPA 2006).

Report of Chemical Emissions. At the end of the year, the EPA requires each industry to report the quantities of toxic chemicals that were released or emitted.

EPCRA Structure

Figure 6.1 demonstrates the hierarchical structure of EPCRA where the regional EPA offices work through a SERC, and the SERC provides direction to LEPC. The SERC determines how the state will be divided into planning districts.

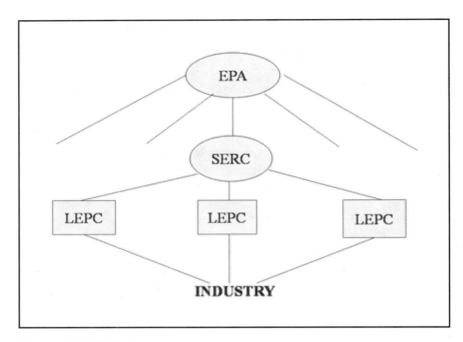

Figure 6.1 EPCRA structure.

Covered Facilities. A determination needs to be made whether a facility storing hazardous chemicals is covered under EPCRA; it is necessary to compile an inventory of the types and amounts of chemicals stored at the facility(s) and determine if any of those chemicals exceed the reportable quantities (EPA 2006).

Covered Chemicals. There are a number of governmental and industrial sources that must be consulted to determine if a specific type of chemical is covered under EPCRA. The most important of these sources are:

- EPA's list of extremely hazardous substances (EHSs)
- OSHA's *Hazard Communication Standard* (OSHA 1996)
- Toxic chemical lists from manufacturers
- Chemicals that would be reportable under CERCLA (EPA 2001a)

Federal Insecticide, Fungicide and Rodenticide Act (FIFRA)

The Federal Insecticide, Fungicide and Rodenticide Act (FIFRA 1996) is the law that addresses the need for safety in the manufacture and use of pesticides. Most healthcare facilities use certified pest control operators. Therefore, FIFRA should not be a major issue for these facilities. Those facilities that conduct in-house rodent or insect control need to insure that the staff is properly trained and certified. This includes those instances where in-house staff decides to handle small problems on its own. The EPA also classifies environmental disinfectants as pesticides (EPA 2003). Germicides that are used to disinfect a critical device are regulated by the Food and Drug Administration, not the EPA. See Chapter 4 for more details on disinfectants.

Resource Conservation and Recovery Act (RCRA)

The Resource Conservation and Recovery Act (RCRA 1976) is EPA's program to manage solid waste, hazardous waste, and underground storage tanks holding petroleum products or certain chemicals. According to the EPA, the goal of RCRA is ". . . to protect human health and the environment from the hazards posed by waste disposal; conserve energy and natural resources through waste recycling and recovery; reduce or eliminate, as expeditiously as possible, the amount of waste generated, including hazardous waste; and ensure that wastes are managed in a manner that is protective to human health and the environment" (EPA 2007).

RCRA violations are the most commonly cited EPA standard in healthcare facilities due to its complexity and confusing definitions. For example, is medical waste a hazardous waste? The answer unfortunately is that it depends on factors such as the degree of contamination, storage and handling methods, and many others.

Some of the concerns that an EPA inspector will address are:

- Has all hazardous waste been identified?
- How much hazardous waste is generated on a monthly basis?
- Is the facility properly managing and disposing of hazardous waste?
- Is there evidence that hospital staff is trained in hazardous waste management?
- Is the hospital prepared for hazardous waste emergencies?
- Have old abandoned underground storage tanks (USTs) been removed or properly decommissioned?
- Do the hospital's USTs have the required corrosion, spill and overfill protection?
- Does the hospital have required records? Maintaining all required records can be a huge program for facilities. Records must be maintained and available at all times.

The answers to these questions may cause an inspector to dig deeper and ultimately cite the healthcare organization for RCRA violations. Note that Subtitle C deals with hazardous waste, and this subpart is regulated directly by the EPA (EPA 2001b).

EPA also offers audit protocols for facilities regulated under subtitle D of RCRA. Subtitle D deals with wastes that EPA considers to be non-hazardous or otherwise exempt from Subtitle C. This also includes small quantity generators of hazardous waste. Subtitle D is generally regulated by state or local jurisdiction (EPA 2000a), along with the audit protocols for USTs and hazardous waste treatment and storage (EPA 2000d). See also Chapter 9, "Waste Management" for locations where hazardous waste may be found.

Safe Drinking Water Act (SDWA)

The Safe Drinking Water Act (SDWA 1974) should have little effect on most healthcare organizations. Hospitals in remote locations may be required to provide their own drinking water. For those facilities, the EPA requires monitoring of the water for biological, chemical and radiological quality (EPA 2000c).

Toxic Substance Control Act (TSCA)

The Toxic Substance Control Act (TSCA 1976) protects human health and the environment from exposure to substances containing toxic chemicals. In healthcare facilities, there are three types of hazardous substances that are of particular concern under TSCA: polychlorinated biphenyls (PCBs), asbestos, and lead-based paint. PCBs are a class of chemical that are no longer manufactured in the U.S. In the past, they were often used as fluid electrical insulators in transformers and other devices. PCBs were banned due to their acute toxic effects and concerns that they may cause reproductive effects and cancer (EPA 2000b). The hazards of asbestos and lead-based paint are discussed in Chapter 2.

Oil Pollution Act (OPA)

The Oil Pollution Act (OPA) was passed in response to incidents involving oil spills from tankers or from land operations (OPA 1990). Healthcare facilities with storage facilities for emergency power or other uses that contain more than or equal to 1320 gallons of oil in above-ground tanks, or 42,000 gallons below ground, must have plans in place to prevent spillage. Procedures must prevent the overfilling of tanks, and containment must be provided; violations are prosecuted under the CWA. For example, in 2005, hospitals in Maine and New Hampshire were fined by the EPA for a violation of the CWA because they failed to have spill prevention, control and countermeasure plans in place (EPA 2005a).

COMPLIANCE WITH EPA REGULATIONS

The EPA acknowledges that compliance with their regulations is complex and costly (EPA 1997). However, failure to comply with these regulations may be even more costly and may result in jail time for chief executive officers (CEOs) who ignore them. Such liability for criminal charges may even be applied to managers who were unaware of the violations, which the EPA calls *willful ignorance*. In other words, the manager should have known that the operation was violating EPA regulations and should have taken steps to correct these violations. At a minimum, if a facility is found to be negligent in meeting regulatory requirements, the facility will be placed under a heavy administrative burden to document the corrective action taken, as well as continued regulatory compliance.

How does a healthcare facility's CEO avoid jail time and large fines for being willfully ignorant? The answer is to maintain an effective environmental management program and to periodically conduct an environmental audit.

This audit may be done using either in-house staff or contractors. The choice of doing an in-house or contract audit depends on many factors, such as the purpose and scope of the audit and the knowledge and skills of the facility's environmental health and safety personnel.

The EPA offers incentives for identifying and self-disclosing environmental violations. In 1995, the EPA issued a policy, which is known as the EPA Audit Policy (EPA 1999). Those who voluntarily disclose violations before they are identified by the EPA and take steps to correct those violations may have penalties waived or significantly reduced. This is a slight departure from EPA's policy of "command and control" and could be described as a "carrot-and-stick" approach. All EPA policies are subject to current administrative priorities, and a change in a presidential administration can result in a change in focus. For example, there may be more use of the stick than the carrot.

Environmental Auditing

According to the EPA, an environmental audit should accomplish three objectives (EPA 1997):

- Verify compliance with environmental requirements;
- Evaluate the effectiveness of in-place environmental management systems; and
- Assess risks from regulated and unregulated materials and practices.

The schematic for an audit in Figure 6.2 is intended for use in federal facilities. However, the same basic approach can be applied to any industry, including healthcare industries.

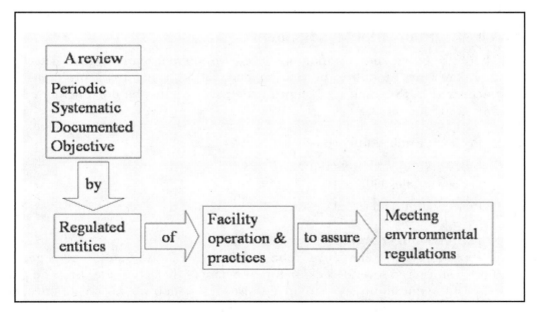

Figure 6.2 EPA's Definition of environmental auditing.

EPA defines an *environmental audit* as a review that is *periodic, systematic, documented,* and *objective* by regulated entities of facility operation and practices to assure that they are meeting environmental regulations:

- *Periodic:* This depends on the size and scope of your operation. It must be frequent enough that it assures that liabilities are managed. In a small satellite clinic, periodic audits may be only necessary once every ten years, whereas a large medical center may require an audit at least every three years.

- *Systematic:* This means that the facility is using a system to monitor compliance with these regulations. The key question is whether or not the system assures comprehensive assessment of all significant environmental hazards. Using the model audit protocols, discussed earlier in this chapter, would meet the definition of systematic.

- *Documented:* As far as the EPA is concerned, if there are no records, it was not done. Therefore, a system of recordkeeping is necessary to meet the intent of EPA's requirements for an audit. Later in this chapter some of the information that should be collected and maintained for an audit will be described.

- *Objective:* Objectivity required that a system be in place that defines which conditions or hazards are significant. Significance is determined by the likelihood and severity of damage to human health and the environment if a condition is allowed to exist. What is the organization's priority ranking plan? An objective method must be in place for determining when a significant hazard needs immediate attention. See Chapter 10 for an example of a hazard ranking system.

Steps in Environmental Management

There are four major components in environmental management. The first three are types of audits; the fourth, remediation, is needed if problems are uncovered in the audits. All steps in the process must be documented. The four components are:

- Pre-survey questionnaire (Phase I)
- Environmental site assessment (Phase I)
- Special studies (Phase II)
- Remediation (Phase III)

Pre-survey Questionnaire

The pre-survey questionnaire is the first step in a Phase I audit and is generally administered several weeks before the date of the actual site visit. The purpose of the questionnaire is to obtain historical data from key documents and records, such as title searches. The pre-survey audit is an attempt to determine the scope of the operation and a general picture of the potential issues that may arise. Based on the results of this pre-survey, a decision may be made to proceed with the Phase I site assessment, conduct a special study (Phase II audit), or remediate known hazards (Phase III). If the operation is small, and there is a reliable historical record that indicates there is no significant potential for environmental harm, a site assessment may not be necessary.

Phase I Environmental Site Assessments

Phase I environmental site assessments are sometimes called due diligence surveys. The purpose of this audit is to define customary practice in the U.S. for conducting environmental site assessments for commercial real estate. The audit findings can be used to define the extent of liability as defined in CERCLA (VanHouten 2007). The goal of this type of audit is to identify recognized environmental conditions. The term *environmental conditions* means the presence or likely presence of any hazardous substances on the property or in the ground, groundwater, or surface water of the property. The audit team attempts to identify an existing release, a past release, or a material threat of a release of these hazardous substances. A Phase I environmental site assessment involves visual inspection of materials and processes to identify potential violations of environmental rules. For example, building materials may be identified as known to contain asbestos or presumed to contain asbestos based on their appearance. The audit team should identify any above-ground or underground storage tanks and their contents. Other concerns may be identifying old transformers that may contain polychlorinated biphenyls (PCBs) or uncovering evidence of prior activities that may have resulted in a release or discharge of potentially hazardous materials. The results of the Phase I audit are compiled in a report that should highlight any areas of concern.

Conducting a Phase I Site Assessment. In-house site assessments may be done on smaller healthcare facilities if the staff is trained in environmental policies and rules. As mentioned above, in the case of small facilities, such as satellite outpatient clinics, it may only be necessary to complete the pre-survey questionnaire. In the case of more complex institutions, it may be necessary to add "team extenders" to supplement the knowledge and skills of local staff. In other cases, it is advisable to use specially trained contractors to do the Phase I or Phase II assessments. This is especially important for complex jobs or if land is being transferred to a new owner.

The methodology for conducting the assessment should be fully documented in an operating manual that describes program components. The Department of Defense (DOD) and the EPA have audit manuals that could be modified for used at healthcare facilities (Orr 2007).

Special Studies (Phase II Audits)

A *special study* or *Phase II audit* may be triggered by either the pre-audit questionnaire or the site visit. This audit will allow the auditors to confirm whether environmental contamination exists, according to CERCLA. During this phase of the audit process, samples or measurements are made to determine the types and quantities of hazardous substances that may be present at the facility. The goal is to document potential hazards. For example, an old hazardous waste site on the property may be of concern. Some other examples would be testing materials for the presence of asbestos or lead, or checking radon levels.

Special studies should only be performed by trained individuals and may require the use of personal protective equipment (PPE). Only laboratories with established expertise should be used in the analysis of environmental samples. The Phase II audit should also include an estimate for the cost of abatement.

Priorities for Correction

The purpose of Phase I and II audits is to uncover potential environmental violations. The results of these audits should be categorized by risk level. Those items rated as a high-priority risk must be corrected, and some may require immediate action. Items that are rated in the medium- and low-priority categories should be entered into a remediation plan. Remember that the EPA encourages full disclosure of environmental violations, and failure to do so can have serious consequences.

Remediation

The results of the audits may identify problems that must be corrected. The EPA refers to this as a *remediation* or as *Phase III*. Figure 6.3, the expanded corrective action process, is the approach that the EPA uses to identify and correct these problems. The process is more than simply identifying and fixing problems but also promotes the analysis of results to identify trends and to uncover the root causes of problems. It is important to focus on root causes to prevent recurring violations. The process of uncovering and correcting violations should be viewed as an opportunity to learn to better manage the environment.

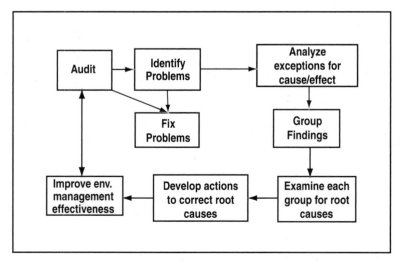

Figure 6.3 EPA's expanded corrective action process.

One final comment on the audit process: If you use contractors, it may be best to use different firms to do the Phase I and Phase II audit and the remediation to avoid any appearances of conflict of interest.

ENVIRONMENTAL MANAGEMENT

As we have previously discussed in Chapter 1, there is a range of environmental compliance from simple property conveyance to "going green." See the EPA's pyramid of audits in Chapter 1 at Figure 1.1. Property conveyance is the simplest and most basic form of environmental management. An environmental audit for a property transfer assures the buyer that the property is free from environmental hazards such as lead-based paint, asbestos, undiscovered hazardous waste and so on. An audit to establish a totally "green" operation would focus on the types of products and practices currently in use and compare them to those considered to be most environmentally sustainable. Assuring lawful property conveyance and regulatory compliance must be done. Using environmental management systems, assessing total environmental risk, and going green should be done.

One important component of environmental management is the selection process, looking both at quantity and quality of products used by the institution. Obviously, it is important to avoid using products that may result in injuries or environmental harm. There has been a gradual evolution from avoiding harmful products to selecting sustainable products. This process has been described as *going green* and is discussed below under energy efficiency and pollution prevention (P2).

Some environmental management approaches that can be applied to institutions are:

- ISO 14000
- Six Sigma
- Energy efficiency and P2

ISO 14000

The International Organization for Standardization (ISO) developed an international standard for environmental management (Goetsch and Davis 2001). The objective of ISO 14000 is to support environmental protection and prevention of pollution in balance with socioeconomic needs (ANSI 1996). ISO 14000 criteria are comprehensive and costly to implement (Goetsch and Davis 2001). A healthcare facility that hopes to comply with the standard must meet specific requirements; the following is a partial list:

- Design a management system that meets the intent of the standard, including an environmental policy, which contains specific objectives and plans to meet them.

- Identify activities, products/wastes, and services that may affect the environment. This would require environmental audits, as described above, to uncover weaknesses and potential code violations.
- Include environmental emergencies in the disaster preparedness plan. (See Chapter 7 for more details.)
- Develop a program to address areas of noncompliance.
- Identify needs for training and communicating (both internally and externally) about environmental protection.
- Maintain a recordkeeping system to document all aspects of the program.

While compliance with ISO 14000 is currently voluntary, a major incentive to meet the certification standards is that it establishes a company's international credibility and may facilitate overseas trade. Compliance with ISO 14000 would be expected to result in long-term cost savings from pollution prevention (discussed below) and avoidance of liability in the event of a spill or other environmental harm. The avoidance of liability could result in savings from lower insurance costs and avoidance of fines or lawsuits.

What is Six Sigma?

Six Sigma is a concept that was originally applied to product quality control to reduce the chance of a manufacturing defect. This concept is now used in a wide range of applications, including the prevention of environmental damage or occupational injuries. The approach is to train corporate staff to achieve performance levels (known as white belt through black belt) and to take on increasingly complex projects. For example, Motorola's Six Sigma training program stresses the following five action items:

- Define opportunity
- Measure performance
- Analyze opportunity
- Improve performance
- Control performance

See the "Additional Resources" section for the Web Site for the Motorola Six Sigma process.

The key to successful implementation of a Six Sigma project is to be sure that outcomes are measurable. In terms of environmental management, an obvious undesired outcome would be an accidental release of a toxic product.

Energy Efficiency and P2

Industries, including the healthcare sector, are discovering that it pays to prevent pollution and be environmentally responsible. For example the National Institutes of Health (NIH) Clinical Center and research laboratories invested millions of dollars in utilities improvements such as high efficiency chillers (Ficca et al. 2000). These investments yielded annual cost savings from lower electricity bills. In some cases, utility rebates paid for the entire cost of the upgrades. Even without utilities rebates, these types of improvements yield a rapid return on investment. At their Louis Stokes Laboratories facility, they estimated a 40% reduction in energy costs from these improvements.

The obvious question is: If protecting the environment saves money, why aren't more organizations actively pursuing energy efficiency and pollution prevention projects? One likely reason is the lack of education of managers about these benefits and the means to achieve those (Wilson et al. 2000). Another likely reason that these improvements have not been quickly implemented is the upfront costs of purchasing these energy-saving appliances and equipment. If there were more financial incentives in the form of government grants or utility rebates, all industries, including healthcare organizations, would be more willing to make the necessary changes. To take advantage of energy efficiency and pollution prevention initiatives, what is needed is a national database of cost-effective approaches, training of health facility managers, and financial incentives to reduce the time interval for return on investment.

RESOURCES

There are several organizations and consensus standards available to assist healthcare organizations with managing the environment. The EPA is active on several fronts to assist healthcare organizations. In 2005, the EPA published *Profile of the Healthcare Industry* (EPA 2005b). Although intended as an overview for staff in their Office of Enforcement and Compliance Assurance (OECA), the information can assist healthcare organizations in identifying environmental issues and concerns.

Healthcare without Harm (HCWH) is an international coalition of healthcare organizations and other related groups the mission of which is to transform the healthcare sector worldwide to be sustainable without compromising patient safety or care. More than 473 organizations in 50 countries have joined HCWH in its decade of existence. See "Additional Resources" at the end of this chapter for the HCWH Web site.

In addition, the EPA and HCWH, along with the American Hospital Association (AHA) and the American Nurses Association (ANA), created Hospitals for Healthy Environment (H2E), the mission of which is to assist hospitals in achieving sustainability in their routine operations. In 2006, H2E became part of Practice Greenhealth, an independent nonprofit organization. See "Additional Resources" at the end of this chapter for the Practice Greenhealth Web site.

The American Society for Testing and Materials (ASTM) has published several standards that can be used to conduct environmental audits' see below in "Additional Resources."

SUMMARY AND CONCLUSIONS

There are important reasons for health and safety professionals to care about environmental health management. First, environmental laws and regulations require it. Failure to comply with these requirements can have serious consequences, including civil and criminal prosecution. Also, a lack of awareness of environmental violations will not protect an individual or organization from these penalties. Therefore, it is prudent to conduct environmental audits to uncover any serious problems. We also have a moral and ethical responsibility to be good stewards of the land, protect public health and the environment, and finally, a visible commitment to environmental protection is good for public relations with the local community. Compliance with the myriad rules and regulations is challenging. Fortunately, there are environmental management systems, such as Six Sigma or ISO 14000 and informal approaches, such as pollution prevention or "going green," that may significantly reduce the liabilities associated with environmental management.

Review

1. Why should healthcare programs concern themselves with environmental management?
2. Healthcare organizations may be cited for violating environmental laws. Which environmental laws are most likely to result in a citation? Identify the two most frequently cited environmental laws.
3. Discuss a recent issue associated with the CWA that may affect healthcare facilities.
4. Describe the major goals of EPCRA.
5. Identify the major sources of information to identify chemicals covered under EPCRA.
6. Discuss one of the biggest problems in complying with RCRA.
7. What are three examples of hazardous materials that would be covered under TSCA?
8. What are the four elements contained in the EPA's definition of an environmental audit?
9. Explain the difference between Phase I and II audits.
10. Summarize the EPA's expanded corrective action process.
11. Explain why healthcare facility administr ators can be prosecuted for environmental violations, even if they are unaware of the problem.
12. Explain the concept behind the EPA's environmental management pyramid.
13. What is ISO 14000, and why should it be implemented?
14. Describe how the Six Sigma concept might be applied to environmental protection in a healthcare facility.

15. What are some reasons that managers have been slow to embrace energy efficiency and pollution prevention projects that save money? What might be necessary to encourage these managers to move forward on these projects?

Additional Resources

American Society for Testing and Materials (ASTM). 2006. *Standard Practice for Environmental Regulatory Compliance Audits* (E-2107–06). West Conshohocken, PA: American Society for Testing and Materials.

———. 2005. *Standard Practice for Environmental Site Assessments: Phase I Environmental Site Assessments* (E-1527–05). West Conshohocken, PA: American Society for Testing and Materials.

———. 2002. *Standard Practice for Environmental Site Assessments: Phase II Environmental Site Assessments* (E-1903–97 (2002)). West Conshohocken, PA: American Society for Testing and Materials.

Environmental Protection Agency (EPA). *Underground Injection Control Program* (retrieved September 2, 2008) (http://www.epa.gov/safewater/uic/index.html)

Healthcare Without Harm (HCWH). *The HCWH Story* (retrieved September 2, 2008) (http://www.noharm.org/us/aboutUs/HCHWStory).

Motorola. *FAQs: What is Six Sigma* (retrieved September 2, 2008) (http://www.motorola.com/content.jsp?globalObjectId=3088)

Practice Greenhealth. *Vision, Mission, Goals and MOU* (retrieved September 5, 2008) (http://www.practicegreenhealth.org).

Reference List

American National Standards Institute (ANSI). 1996. *Environmental Management Systems-Specification with Guidance for Use.* Milwaukee, WI: American National Standards Institute.

Clean Air Act (CAA). 1990. 42 U.S.C. §7402 et seq. (September 2, 2008) (http://www.access.gpo.gov/uscode/title42/chapter85_.html).

Clean Water Act (CWA). 1972. 33 U.S.C. §1251 et seq. (retrieved September 2, 2008) (http://www.access.gpo.gov/uscode/title33/chapter26_.html).

Comprehensive Environmental Response, Compensation and Liability Act (CERCLA). 1980. 42 U.S.C. 9601 et seq. (retrieved September 2, 2008) (http://www.access.gpo.gov/uscode/title42/chapter103_.html).

Emergency Planning and Community Right-to-Know Act (EPCRA). 1986. 42 U.S.C. 1101 et seq. (retrieved September 2, 2008) (http://www.access.gpo.gov/uscode/title42/chapter116_.html).

Environmental Protection Agency (EPA). 1997. *Environmental Audit Program Design Guidelines for Federal Agencies* (Rep. No. 300-B-96-011). Washington, D.C.: Environmental Protection Agency.

———. 2008a. *General Permit for Stormwater Discharges From Construction Activities. Appendix B: Permit Areas Available for Coverage* (retrieved September 2, 2008) (http://cfpub1.epa.gov/npdes/pubs/cgp2008_finalpermit.pdf).

―――. 2005a. *Hospitals in Maine and New Hampshire Are First to Sign Expedited Agreement for Violations of Oil Spill Prevention Laws* (retrieved September 2, 2008) (http://yosemite.epa.gov/opa/admpress.nsf/e68221692a2177fb852572a000650c03/28283ef1f9c6fd9d852570ce004c6d75!OpenDocument)

―――. 1999. "Incentives for Self-Policing: Discovery, Disclosure, Correction and Prevention of Violations." *Federal Register,* 64:26745-26756.

―――. 2008b. *Managing Wet Weather with Green Infrastructure; Action Strategy* (retrieved September 2, 2008) (http://cfpub.epa.gov/npdes/pubs/gi_action_strategy.pdf).

―――. 2005b. *Profile of the Healthcare Industry* (EPA/310-R-05-002), (retrieved September 2, 2008) (http://www.epa.gov/compliance/resources/publications/assistance/sectors/notebooks/health.htm)

―――. 1998. *Protocol for Conducting Environmental Compliance Audits and the Comprehensive Environmental Response, Compensation and Liability Act* (EPA 305-B-98-009), (retrieved September 2, 2008) (http://www.epa.gov/compliance/resources/policies/incentives/auditing/apcol-cercla.pdf)

―――. 2001a. *Protocol for Conducting Environmental Compliance Audits under the Emergency Planning and Community Right-to-Know Act and CERCLA Section 103* (EPA 305-B-01-002), (retrieved September 2, 2008) (http://www.epa.gov/Compliance/resources/publications/assistance/sectors/epcra.pdf)

―――. 2000a. *Protocol for Conducting Environmental Compliance Audits of Facilities Regulated under Subtitle D of RCRA* (EPA 3-B-00-001, (retrieved September 2, 2008) (http://www.epa.gov/compliance/resources/policies/incentives/auditing/apcol-rcrad.pdf)

―――. 2000b. *Protocol for Conducting Environmental Compliance Audits of Facilities with PCBs, Asbestos, and Lead-Based Paint* (Rep No. EPA 300-B-00-004), (retrieved September 2, 2008) (http://www.epa.gov/compliance/resources/policies/incentives/auditing/apcol-tsca.pdf).

―――. 2003. *Protocol for Conducting Environmental Compliance Audits under the Federal Insecticide, Fungicide and Rodenticide Act (FIFRA)* (EPA 300-B-00-003), (retrieved September 2, 2008) (http://www.epa.gov/compliance/resources/policies/incentives/auditing/apcol-fifra.pdf)

―――. 2001b. *Protocol for Conducting Environmental Compliance Audits for Hazardous Waste Generators under RCRA* (EPA 305-B-01-003), (retrieved September 2, 2008) (http://www.epa.gov/compliance/resources/policies/incentives/auditing/apcol-rcragen.pdf)

―――. 2000c. *Protocol for Conducting Environmental Compliance Audits of Public Water Systems under the Safe Drinking Water Act* (EPA 300-B-00-005), (retrieved September 2, 2008) (http://www.epa.gov/compliance/resources/policies/incentives/auditing/apcol-sdwa.pdf)

―――. 2000d. *Protocol for Conducting Environmental Compliance Audits of Storage Tanks under the Resource Conservation and Recovery Act* (EPA 300-B-00-006), (retrieved September 2, 2008) (http://www.epa.gov/compliance/resources/policies/incentives/auditing/apcol-rcratanks.pdf)

―――. 2007. *RCRA Statute, Regulations, and Enforcement* (retrieved September 2, 2008) (http://www.epa.gov/compliance/civil/rcra/raraenfstatreq.html).

————. 2006. *Title III Consolidated List of Lists—October 2006 Version* (retrieved September 2, 2008). (http://www.epa.gov/emergencies/tools.htm#lol.)

Environmental Science Center, with Bristol-Myers Squibb Company. 2007. *Greener Hospitals: Improving Environmental Performance.* Augsburg, Germany: Wissenschaftzentrum Umwelt.

Federal Insecticide, Fungicide and Rodenticide Act (FIFRA). 1996. 7 U.S.C. 136 et seq. (retrieved September 2, 2008) (http://www.access.gpo.gov/uscode/title7/chapter6_.html).

Ficca, S. A., Y. D. Chyun, M. Ebrahimi, F. Kutlak, and F. Memarzadeh. 2000. "Activities of the National Institutes of Health Relating to Energy Efficiency and Pollution Prevention." *Environ.Health Perspect.* 108 Suppl 6:939-44.

Goetsch, D. L. and S. B. Davis. 2001. *ISO 14000 Environmental Management.* Upper Saddle River, NJ: Prentice Hall.

Occupational Health and Safety Administration (OSHA). 1996. 29 CFR 1910.1200, *Hazard Communication Standard* (retrieved September 2, 2008) (http://www.osha/pls/oshaweb/owadisp.show_document?p=table=standards&p_id=10099).

Oil Pollution Act (OPA). 1990. 33 U.S.C. §2702 et seq. (retrieved September 2, 2008) (http://www.access.gpo.gov/uscode/title33/chapter40_.htm)

Orr, J. Environmental Health Officer, U.S. Public Health Service. Personal Communication (7-30-2007).

Resource Conservation and Recovery Act (RCRA). 1976. 42 U.S.C. §6901 et seq. (retrieved September 2, 2008) (http://www.access.gpo.gov/uscode/title42/chapter82_.html).

Safe Drinking Water Act (SWDA). 1974. 42 U.S.C. §300f et seq. (retrieved September 2, 2008) (http://www.access.gpo.gov/uscode/title33/chapter6a_subchapterxii_.htm)

Toxic Substances Control Act (TSCA). 1976. 15 U.S.C. §2601 et seq. (retrieved September 2, 2008) (http://www.access.gpo.gov/uscode/title15/chapter53_.html).

VanHouten, J. W. 2007. *Phase I and II Environmental Site Assessments: International Implications.* West Conshohocken, PA: ASTM International.

Wilson, S. H., S. Merkle, D. Brown, J. Moskowitz, D. Hurley, D. Brown. 2000. "Biomedical Research Leaders: Report on Needs, Opportunities, Difficulties, Education and Training, and Evaluation." *Environ.Health Perspect.* 108 Suppl 6:979-95.

CLASSROOM ACTIVITY

Environmental Management Scenario

Scenario: You are the Environmental Health and Safety Managers for BroJoe Hospital, a 150-bed, acute-care facility. You have just returned from a conference where representatives from a large national healthcare organization presented some of their approaches to environmental sustainability in the hospitals and clinics. The presenters described "green" approaches in both new construction and in routine operations. All changes were determined to be cost-effective and some provided a return on investment within the first year.

The assignment is to assemble into small groups of three to five people and develop a plan to achieve sustainability. In the table below, the first column describes an issue, and the second column identifies the current practice. In the third column, your group should identify an environmentally friendly option to replace the current practice. Do not include sustainability in renovations or new construction.

Current Operations

Issue	Current Practice	Sustainable Options
Energy–Lighting & electricity	Incandescent lights	
Energy–Heating	Natural gas-fired furnaces, boilers providing perimeter hot-water heating	
Energy–Ventilation & AC	Combination of variable air volume recirculated systems and single-pass exhaust systems (isolation rooms & toilets)	
Storm water	Directed to the city storm water drainage system	
Water use	Standard toilets, showerheads & mop heads	
Hazardous waste management	Examples of hazards ▪ Mercury present in medical devices, ▪ Xylene used in lab and maintenance ▪ Glutaraldehyde used for disinfection & in film processing ▪ Standard housekeeping chemicals	
Solid waste management	No recycling, heavy use of disposable items	
Other areas (In the second column, list other potential problem areas that interfere with our efforts to be more environmentally responsible. In the third column, identify your solutions to the problem.)		

CHAPTER 7

Emergency Preparedness

George Byrns and George Stevens

Learning Objectives

1. Describe the types of disasters that may affect a healthcare facility.

2. Explain the difference between internal and external emergencies.

3. Define the concepts RACE and ILSM as applied to internal emergency planning.

4. Explain the four major elements of emergency management.

5. Describe the development of a plan to manage emergencies.

6. Describe the Joint Commission's approach to community emergency management.

7. Discuss the implementation of an emergency preparedness plan.

8. Explain the differences between emergency planning drills and exercises.

Ever since the attacks on September 11, 2001, there have been concerns whether or not communities or institutions, including healthcare facilities, will be prepared to respond in an emergency (JCAHO 2005). One only needs to look at overcrowded hospital emergency rooms across the country to realize that healthcare facilities may easily be overwhelmed in during a major disaster (JCAHO 2003). Therefore, a key issue in community emergency preparedness is the capacity and capability of healthcare institutions to respond in a crisis. This situation is complicated because, for many years, hospitals have been using the "just-in-time" supply system. This approach relies on vendors to quickly deliver any needed supplies. While it eliminates the need to maintain expensive storage space and substantial inventories of supplies, this efficiency measure could spell disaster during a major emergency. The Joint Commission on Accreditation of Healthcare Organizations (known as the Joint Commission or JCAHO) requires that a hospital's emergency plan identify capabilities and response efforts when the hospital cannot be supplied by the local community for at least 96 hours (JCAHO 2009). In these 2009 standards, the Joint Commission makes it clear that hospitals are not required to maintain supplies necessary for 96 hours of operation. This means that, according to the Joint Commission, an acceptable response effort would be to close or evacuate the facility. If this is the only healthcare delivery system in the area, this is likely to cause additional hardship to the community.

A disaster or emergency is an event that occurs suddenly, disrupting normal operations and requiring immediate attention (Brauer 2006). Disasters come in all sizes. Some affect the community for a short period and quickly dissipate, while others have longer lasting effects (AHA 2000). In a major disaster, small rural communities and healthcare institutions may be on their own for 24 to 72 hours before help arrives (JCAHO 2005). A major concern is that while hospitals have a good track record in managing smaller, short-term disasters, it is unclear how well these facilities will be able to manage major disasters.

The Government Accountability Office (GAO) investigated limitations in the National Disaster Medical System (NDMS) in its ability to support hospitals and nursing homes in a disaster (GAO 2006). The NDMS is a federally coordinated system designed to support states and local governments in their ability to support hospitals during a natural disaster, major transportation accident, technological disaster or acts of terrorism. The GAO investigation revealed that nursing homes were never considered for inclusion in this program (see Chapter 14 for more information) and there were some serious transportation supply gaps in the existing program (GAO 2006). A primary concern was that in a major disaster, the demand for ambulances and other transport vehicles would exceed the supply of these critical vehicles. GAO's recommendation to the U.S. Department of Health and Human Resources was to include nursing homes in this support system and to devise means of increasing the availability of emergency transportation.

TYPES OF EMERGENCIES

The Joint Commission defines an emergency as, ". . . an unexpected or sudden event that significantly disrupts the organization's ability to provide care, or the environment of care itself, or that results in a sudden, significantly changed or increased demand for the organization's services. Emergencies can be either human-made or natural (such as an electrical system failure or a tornado), or a combination of both, and they exist on a continuum of severity" (JCAHO 2008).

The National Fire Protection Association (NFPA) classifies emergencies and disasters as (NFPA 2004):

- Geological hazards (earthquake, tsunami, volcano, landslide, mudslide, subsidence, glacier, and iceberg)
- Meteorological hazards (flood, drought, fire, snow, windstorm, extreme temperatures, lightning strikes, and famine)
- Biological hazards (diseases that impact humans and animals and animal or insect infestation)
- Human-caused events:
  1. Accidental (hazardous material spill or release, explosion/fire, transportation accident, building/structure collapse, energy/power/ utility failure, fuel/resource shortage, air/water pollution or conta- mination, water control structure/dam/levee failure, financial system emergencies, and communications systems interruptions)
  2. Intentional (terrorism, sabotage, civil disturbance, public unrest, mass hysteria, or riot, enemy attack or war, insurrection, strike, misinformation, crime, arson, and electromagnetic pulse)

These emergencies can be grouped into natural events, human events, or technology-related events. A technological system failure might be a boiler explosion, loss of water, or many other types of utilities failures. Transportation disasters are one type of human event that may involve airplanes, buses, trains, or car and truck crashes. Healthcare organizations are particularly concerned about their ability to handle world-wide pandemics of diseases such as avian influenza. One unique concern in hospitals is the potential for exposures to biological, chemical, or radiological materials when a hospital receives con- taminated patients during mass casualty incidents (OSHA 2005).

Emergencies can also be categorized as internal or external. An *internal emergency* occurs on the grounds of the healthcare facility. An *external emergency* occurs away from the facility and results in the need to manage large numbers of casualties. Regardless of the type of emergency, the healthcare facility must be prepared to react and respond appropriately.

EXTERNAL DISASTER PLANNING

The Federal Emergency Management Agency (FEMA) developed a useful framework for emergency planning. Figure 7.1 shows FEMA's four phases and discusses the steps for each.

Notice that successful planning prepares the healthcare organization and the community for contingencies before the emergency, during the emergency, and in the aftermath of an emergency. The *response* phase must have a written description of the processes used to initiate the plan, including how, when, and

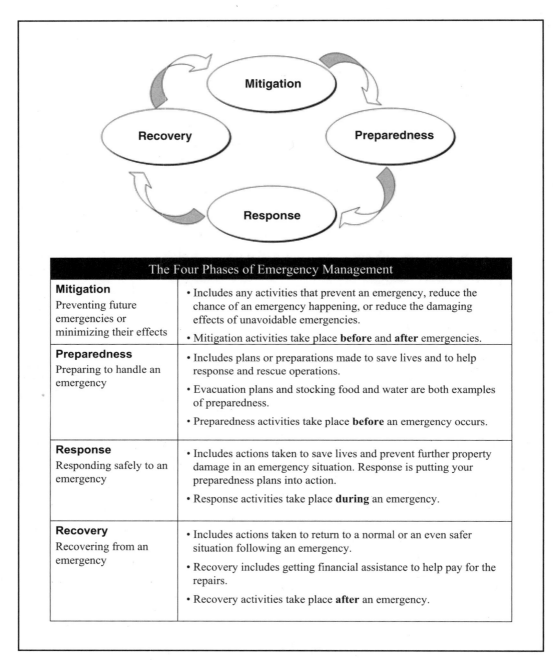

The Four Phases of Emergency Management	
Mitigation Preventing future emergencies or minimizing their effects	• Includes any activities that prevent an emergency, reduce the chance of an emergency happening, or reduce the damaging effects of unavoidable emergencies. • Mitigation activities take place **before** and **after** emergencies.
Preparedness Preparing to handle an emergency	• Includes plans or preparations made to save lives and to help response and rescue operations. • Evacuation plans and stocking food and water are both examples of preparedness. • Preparedness activities take place **before** an emergency occurs.
Response Responding safely to an emergency	• Includes actions taken to save lives and prevent further property damage in an emergency situation. Response is putting your preparedness plans into action. • Response activities take place **during** an emergency.
Recovery Recovering from an emergency	• Includes actions taken to return to a normal or an even safer situation following an emergency. • Recovery includes getting financial assistance to help pay for the repairs. • Recovery activities take place **after** an emergency.

Figure 7.1 FEMA's four phases of emergency management.

by who the steps are to be activated. This is commonly demonstrated by having pre-made action checklists by function tabbed for immediate use by responders. Step one is often how staff are notified that an emergency situation has developed, and that the disaster plan is in effect. Step two is notification of the external community of its status, or, if the condition is first discovered by the hospital, then the alert is a warning of an epidemic or bioterrorism attack so that the community can take action to limit the spread. After this point, the plan will then generally list the responsibilities of individual staff for the performance and support of the healthcare mission.

Success in managing a major external disaster requires collaboration and cooperation between a variety of organizations and institutions within a community. An effective incident command system (ICS) is necessary to assure that the collaboration and cooperation takes place. The purposes of the ICS are as follows (California EMSA 2006):

- Manage all routine or planned events, of any size or type, by establishing a clear chain of command.
- Allow the integration of personnel from different agencies or departments into a common structure that can effectively address issues and delegate responsibilities.
- Provide operational personnel needed for logistical and administrative support.
- Ensure key functions are covered, and duplication is eliminated.

A typical ICS command structure is shown in Figure 7.2.

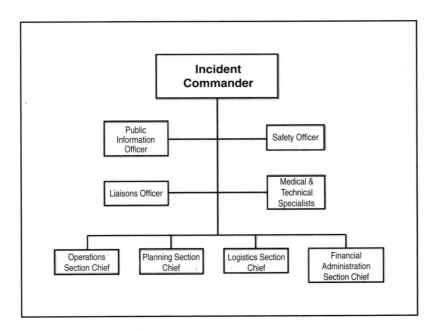

Figure 7.2 ICS command structure.

A local healthcare organization would organize its emergency response command structure along similar lines. The overall incident commander would be the CEO or his/her designee; other members may include:

- Health and Safety Manager (a part of the incident command unit)
- Clinical Director and Director of Nursing
- Risk Manager (filling the role of information officer and liaison officer)
- Director of Finance
- Director of Human Resources
- Director of Central Supply
- Director of Facilities Management

The Joint Commission recommends a thirteen-step approach to planning for community-wide disasters (JCAHO 2005):

1. Define the community.
2. Identify and establish the emergency management preparedness and response team.
3. Determine the risks and hazards the community faces.
4. Set goals for preparedness and response planning.
5. Determine current capacities and capabilities.
6. Develop the integrated plan.
7. Ensure thorough communication planning.
8. Ensure thorough mental health planning.
9. Ensure thorough planning related to vulnerable populations.
10. Identify, cultivate, and sustain funding sources.
11. Train, exercise, and drill collaboratively.
12. Critique and improve the integrated community plan.
13. Sustain collaboration, communication, and coordination.

Define the Community

The first step in planning for an external disaster is to determine key stakeholders within the community (JCAHO 2005). Some of examples of key stakeholders include:

- Law enforcement, fire department, emergency medical services
- Public works
- Public health
- Schools, colleges, and universities
- Housing agencies

- Utilities (energy, water, communications)
- Healthcare facilities
- Private industry
- Service and religious organizations
- Federally funded local response initiatives, such as community emergency response teams (CERTs)

Each of the above groups can play an important role in emergency response.

Identify and Establish the Team

Effective emergency preparedness requires a team approach. Fortunately, linkages between the key players, such as the fire department, emergency medical services and area hospitals may already exist. One way of fostering this team approach is the formation of community emergency response teams (CERTs) (Citizen Corps 2007). This is a program that is funded through Congress to help train local communities in improving their preparedness and response to better manage such things as: fire safety hazards, light search and rescue, team organization, and disaster medical operations.

The next step is to identify appropriate planning partners. Some examples of potential partners are listed above. Healthcare organizations need to play a leading role in planning for and responding to a mass casualty event that could overwhelm any single healthcare facility. Nursing homes may have additional bed capacity, supplies and skilled staff to care for non-critical disaster victims. Ambulatory facilities can assist in triage and by providing additional skilled personnel, and even home health agencies can assist by providing trained staff and supplies (JCAHO 2005).

Local colleges and universities may have healthcare staff that can assist in the disaster response. In addition, they may have vehicles to transport injured victims. Other potential partners might include local industries to assist in communications, utilities and other functions. For example, a heavy machinery manufacturer or large construction company could provide heavy equipment that might be useful in removing debris in a disaster. Obviously, the American Red Cross will play a significant role in assisting the community with emergency response. Each community may have unique assets that may be valuable in an emergency.

Determine the Community's Risks and Hazards

Once the planning team is in place, the next step is to conduct a hazard vulnerability analysis (JCAHO 2005). A list of all potential hazards should be compiled. There are two challenges in developing such a list. First, it is relatively easy to overlook a potential hazard. For example, a local industry may have large quantities of a hazardous chemical that has not been reported through the SARA Title III Community Right-to-Know program. Also, new hazards may emerge over time, such as pandemic influenza. Once the list is prepared, it should then be assessed and prioritized based on likelihood of occurrence and severity. See Chapter 10 for more information on priority setting.

Set Preparedness and Response Planning Goals

Preparing for an external disaster requires that realistic goals must be set, recognizing that some risk remains even with good planning. According to the Joint Commission, three goals are most important (JCAHO 2005):

1. Save lives and protect health.
2. Protect and sustain the critical infrastructure, property, and the environment needed to save lives and protect health.
3. Find dual uses for existing or emerging capabilities. (This goal simply allows you to stretch limited resources and cover more needs.)

In addition to the three basic goals, the planning process should cover each of the four phases of emergency management, as described in Figure 7.1.

Determine Current Capacities and Capabilities

For healthcare facilities, this means determining the patient surge capacity. In a major disaster, patient surge would likely overwhelm any individual facility and possibly all the facilities in the community. The American Hospital Association (AHA) recommends that surge capacity be based not on the numbers of inpatient beds, but on the numbers of skilled staff available to respond (AHA 2000). This includes the identification of reserve staff, such as healthcare workers who have recently retired or who have taken jobs outside of the healthcare field. Alternate care and shelter facilities should also be identified. This could include churches, college dormitories, motels, and other structures that could provide care and shelter (JCAHO 2005). Finally, federal facilities, such as military bases, often contain a wide range of resources that would be beneficial in an emergency.

Develop the Integrated Plan

There are four basic approaches to developing the plan that may be used alone or in combination (JCAHO 2005):

1. Develop the plan from scratch;
2. Adapt a plan that already exists (for example, from another hospital);
3. Adapt a plan obtained through the emergency management literature; or
4. Adapt a county, regional, state, or national plan.

The Joint Commission strongly advises against using a "cookie-cutter" approach of adopting another facility's plan as is. The best approach is to review local and state laws, regulations, and executive orders that have a bearing on the plan, and use the results from the hazard vulnerability analysis as a guide in developing the plan. FEMA offers an approach to plan development in their, *Guide for All-Hazard Emergency Operations Planning* (FEMA 1996). FEMA does not mandate one particular approach, but they do suggest some topics:

- **Purpose:** The plan should provide a general statement of what it is meant to do.

- **Situation and Assumptions:** This part of the plan should outline assumptions for the types of hazards it will address and which information will be used in preparing it.

- **Concept of Operations:** This area of the plan should describe the general sequence of actions before, during, and after the emergency situation.

- **Assignment of Responsibilities:** One of the most important issues in the plan is the command structure. The hierarchy of command should be clearly identified, including who will be reporting to whom. Clearly, the organization's chief executive officer will be ultimately responsible; however, emergencies may occur at night and on weekends, so it must be clear who has authority to trigger the response plan in the facility at any given time.

- **Administration and Logistics:** Another major issue is the availability of medical supplies to meet a patient surge. In the past, most facilities used the "just-in-time" approach to supply management, which meant that there were limited amounts of material onsite at any given time. However, the Joint Commission, in their 2009 standards, requires that a hospital's emergency plan identify capabilities and response efforts when the hospital cannot be supplied by the local community for at least 96 hours (JCAHO 2009). The Joint Commission did make it clear, however, that hospitals were not expected to maintain a 96 hour supply system onsite (JCAHO 2009).

- **Plan Development and Maintenance, and Authorities and References:** For a healthcare facility, this would consist of a written authority statement from the governing board.

Some steps in preparing the healthcare facility's plan include:

1. Identify the individual or program responsible for organizing plan development (in all likelihood, the health and safety manager).
2. Develop a rough outline of the basic plan.
3. Organize a planning committee and schedule an initial meeting.

4. Establish subcommittees for parts of the plan; appoint subcommittee chairs, and schedule completion dates and follow-up meetings.

5. Work with subcommittees on successive drafts.

6. Integrate the contributions of the subcommittees into a draft plan.

7. Contact organizations who have roles in implementing the plan for their written concurrence. (For example, contact local law enforcement, the fire department, public utility authorities and others who may be expected to respond and assist.)

8. Circulate the draft to the planning committee for review and comment.

9. Meet with the planning committee to incorporate final changes and discuss the implementation strategy.

10. Print and distribute the plan to department and service directors and brief them and their staff about the plan.

There should be only *one* external emergency plan, which is flexible enough to deal with a wide variety of disasters. However, the plan will need hazard-specific appendices to deal with some of the unique issues raised by different types of events (JCAHO 2005). The plan should be written in simple language; it should clearly delineate all employees' roles and responsibilities. In order for employees to be able to understand the plan, a table of contents and glossary of terms are helpful.

Communication Planning

Ensuring thorough communications with the community in a disaster is a complex, multifaceted process. Ensuring good communications within a healthcare institution is also challenging, but no less important. The options are electronic—conventional telephones, cellular phones, two-way radios, pagers, the intercom—as well as human. It is critical that local emergency medical services' (EMS) radio dispatching can communicate with your facility and that your facility can communicate with fire, police, and other important disaster response personnel (JCAHO 2005). Generally, one radio frequency is reserved for the community-wide emergency response effort. The healthcare facility communications plan should address the need for routine maintenance of radios and other pieces of communications equipment so that they will be reliable when needed. Emergency communications equipment should be connected to the facility's emergency power system; nevertheless, the plan should also address back-up procedures in the event that the primary communications method is down. For example, if the two-way radios are not working, all of the key players should have cell phones with the numbers available to one another.

In a major emergency, members of the general public and the media will require information from all local healthcare providers. This communication is necessary and appropriate, but it should also be well-controlled to avoid the release of misinformation. The communications plan must also describe who will speak to the public and the media, and what training will be received. See Chapter 11 for more information on critical issues in risk communications.

Mental Health Planning

There may be serious mental health issues in the aftermath of any major disaster, and certain healthcare providers, such as EMTs, may be particularly affected after responding to these traumatic events. Terrorist attack and mass violence can present particularly serious mental health challenges; unfortunately, these attacks have become more common in the last few decades (DHHS 2004). In order to provide good mental health planning, the Department of Health and Human Services (DHHS) offers useful documents in planning and preparing for mental health needs associated with an emergency (DHHS 2003; DHHS 2004).

Planning and Vulnerable Populations

The Joint Commission recommends that the emergency preparedness plan consider the needs of vulnerable populations (JCAHO 2005), including children, the aged, disabled, and non-English speaking persons. As the American Academy of Pediatrics (AAP) points out, children are not small adults and should be cared for by healthcare practitioners who are knowledgeable in pediatrics (AAP 2006). Children and infants are more vulnerable to biological, chemical, and radiological agents and are more susceptible to the effects of dehydration. Also, it is important to remember that the immune systems of the disabled, aged and small children may be compromised, decreasing their chance of surviving infections. In addition, the response plan for vulnerable populations should include translators to assist caregivers in the triage of non-English speaking patients. Therefore, it is important that EMTs and other healthcare providers are aware of these increased vulnerabilities.

Identify, Cultivate, and Sustain Funding Sources

There will be significant costs associated with emergency preparedness. These costs fall into three areas: personnel time, equipment and supplies, and capital improvements. The healthcare organization's chief executive officer must make emergency planning a priority and allow the planning committee the time and resources to meet the need, based on the vulnerability analysis described earlier. Equipment and supply costs vary greatly, from batteries to portable high efficiency particulate air (HEPA) units. HEPA units may be necessary in the Emergency Services (ES) department to assist in the control of infectious agents spread via the air, such as severe acute respiratory syndrome (SARS). In colder climates, it may be difficult to decontaminate patients in the hospital parking lot. Therefore, capital improvements might be necessary to provide decontamination rooms within the ES. Also, as a part of the healthcare facility's internal emergency preparedness effort, it may be necessary to modify the building structure to "harden" it and make it less vulnerable to a terrorist attack. One such issue is the need to protect the building ventilation system from biological, chemical or radiological attack. Examples of building modifications may be found in Chapter 8. Capital building improvements may be costly, and additional revenue sources, such as federal grants, may be needed.

Train, Exercise, and Drill Collaboratively

Training for an external disaster is best handled as a community-wide event. Training programs should be competency-based and will depend on an individual's role in emergency preparedness (JCAHO 2005). Some types of training, such as CPR, should be offered to members of the community, while other types of training, such as decontamination of victims of hazardous materials spills, should only be offered to hospital personnel. The CERT program described earlier in this chapter is an example of a 20–hour, federally funded training program (Citizen Corps 2007). There are additional training programs on a variety of topics offered through FEMA. One such program deals with incident command training. A representative from the health care organization should be a part of the incident command team and should receive this training.

Drills and Exercises

While preparatory training is helpful, it does not take the place of community-wide drills and exercises. These are the most effective way to uncover weaknesses in the healthcare facility's or community's emergency preparedness plan (JCAHO 2005). The healthcare facility or the community may also do tabletop exercises. These are the simplest type of exercise in terms of planning, preparation, and coordination since they involve no equipment or use of simulated casualties. Guidance to assist in planning for fires, floods, hurricanes and other disasters is available from FEMA (FEMA 1993).

The U.S. Department of Homeland Security (DHS) also distinguishes between *games* (one step above a tabletop exercise but still does not use resources) and *operations-based exercises* (which may be a drill, a functional exercise, or a full-scale exercise). Operations-based exercises involve an actual response, use of equipment and resources, and the commitment of personnel (DHS 2003).

Homeland Security defines a *drill* as "a coordinated test used to evaluate a specific operation or function in a single department or nursing unit" (DHS 2003). These drills can focus on new equipment, test new policies or procedures, or practice skills. They define functional exercises, also called *command post exercises,* as "tests of individual capabilities, multiple functions or activities within a function, or interdependent groups of functions" (DHS 2003). The objective is to implement specific plans and procedures under crisis conditions, within or by particular teams. A full-scale exercise is the most complex event and usually includes multi-departmental, multi-organizational, multi-jurisdictional agencies. The full-scale exercise also involves realistic problems requiring critical thinking, rapid problem-solving, and effective responses. The major differences between drills, functional exercises, and full-scale exercises are simply a matter of scope. The drill is generally limited to the healthcare organization, whereas exercises involve varying amounts of community resources.

The Joint Commission requires an accredited hospital to have a drill or exercise at least once every four to six months, and at least one of these drills must involve a community event that involves a patient surge (JCAHO 2009).

Training and drilling for internal disasters are covered later in this chapter.

Critique and Improve the Integrated Community Plan

Each drill or exercise is an opportunity to critique and improve both the healthcare facility and the community plans. At a minimum, these plans should be reviewed annually and revised as necessary. Good recordkeeping is essential to document areas of weakness. Schedule a post-test evaluation session with the emergency preparedness planning team to discuss the major problems uncovered in the evaluation. Once the plan is modified, the Joint Commission recommends conducting a tabletop exercise to determine the effectiveness of the changes (JCAHO 2005). It is important to remember that while the Joint Commission considers these tabletop exercises to be useful, they do not consider them to be a replacement for exercises that involve simulated or real patient victims (JCAHO 2009).

Sustain Collaboration, Communication, and Coordination

The final activity recommended in the Joint Commission emergency planning guide is to maintain the collaborative efforts between the major players in the community (JCAHO 2005). In a random sample of U.S. hospitals, researchers found that there was a lack of involvement in emergency planning by media outlets and volunteer organizations, both of which are integral to an effective response (Braun et al. 2006). The Joint Commission also recommends collaborating with other communities to discover lessons they have learned (JCAHO 2005). DHS even has a Web site where communities can share their lessons and best practices (DHS 2008). Lastly, they recommend continuing open communications with the public about the importance of the community-wide plan.

STAFFING AND SURGE PLANNING

Terrorist attacks and pandemic disease outbreaks may result in a surge of patients that would overwhelm healthcare facility capacities (Hick et al. 2004). As previously stated, the AHA recommends that a facility's capacity be based on the number of skilled personnel available to respond and not simply the number of inpatient beds (AHA 2000). Once the acute care facility's capabilities are exceeded, it may be necessary to use alternate care sites such as schools, churches, and other places of assembly. The primary function of these alternate sites would be in triage and caring for first aid cases (Lam et al. 2006). However, the ability of these sites to play an effective role in disaster management has received relatively little attention (Lam et al. 2006). A particular concern is a lack of plans to provide these alternate sites with pharmaceuticals, supplies, and equipment (Braun et al. 2006).

The Joint Commission produced a report on surge hospitals that included (JCAHO 2006b):

- types of surge hospitals, such as closed hospitals or wards, facilities of opportunity (nonmedical buildings that can be adapted into surge hospitals because of their size or proximity to a medical center), mobile medical facilities, portable facilities;
- planning for, establishing and operating surge hospitals;
- sufficiency of care; and
- legal and reimbursement issues.

Issues discussed under planning for, establishing and operating surge hospitals are (JCAHO 2006b):

- Evaluating the options for surge capability;
- Design considerations of dual use in existing buildings;
- Coordinating effects with local, state, and federal emergency management;
- Obtaining necessary equipment and supplies;
- Selecting leaders in charge of establishing and operating the facilities; and
- Communicating effectively in and with surge hospitals.

The report also discusses how to ensure that long-term surge hospitals offer safe care and the possibility of the Joint Commission developing standards for surge hospitals. Case studies are also included based on facilities that opened after Hurricane Katrina, such as:

- the "Katrina Clinic" in Houston,
- the Dallas Convention Center,
- a basketball arena and field house at Louisiana State
- an empty former retail store in Baton Rouge, and
- a veterinary hospital in College Station, Texas.

Both the advantages and disadvantages of these facilities were discussed, as well as lessons learned (JCAHO 2006b).

INTERNAL EMERGENCY PREPAREDNESS

An internal emergency is one that occurs within the healthcare facility, on the grounds of the facility, or in some way directly affects the operation of the healthcare facility. For example, a water main break could directly affect a hospital's water supply.

Types of Internal Emergencies

There are many types of internal emergencies that can occur inside of health-care facilities, including:

- Explosions, fires, smoke and/or fumes;
- Equipment and utilities failure; and
- Violence and terrorism.

Each of these types of emergencies is discussed below.

Explosion, Fire, Smoke and/or Fumes

An explosion or a fire that releases large amounts of smoke and fumes is one of the most devastating events that can occur in a healthcare facility. As a result, building compartmentalization is extremely important. *Compartmentalization* is a method of constructing a building so that it will delay the spread of fire long enough to allow the fire department to arrive or sufficient time to evacuate building occupants. For example, patient room doors should be capable of delaying the spread of fire for 20 minutes. Corridor smoke and fire doors should delay the fire for at least one hour, and the building slab or walls separating buildings should delay the spread for at least two hours. Building stairwells are also fire rated to allow a safe means of escape.

Fire preparedness plans use the concept of *RACE*, which stands for:

- **Rescue:** Rescue anyone in immediate danger.
- **Alarm:** Activate the fire alarm.
- **Contain:** Contain the fire by closing the door.
- **Extinguish or evacuate:** Extinguish the fire, if it is small, or evacuate, if the fire cannot be contained with one portable fire extinguisher.

Personnel should not attempt to use portable fire extinguishers unless they have been properly trained. The fire plan should address the need for this type of training to assure that there are trained personnel on hand at all times.

There are two types of building evacuations, horizontal and vertical. *Horizontal evacuation* means that occupants are moved to another fire zone on the same floor of the hospital. This is always the preferred choice because of the difficulties and dangers associated with transporting non-ambulatory patients down stairwells. *Vertical evacuation* means exiting the building; this should only occur if there is no hope of containing the fire. Evacuation plans and drills should consider both types of evacuations.

Fortunately, the need for building evacuations has significantly diminished over the years. Modern healthcare facilities are equipped with automatic sprinkler systems that activate in a fire. It is important to note however, that these sprinkler systems are designed to protect the building rather than the occupants. Most deaths are due to smoke inhalation and not fire injury.

Equipment and Utilities Failures

Equipment or utilities failures may be severe enough to disrupt normal hospital operations. For example, the loss of the heating system in an Alaskan hospital during the winter could result in a building evacuation. Some examples of equipment or utilities failures are: telecommunications failure, loss of water, loss of medical gases, and medical equipment failure. Each will be discussed separately below.

Telecommunication Failure. Loss of communications systems, such as the intercom system, could result in a loss of life if it prevents a call for medical assistance during a patient resuscitation. However, even the loss of the telephone system or the internet could have serious consequences if it interferes with access to important information. Therefore, the internal plan should address the need for maintaining a functional communications system. It should also provide a backup system for a short-term interruption of services.

Loss of Water. A modern healthcare facility can not operate without a safe and reliable water supply. Even a short-term disruption, such as a broken water main, is not acceptable. Therefore, a hospital should have at least two independent sources of water mains. In the event that both water mains are disrupted, there should be a back-up system that involves the provision of water using water trucks. Ensuring that the water supply remains safe during one of these emergencies is an important responsibility of the facility's health and safety manager.

Loss of Medical Gases. Modern healthcare facilities have piped systems for suction, oxygen, and other medical gases. The internal plan should include the use of portable suction units or medical gas cylinders in the event of a temporary loss of one or more of these utilities.

Medical Equipment Failure. Biomedical engineering personnel have the responsibility of testing and maintaining medical equipment so that it functions reliably when needed. These personnel may be either staff members or hired on contract. The internal plan should identify back-up systems or replacements for certain critical medical equipment. The plan should also address the Food and Drug Administration's reporting requirements for critical equipment failures under the Safe Medical Devices Act of 1990 (SMDA), which requires all healthcare facilities to report deaths and serious injuries "caused or contributed to" by medical devices. In addition, it is critical that all personnel be properly trained in the use of medical equipment before they are asked to use it.

Violence and Terrorism

Violence and terrorism may target a community's healthcare institutions. Some examples of these types of emergencies include:

- Bomb threats
- Public disturbances
- Hostage situations
- Work-place violence
- Infant abductions

Each of these emergencies requires specific planning. The bomb threat plan should emphasize the importance of reporting suspicious packages or devices. The plan must designate who will respond to this report and when occupant evacuation is warranted. Public disturbances and hostage situations would typically be reported to the local law enforcement agency and not be handled using healthcare personnel. Planning for and preventing workplace violence is such a complex topic that it will be addressed in Chapter 12 of this book. Infant abduction is an issue that is best handled through prevention and having policies on who can have access to the infants. However, in the event of abductions, this would typically be referred to the police.

Hazardous Material Decontamination

One essential component of any healthcare facility emergency preparedness plan is the decontamination of individuals presenting at the emergency department. Decontamination of patients with biological agents should only be considered in instances of gross contamination (Hospital and Healthcare System Disaster Interest Group and California EMSA 2005). Victims who have been contaminated with hazardous chemicals or radioactive materials present a special problem. It is essential to decontaminate these patients as quickly as possible to prevent them from suffering any additional harm but it is also vital to avoid spreading the contamination to the healthcare providers and to the rest of the facility (Jagminas and Erdman 2006). The two basic approaches in decontamination are *chemical dilution* and *chemical inactivation*. Dilution simply means flushing the victim with large quantities of water to reduce the concentration of the contaminant. Inactivation means another chemical is applied to neutralize the contaminant of concern.

Emergency medicine personnel performing triage must make judgments regarding the immediacy of the need for treatment and the risks associated with the contaminant(s). Based on this initial assessment, the patient may be placed in either the red (hot) zone, yellow (warm) zone or considered to be uncontaminated in the green (cold) zone (Hospital and Healthcare System Disaster Interest Group & California EMSA 2005). Errors in properly classifying the risk of a contaminated patient may result in the closure of the emergency room, which could be disastrous in an emergency (Jagminas and

Erdman, 2006). The California Emergency Medical Services Authority (EMSA) and the Hospital and Healthcare System Disaster Interest Group developed an algorithm to assist emergency medicine personnel in making these difficult decisions. See Figure 7.3.

The initial assessment also determines the level of personnel protective equipment (PPE) required in treating the victim. PPE ranges from Level D (full face shield, hood or hair covering, gloves, water-repellent gown, and water-repellent boots or shoe covers) to Level A (full containment with a vapor protective suit and supplied air respirator). A similar approach is used with victims of radiological contamination. See Figure 7.4 for an example of a management approach for patients contaminated with radiation.

Another issue that must be considered in a facility's hazard vulnerability assessment (HVA) is contaminated water and run-off. For example, residual chemicals from patient decontamination procedures may be too toxic to discharge directly into the sewer. One approach to the HVA is to determine the types of chemical hazards in the community and their aquatic hazards. It must be recognized that an accident involving an interstate shipment of a hazardous product may be difficult to predict. Also, each state may have special criteria regarding acceptable contaminant levels in effluents discharged to the sanitary sewer. It is best to consult with the state EPA office when preparing the HVA. Another approach is to construct temporary holding tanks that may be tested and treated as needed, after the emergency has passed.

Emergency Power

Healthcare institutions rely on electricity for many critical services; providing a reliable supply of electricity for critical care systems is of the utmost importance (JCAHO 2006a). Therefore, the healthcare facility internal emergency preparedness plan must include provisions for emergency power.

Loss of power can range in magnitude from minor disruptions to catastrophic system-wide failures. The Joint Commission recommends that healthcare organizations do a vulnerability analysis and develop a plan that goes beyond the minimum requirements of NFPA 110 in providing emergency power (NFPA 2004). Their concern is that, in a major disaster such as Hurricane Katrina, hospitals may lose electrical service for 72 hours or longer. Therefore, planning for minor disruptions may be insufficient. In a *Sentinel Event Alert,* the Joint Commission amended their Environment of Care (EC) standards to require accredited hospitals to provide emergency power for extended periods of time (JCAHO 2006a). In 2009, the Joint Commission removed provisions on emergency preparedness from the EC standards and created two new sections, Emergency Management (EM) and Life Safety (LS). Most of these were minor wording changes did not affect the intent. One major change was to require the testing of emergency generators over and above the current requirement of monthly tests for 30 continuous minutes. The new requirement is to test at least once every 36 months

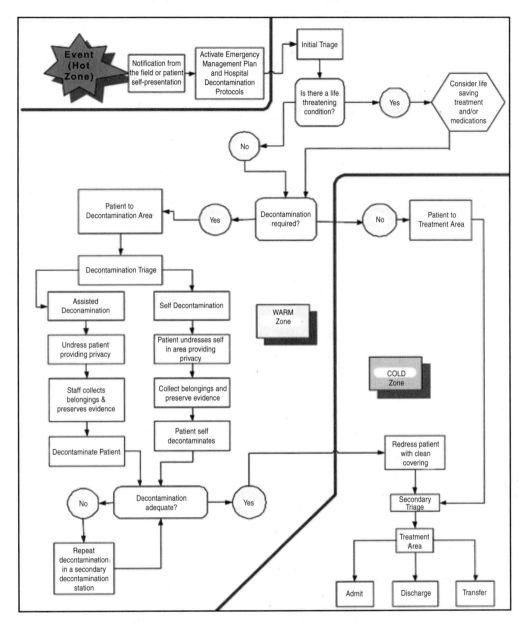

Figure 7.3 Algorithm for chemical decontamination in a hospital setting. (Source: California EMSA and Hospital and Healthcare System Disaster Interest Group 2005)

for a minimum of four hours (JCAHO 2009). In addition, some of the factors that should be considered in the vulnerability assessment are the availability of fuel supplies for the generators and the need for additional truck-mounted, portable generators to provide a redundant power source. The results of generator testing and the vulnerability analysis, as well as

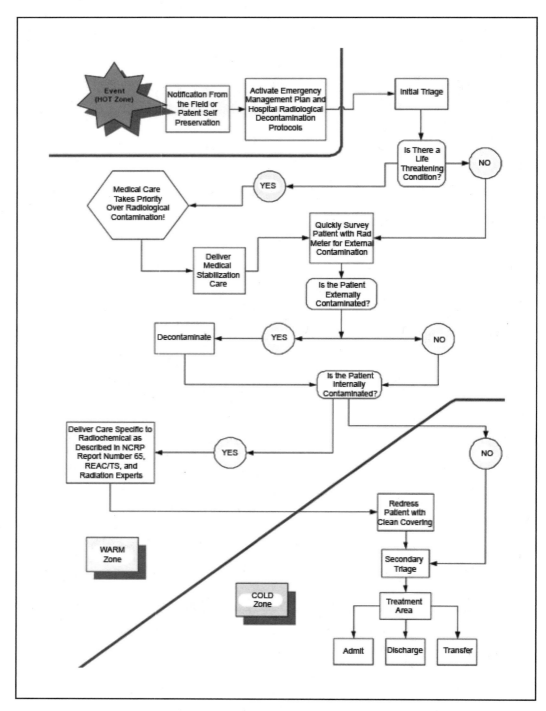

Figure 7.4 Algorithm for treatment of radioactive contamination. (Source: California EMSA and Hospital and Healthcare System Disaster Group 2005)

other records regarding the provision of emergency power, must be maintained and available for review by a Joint Commission surveyor or OSHA inspector (JCAHO 2009).

Interim Life Safety Measures (ILSMs)

The Joint Commission Standard LS.01.02.01 requires the establishment of ILSMs when life safety protections are compromised due to construction or any other disruption that causes the facility to be non-compliant with the Life Safety Code (JCAHO 2009). Of particular concern are actions that affect fire barriers, the alarm system, the automatic sprinklers, or the means of building egress. Temporary construction partitions are required to be smoke tight and built with materials that will not contribute to the development or spread of fire. The ILSM policy must address each of the following concerns:

1. Inspects exits in affected areas on a daily basis.
2. Provides temporary but equivalent fire alarm and detection systems for use when a fire system is impaired.
3. Provides additional fire-fighting equipment (such as portable fire extinguishers).
4. Uses temporary construction partitions that are smoke-tight, or made of noncombustible material or made of limited-combustible material that will not contribute to the development or spread of fire.
5. Increases surveillance of buildings, grounds, and equipment, giving special attention to construction areas and storage, excavation, and field offices.
6. Enforces storage, housekeeping, and debris-removal practices that reduce the building's flammable and combustible fire load to the lowest feasible level.
7. Provides additional training to those who work in the hospital on the use of fire-fighting equipment.
8. Conducts one additional fire drill per shift per quarter.
9. Educate staff hospital-wide to promote awareness of building deficiencies, construction hazards, and temporary measures.

These temporary measures must be inspected at least monthly and, as with other aspects of the emergency preparedness plan, records of activities relating to ILSMs must be maintained.

Terrorism

A terrorist attack could either target the community or the healthcare facility. Either way, it is critical to quickly identify details about the type of agent (biological, chemical, or physical) that was used in the attack. According to the

Institute of Medicine, it is important to determine (Institute of Medicine 2005):

- where the agent is,
- where it will spread,
- who may have been exposed,
- the quantity of the agent,
- the effects of exposure,
- what must be done to reduce exposure, and
- how to treat victims.

A terrorist attack is intended to create fear and panic. As discussed earlier in this chapter, part of the emergency response to this type of attack must involve treating the mental health of victims. One of the critical concerns is a terrorist attack on a healthcare facility's heating, ventilating, and air conditioning (HVAC) system. The concern is that HVAC fresh air inlets need to be protected; thus, terrorists would be unable to spread a hazardous chemical, biological agent, or radioactive material through the building ventilation system. See Chapter 8 for details on protecting the HVAC from a terrorist attack.

SUMMARY AND CONCLUSIONS

Healthcare organizations must effectively respond to internal or external disasters. Emergencies may result from natural, human, or technologically related events. While most hospitals are equipped to handle small-scale, short-term emergencies, there is concern that many hospitals will be unable to manage larger, long-term emergencies. According to FEMA, there are four phases to disaster management: mitigation, preparedness, response, and recovery. An effective incident command system (ICS) must be in place in order to manage these four phases. According to the Joint Commission, effective response to an external disaster requires close and continuous cooperation between the healthcare organization and the local community. There are three goals in emergency preparedness: saving lives and protecting health; protect and sustaining the critical infrastructure, property, and the environment; and finding dual uses for existing or emerging capabilities. A key concern for healthcare organizations is their capability, including the availability of adequate staffing, during patient surges. One unique concern that healthcare facilities may face is treatment of patients who have been contaminated by biological, chemical, or radiological agents. Failure to properly manage these patients could result in the spread of contamination and the need to close the facility. One of the most critical needs of a modern healthcare facility is the need for reliable and continuous emergency power. In a major disaster, emergency power may be required for more than 72 hours. One of the final major issues is the potential for a hospital to be selected as a "soft target" for a terrorist attack. Emergency plans must be designed to minimize this threat and to quickly limit any damage from such an attack.

Review

1. Give an example of an emergency associated with a natural event, a human event, or a technology-related event.
2. Describe the elements of each of the four phases of disaster management.
3. What does CERT stand for?
4. Describe the different types of external emergency drills and exercises.
5. What does the term "RACE" stand for, as it relates to internal disaster planning?
6. What is ILSM?
7. The Institute of Medicine recommends a specific approach when dealing with terrorism. Describe their approach.

Reference List

American Academy of Pediatrics (AAP). 2006. *Pediatric Terrorism and Disaster Preparedness: A Resource for Pediatricians* (Publication. No. 06-(07)0056-EF). Rockville, MD: Agency for Healthcare Research and Quality (AHRQ).

American Hospital Association (AHA). 2000. *Hospital Preparedness for Mass Casualties* (retrieved August 13, 2008) (http://www.aha.org/aha/content/2000/pdf/2000forumreport.pdf).

Brauer, R. L. 2006. "Emergencies." In Brauer, R.L., *Safety and Health for Engineers* (pp. 537–545). Tolono, IL: Willey-Interscience.

Braun, B. I., N.V. Wineman, N.L. Finn, J.A. Barbera, S.P. Schmaltz, and J.M. Loeb. 2006. "Integrating hospitals into community emergency preparedness planning." *Ann.Intern.Med,* 144:799–811.

California Emergency Medical Services Authority (EMSA). 2006. *Hospital Incident Command System Guidebook* (retrieved August 11, 2008) (http://www.emsa.ca.gov/HICS/files/Guidebook_Glossary.pdf).

Citizen Corps. 2007. "Community Emergency Response Teams (CERT)." (retrieved August 11, 2008) (https://www.citizencorps.gov/cert/index.shtm).

Department of Health and Human Services (DHHS). 2003. *Mental Health All-Hazards Disaster Planning Guidance* (Rep. No. SMA 3829). Rockville, MD: Center for Mental Health Services, Substance Abuse and Mental Health Services Administration.

———. 2004. *Mental Health Response to Mass Violence and Terrorism* (Rep. No. SMA 3959). Rockville, MD: Center for Mental Health Services, Substance Abuse and Mental Health Services Administration.

Department of Homeland Security (DHS). 2003. *Homeland Security Exercise and Evaluation Program, Volume 1: Overview and Doctrine* (Rep. No. NCJ199536). Washington, D.C.: Office for Domestic Preparedness.

———. 2008. *Lessons Learned Information Sharing (LLIS)* (retrieved August 13, 2008) (https://www.llis.dhs.gov/index.do).

Federal Emergency Management Agency (FEMA). 1996. *Guide for All-Hazard Emergency Operations Planning* (State and Local Guide (SLG) 101). Washington, D.C.: Federal Emergency Management Agency.

Government Accountability Office (GAO). 2006. *Disaster Preparedness: Limitations in Federal Evacuation Assistance for Health Facilities Should Be Addressed* (Rep. No. 06-826). Washington, D.C.: U.S. Government Accountability Office.

Hick, J. L., D. Hanfling, J.L. Burstein, C. DeAtley, D. Barbisch, G.M. Bogdan. 2004. "Health Care Facility and Community Strategies for Patient Care Surge Capacity." *Ann.Emerg.Med.* 44:253–261.

Hospital and Healthcare System Disaster Interest Group (California) and California Emergency Medical Services Authority (EMSA). 2005. *Patient Decontamination Recommendations for Hospitals* (EMSA #233) (retrieved August 11, 2008) (http://www.emsa.ca.gov/pubs/pdf/emsa233.pdf).

Institute of Medicine. 2005. *Public Health Risks of Disasters: Communication, Infrastructure, and Preparedness—Workshop Summary.* Washington, D.C.: National Academies Press.

Jagminas, L. and D.P. Erdman. 2006. *CBRNE - Chemical Decontamination* (retrieved August 14, 2008) (http://www.emedicine.com/emerg/TOPIC893.htm).

Joint Commission of Accreditation of Healthcare Organizations (JCAHO). 2003. *Health Care at the Crossroads: Strategies for Creating and Sustaining Community-wide Emergency Preparedness Systems.* Oakbrook Terrace, IL: Joint Commission on Accreditation of Healthcare Organizations.

———. 2009. *Hospital Accreditation Standards.* Oakbrook Terrace, IL: Joint Commission on Accreditation of Healthcare Organizations.

———. 2006a. "Preventing Adverse Events Caused by Emergency Electrical Power System Failures." *Sentinel Event Alert* (Issue 37, September 26, 2006), (retrieved August 13, 2008) (http://www.jointcommission/org/SentinelEventApert/sea_37.htm).

———. 2008. "Revision to Standard EC.4.12, Element of Performance 6 Note Text. Joint Commission Perspectives" (retrieved August 13, 2008) (http://www.jcrinc.com/fpdf/pubs/pdfs/JCReqs/JCP-01-08-S5.pdf).

———. 2005 *Standing Together: An Emergency Planning Guide for America's Communities.* Chicago, IL: Joint Commission on Accreditation of Healthcare Organizations.

———. 2006b. "Surge Hospitals: Providing Safe Care in Emergencies. Oakbrook Terrace, IL: Joint Commission on Accreditation of Healthcare Organizations.

Lam, C., R. Waldhorn, E. Toner T.V. Inglesby, and T. O'Toole. 2006. "The Prospect of Using Alternative medical care facilities in an influenza pandemic." *Biosecur.Bioterror,* 4:384–390.

National Fire Protection Association (NFPA). 2004. *Standard on Disaster/Emergency Management and Business Continuity Programs* (NFPA 1600). Quincy, MA: National Fire Protection Association.

————. 2005. *Standard for Emergency & Standby Power Systems* (NFPA 110).Quincy, MA: National Fire Protection Association.

Occupational Safety and Health Administration (OSHA). 2005. "OSHA Best Practices for Hospital-Based First Receivers of Victims from Mass Casualty Incidents Involving the Release of Hazardous Substances" (retrieved August 13, 2008) (http://www.osha.gov/dts/osta/bestpractices/html/hospital_firstreceivers.html).

CLASSROOM ACTIVITY

Emergency Preparedness Strategies

Scenario: You will play the part of an environmental health and safety manager for a 400-bed, acute care hospital. Working in groups of three or four, you will be assigned the responsibility to develop a strategy for emergency management. Your vulnerability analysis identified the following as examples of potential emergencies:

- A terrorist attack at a nuclear power plant that results in radiation contamination (assume that at least ten of the 50 injured victims are contaminated).
- An airplane carrying 150 passengers crashes at the local airport. (assume there are at least 50 injured survivors).
- A hazardous material accident involving a pesticide truck spill and secondary explosion on a busy street in town (assume at least ten injured victims are contaminated and all 20 survivors have first degree burns).
- A community-wide outbreak of avian influenza (assume there are at least 75 infected persons).
- A tornado touches down and destroys 20 homes (assume there are at least 30 injured persons).

In developing the strategy, you should consider the following:

1. Which community members need to be involved with each of the above scenarios?
2. Which hospital staff positions should be part of the executive planning committee?
3. What are the risks (if any) that the hospital will face as a result of the above disasters?
4. What are reasonable goals in preparing for and responding to each of the above emergencies.

5. In developing a plan discuss the following elements:
   - Purpose: Make a general statement of what the plan is meant to do.
   - Situation and Assumptions: For each of the above situations, what are the assumptions that you will make when you prepare the plan?
   - Concept of Operations: What is the general sequence of actions before, during, and after the emergency situation?
   - Assignment of Responsibilities: What is the hierarchy of command; in other words who will be reporting to whom? Who in the facility has authority to trigger the response plan at any given time?
   - Administration and Logistics: Do you have sufficient medical supplies to meet a patient surge? Use the "just-in-time" approach to supply management.
   - Plan Development and Maintenance, and Authorities and References: Give an example of the kind of written authority statement that would be issued by the governing board.

6. In the large-group setting, evaluate the effectiveness of each plan.

CHAPTER 8

Indoor Air Quality in the Healthcare Environment

George Byrns, David Regelbrugge and Lee Shands

Learning Objectives

1. Identify the four key elements to consider when investigating an indoor air quality (IAQ) problem.

2. Define the major types of health complaints associated with poor IAQ.

3. Explain why relative humidity (RH) and carbon dioxide (CO_2) measurements are made when investigating IAQ complaints.

4. Describe the basic approach to the evaluation of IAQ.

5. Explain the importance of mold in IAQ, including issues involved in sampling for indoor mold.

6. Discuss terrorism as an IAQ issue.

7. Describe IAQ prevention and control measures.

The investigation of indoor air quality (IAQ) problems is often one of the most challenging tasks of an institutional environmental health and safety (IEHS) professional. Initial complaints by building occupants are often ignored, creating a high stress environment. In addition, it is often difficult to pinpoint the source of these complaints because many of the symptoms may be confused with the common cold, psychological stress, and allergies (American Lung Association et al. 1994). OSHA lists potential sources of these complaints, such as: odors, low-level contaminants, poor air circulation, thermal gradients, humidity, job pressures, lighting, work-station design, and noise (OSHA 1999). Sometimes even minor building modifications, such as installation of internal room dividers or new equipment, can affect the quality of air (EPA and NIOSH 1991). On the positive side, performing an IAQ investigation tends to reduce occupants' stress.

The typical U.S. resident spends about 90% of the time indoors (EPA 1995). In addition, energy conservation measures in the 1970s made buildings much tighter than they were in the past. Sealing and caulking windows and doors lead to reduced amounts of fresh air entering the building. This, combined with poor building design, construction or material defects, and poor maintenance, may exacerbate poor IAQ. The introduction of new technologies or chemicals in the healthcare environment may also produce indoor pollutants. For example, surgical laser plumes may contain viable infectious agents and a mixture of toxic chemicals. Lastly, increased public awareness may also be a factor. There have been stories on the news suggesting that exposure to *Stachybotrys* mold spores will cause permanent health effects. Most of these reports have been anecdotal, with little scientific support. There is currently considerable debate in the health community about the significance of health risks from exposure to mold.

KEY ELEMENTS IN IAQ

There are four key elements to consider in assessing IAQ:

- Sources of contamination
- Heating, ventilating, and air conditioning (HVAC) system
- Occupants of the building
- Pathways of exposure (EPA and NIOSH 1991)

It is important to note that the HVAC and the building occupants can serve as both sources of contaminants and pathways of exposure. The indoor air environment is not a static situation, but a set of constantly changing interactions among a number of factors. Therefore, our primary goal in an investigation may not be to identify a specific problem, but to improve the occupants' perception of a building's IAQ.

Sources of IAQ Contaminants

Sources of contaminants can be outside, beneath or inside the building. Sources inside the building include broken or cracked plumbing vent lines, plants, aquariums, water fountains, and desktop serenity fountains. If the HVAC fresh air intakes are located at ground level outside, mold spores, gases, or vapors, such as vehicle exhaust, could be pulled into the building. Even if the intakes are located on the roof, there may be other sources of contamination which may be pulled into the system, such as cooling towers, exhaust stacks or plumbing vent pipes that may have been placed too close to the outside air intakes. Standing or recurring moisture on the roof or in crawl spaces promotes the growth of mold or other microorganisms, and these may find their way into the building, which could also result in odors or other potential concerns.

HVAC as a Source of IAQ Complaints. A number of potential IAQ problems may be associated with the building's HVAC system. Due to efforts to conserve energy, one common cause of poor IAQ is an insufficient number of fresh air exchanges. Increasing energy costs, such as the rising prices of natural gas and electricity, create an incentive to increase the amount of recycled air by closing outdoor intakes. Screens on the outside air intakes may become clogged with leaves, grass or other debris, especially if the outside air intakes are located at ground level. In some cases, the source of the contamination may not be identified, but complaints may be resolved by simply increasing the amount of fresh air entering the building. Other problems with the HVAC system may include dirt and microbial growth in drip pans and the ductwork, improper use of biocides, sealants, or cleaning compounds, improper venting of combustion products, and refrigerant leakage (EPA & NIOSH, 1991). A properly designed and operated HVAC system is a critical component of IAQ quality. See below for more information on HVAC.

Improperly Installed or Operated Equipment. In addition, improperly installed or operated equipment could release indoor air contaminants. In some cases, equipment has been installed or operated contrary to the manufacturer's instructions. There are also a variety of supplies that may be important sources of contamination. The laboratory and maintenance departments use solvents and other volatile chemicals that may contribute to poor IAQ. Cleaning and disinfection chemicals can be particularly problematic, and certain chemicals, such as glutaraldehyde, can sensitize susceptible workers (Byrns et al. 2000). The section on "Pollution Prevention and Sustainability" in Chapter 9 discusses the importance of substituting safer alternatives for these toxic products.

Human Activities. Human activities may also be a source of IAQ contamination. Cleaning or maintenance tasks that re-suspend dust or release other contaminants may lead to IAQ concerns, as well as lack of cleaning or ineffective cleaning. A build-up of dust or food may attract dust mites and cockroaches. These insects produce allergens that may cause allergic reactions in sensitive individuals. Another major source of irritation to workers and patients concerns individuals with body odor or who use heavy doses of perfume. In some cases, other building occupants may be allergic to certain types of perfume, and this can create some serious policy and logistical problems. For example, can management require an office to be scent-free, or is this an infringement of personal freedom?

Carpeting and Furniture. Various types of building components may present a variety of IAQ problems. For example, new carpeting or inexpensive furniture may release a variety of volatile organic compounds (VOCs). Carpets can also be a problem because they tend to collect contaminants and are difficult to clean thoroughly.

Plumbing Systems. Plumbing systems may be a source of IAQ contamination. In older buildings, plumbing vent pipes may become clogged or cracked due to aging, releasing sewer gas containing hydrogen sulfide (a gas with an odor similar to rotten eggs) into the building. During dry winter months, it is common for unused plumbing traps to dry out, which may also result in the release of sewer gas into the building.

Disasters. Fires, floods, or sewer back-ups will also affect IAQ by releasing soot, odors and biological contaminants into the building. These contaminants may be difficult to eliminate.

HVAC

A properly operating HVAC system serves two important functions. It provides heating and cooling for occupant comfort, and it removes odors and harmful contaminants from the occupied space (AIHA 2003). The control of harmful air emissions is best accomplished by using *local exhaust ventilation* (LEV). The purpose of LEV is to capture and remove air contaminants at their source. These systems tend to be more cost-effective and efficient than using air dilution for the control of air contaminants. Some important considerations with LEV systems are that the exhaust air should discharge directly to the outside without recirculation, and provision should be made for "make-up" air to replenish the exhausted air. Unfortunately, in most institutions there are relatively few situations that allow the use of LEV. The other approach is called *dilution ventilation* or *general ventilation*. This approach is often necessary in healthcare facilities because there are usually multiple sources that are, in many cases, mobile, such as a patient with a respiratory infection. In order to achieve occupant comfort and the removal of contaminants, the HVAC must add a certain amount of outdoor air; the amount depends on the room's function and the number of occupants present.

Thermal Comfort

Our perception of thermal comfort is based on the combination of temperature and the amount of relative humidity (RH). Thermal comfort is one of the main factors that determine whether or not individuals are happy with a building's IAQ. The acceptable thermal level is dependant on a number of variables, such as the age of the occupants and their level of physical activity (EPA and NIOSH 1991). Because of individual preferences in temperature levels, people tend to accept a relatively narrow range of temperature and relative humidity levels.

According to the American Institute of Architects (AIA), indoor temperatures should fall within the range of 68 to 78° F and RH should be between 30 and 60% (AIA 2006). Temperatures and RHs outside of this range will increase the number of complaints about IAQ. Lower humidity may cause drying of skin and mucous membranes, resulting in irritation of the eyes, nose and throat, whereas too much moisture provides a perfect environment to support mold growth. The American Society of Heating, Refrigerating, and

Table 8.1 Acceptable Ranges of Temperature and
Relative Humidity (RH) During Summer and Winter
(Source: EPA and NIOSH 1999, adapted from ASHRAE 2007)

Relative Humidity (RH)	Winter Temperature	Summer Temperature
30%	68.5°F – 76.0°F	74.0°F – 80.0°F
40%	68.5°F – 75.5°F	73.5°F – 79.5°F
50%	68.5°F – 74.5°F	73.0°F – 79.0°F
60%	68.0°F – 74.0°F	62.5°F – 78.0°F

Air Conditioning Engineers (ASHRAE), in Table 8.1 above, recommends acceptable thermal and RH conditions (ASHRAE 2007).

HVAC Operations

Building HVAC systems typically blend outdoor air with a certain percentage of recirculated indoor air, and most institutions operate either a constant volume or variable volume (VAV) system. Constant volume systems provide a steady amount of airflow to maintain room thermal comfort levels, whereas VAV systems adjust the amount of heating and cooling airflow based on inside or outside air conditions. VAV systems tend to be more challenging to manage. With either type of system, it is critical that the airflow be properly balanced. If a room is designed to be under negative pressure, the amount of cubic feet per minute (cfm) of air that is removed from the room must be slightly greater than the amount of air supplied to the room. Negative pressure is required to control the migration of contaminants from a room; for example, infectious isolation rooms must be under negative pressure relative to the adjacent hallways. On the other hand, clean areas, such as operating rooms, must be under positive pressure to prevent the infiltration of contaminated air into sterile areas. Achieving and maintaining HVAC balance in terms of both the amount of cfm and the pressure relationships is difficult.

A final issue in HVAC operations is the need for air cleaning and filtration. In institutions, the supply air must be provided with roughing or pre-filters that are at least 30% efficient. In addition, certain areas of the hospital, such as the operating rooms, require higher efficiency filters ($\geq 90\%$). Areas with patients who are severely immuno-compromised, such as bone marrow transplant units, should have high-efficiency air filters (HEPA). A HEPA filter is designed to remove 99.97% of particles with an aerodynamic diameter of 0.3 micrometers (µm). (The 0.3 µm particle size tends to be the most difficult to capture in a filter.) HEPA filters must also be installed in certain exhaust systems, for example biological safety cabinets and isolation room exhausts.

Building Occupants

In healthcare institutions, there are significant differences among building occupants. In terms of time spent in the building, employees are typically present for eight to twelve hours each day, patients are present for 24 hours each day during their hospitalization, and visitors are typically present for much shorter time intervals, perhaps an hour or two. Significant differences also exist among building occupants in terms of susceptibility and tolerances, due to genetics or pre-existing health conditions. Obviously, hospital patients have the least tolerance for disruptions in IAQ. Some workers may have allergies (called *atopy*) or respiratory diseases that put them at greater risk of adverse health effects from poor IAQ. Even contact wearers may be at greater risk of eye irritation due to IAQ contaminants.

Pathways of Exposure

The most important pathway of exposure is the HVAC system because it can spread contaminants throughout the building. This is why the investigation of poor IAQ (described below) often centers on the HVAC. Other pathways can include stack effects and wind direction (EPA and NIOSH 1991). *Stack effects* refers to the tendency of warm air to rise. For example, if the building has a trash chute, contaminated air will rise up the chute and may be released on the higher floors every time the access door is open. In older buildings, stack effects may cause continuous leakage through defective door gaskets or floor penetrations. *Wind direction* can be a problem when there is a source of contamination downwind from your building; this is especially a problem if your building envelope is leaky (EPA and NIOSH 1991). Wind effects can also create local areas of high pressure on the windward side of the building; this can result in the movement of contaminants from the high pressure area to areas of lower pressure within the building. Finally, the building occupants themselves can serve as a pathway of exposure by carrying contaminants, such as microorganisms or chemicals, to other parts of the building where they may affect other occupants.

IAQ HEALTH EFFECTS

It is important to distinguish between two similar sounding issues, *building-related symptoms* (BRS) and *building-related illness* (BRI). BRS was formerly called *sick-building syndrome*. BRS consists of a group of building occupants that share similar complaints about air quality. Individuals may report a wide range of symptoms, including headache, dizziness, nausea, tiredness, lack of concentration, and eye, nose, and throat irritation (OSHA 1999). BRS is by far the most common problem because humans have a relatively narrow range of tolerances for changes in environmental conditions, including temperature and humidity levels. The other problem is that people suffering from BRS may be anxious and highly stressed, and this can aggravate pre-existing conditions or exacerbate otherwise minor irritations.

In BRI, however, the problem can be directly attributed to the building; Legionnaires disease is the classic example. Another example is occupational asthma, which has been described as a chronic disease "out of control." It has been estimated that about 15% of all adult onset asthma is due to occupational exposures (CDC 1994; Wheeler et al. 1998; HCWH 2006). There are two types of occupational asthma, allergic and irritant. *Allergic asthma* develops after variable periods of exposure to a sensitizing agent such as latex. *Irritant asthma* immediately follows a single, intense exposure to a known irritant, as in reactive airway dysfunction syndrome (RADS), or after a variable period of repeated exposures to lower doses of irritating chemicals. There are over 350 biological, chemical and physical agents known to cause asthma. In the healthcare setting, common products may trigger an asthmatic attack, such as the sensitizing agents listed below (HCWH 2006):

- Cleaners, floor stripper, disinfectants
- Acrylics
- Drugs
- VOCs
- Latex

A third IAQ health condition is called *multiple chemical sensitivity* (MCS), which is also known as *idiopathic environmental intolerance*. It is defined as "a chronic condition with symptoms that recur reproducibly in response to low levels of exposure to multiple unrelated chemicals and improve or resolve when incitants are removed" (Bartha et al. 1999). In a random telephone survey in the U.S., it was found that 11.2% of Americans reported an unusual hypersensitivity to commonly found chemicals, such as perfume and paint, and 2.5% reported that they had been medically diagnosed with MCS (Caress and Steinemann 2004). Since many in the medical community, including the American Medical Association (AMA), question the existence of MCS, it is a condition that will continue to be debated for the foreseeable future.

Investigating IAQ Problems

Figure 8.1 below is taken from the document, *Building Air Quality: A Guide for Building Owners and Facility Managers* (EPA and NIOSH 1991). It should be noted that it may be necessary to involve IAQ experts when dealing with particularly complex issues.

Initial Walk-through

The first step after receiving a complaint is to gather the necessary supplies and equipment. During the initial investigation, only basic forms are needed to collect information from the affected individuals on their symptoms and from building maintenance workers on the operation of the HVAC. While this information is compiled, a general walk-through is also conducted to become familiar with the location of occupants and HVAC intakes and stack exhausts. There are some simple rules regarding HVAC systems. Plumbing vents or exhaust stacks should be separated from supply intakes with 25 feet of horizontal separation, but prevailing winds may require even greater

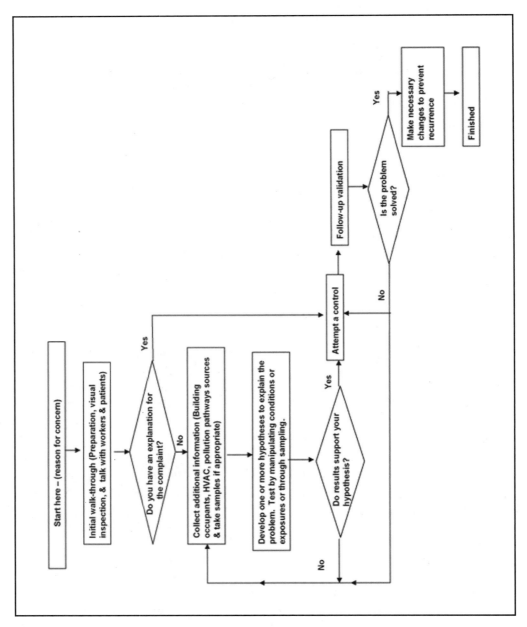

Figure 8.1 IAQ audit.

separations (AIA 2006). Fresh air intakes should be at least 6 feet above ground level or if on the roof, at least 3 feet above the roof level. Vertical or horizontal separation of potential contamination sources from building air intakes is important to prevent re-entrainment of pollutants. In addition, the location of indoor air supply, return and exhaust grilles or diffusers should be noted. Adequate separation between supply grilles and return or exhaust grilles is essential to achieve acceptable dilution ventilation mixing and to prevent *short-circuiting*. (In an airborne infectious isolation room, the supply grill should be located near the entrance to the room and the exhaust grille near the head of the bed.)

During the walk-through, any unusual activities that involve the use of solvents or other volatile chemicals should be noted. It is also helpful to note the location of the individuals reporting the problem in relationship to the air return grilles. Individuals who are located adjacent to the air return grilles may be exposed to higher concentrations of air contaminants. The building maintenance staff should be questioned about any recent changes, malfunctions, or repairs to the HVAC system, possibly providing a useful clue to an IAQ problem. The initial walk-through may provide enough information to identify the problem without taking any samples or measurements. If no obvious cause is apparent, the next step is to develop and test a hypothesis. Some likely causes of poor IAQ are insufficient dilution ventilation, an emissions source inside the building, an outside source that is causing emissions to enter the HVAC building intake, the presence of hypersensitive individuals, or psychogenic causes.

Additional Avenues of Investigation

If the initial walk-through does not present a resolution to the problem, more information on sources, the HVAC, pathways of exposure, and the occupants needs to be collected. At this point, measurements and samples should be taken of temperature, relative humidity (RH) and carbon dioxide (CO_2) to assess whether the HVAC is operating within acceptable limits. As described above, some individuals have relatively limited tolerances for fluctuations in temperature and humidity levels. High carbon dioxide levels (generally above 1000 ppm) are used as an indicator of ineffective air exchange. It is important that these readings are taken later in the day when the maximum number of occupants are typically present.

Tools for Collecting Information

Standardized complaint forms are available from EPA and NIOSH (1991). These forms create a line listing or incident log of case information. In addition, if the symptoms disappear over the weekend and reappear when workers return, they should be asked to keep a diary to help pinpoint activities or locations in the building that may trigger the problem. An occupant diary can be extremely helpful in documenting times and dates that an odor occurs, a description of the odor, outside weather conditions when the odor is noted, or anything unusual occurring in building at that time.

Survey tools that may be useful in an IAQ investigation include: viable or non-viable biological sampling devices, moisture meters, particle counters, ventilation devices (for velocity, pressure, and direction), photoionizing detectors to measure VOCs, and detector tubes for specific contaminants. It may be necessary to do sampling for specific toxic chemicals used in health care that contribute to poor IAQ, such as methyl methacrylate, glutaraldehyde or formaldehyde, to name a few. For example, x-ray film processing involves a number of toxic chemicals, such as glutaraldehyde, acetic acid, and hydroquinone in high concentrations (Byrns et al. 2000). See "Tools for Sampling Mold," below for examples of equipment used in mold surveys.

Evaluating Data

It is important to define the complaint area, look for timing patterns, and look for symptoms patterns. This can be extremely helpful in clarifying where the problem is coming from and who it is affecting. In a healthcare setting, it is unusual to find chemical gases or vapors above occupational exposure limits (OELs). The one major exception is glutaraldehyde. If workers can smell it, it is likely to be above the American Conference of Governmental Industrial Hygienists (ACGIH®) ceiling limit of 0.05 parts per million (ACGIH 2008).

Prevention and Control of IAQ Problems

Prevention and control of IAQ complaints can range from simple solutions, such as adjustment of temperature and RH or increasing the amount of outside air, to complex changes in technology. There are a number of common IAQ problems that are relatively easy to correct. Unused plumbing traps that are allowed to dry out can allow sewer gases to enter the building. These drains should have water poured into them or be permanently sealed. The filters in the HVAC system should be changed on a routine basis to prevent overloading the filter and reducing the HVAC system effectiveness. The frequency may need to be modified due to environmental conditions, such as construction nearby or the spring pollen season, resulting in quicker filter loading. However, the filters should not be changed too often, because some particle loading on the filter actually improves the filter performance. IAQ complaints may be common in new construction or newly renovated areas due to the *off-gassing* (the continuous release of volatile contaminants such as formaldehyde) of the building components. To minimize this problem, construction should be completed with low volatility components, and if odors are still present prior to occupancy, the ventilation system should be adjusted to allow more fresh air into the ventilation cycle. This will help dilute any odors. Room lighting can also affect IAQ complaints. Inadequate lighting can result in feelings of malaise that are mistaken for IAQ problems; improving the lighting conditions can result in resolution of the IAQ complaints.

Whenever possible, source control is the most cost-effective means of protecting IAQ. This can be accomplished by sealing or encasing the source; for example, keeping containers of chemicals like glutaraldehyde tightly covered or substituting safer alternatives for toxic chemicals. Other options include using local exhaust systems to capture and remove contaminants, selecting lower emission equipment, or relocating contaminant-producing equipment to unoccupied areas. In some cases it may be possible simply to reschedule certain tasks to low occupancy periods. For example, methyl methacrylate is a chemical that is used in glues, resins, and plastics; it has a strong odor and is highly irritating. Laboratories using this product could delay casing molds until the end of the work day. Another option might be to relocate susceptible individuals to other areas in the building. While this can work for certain problems, individuals with latex allergies may have a hard time finding a latex-free area in health care. The final control involves risk communication. When the IEHS manager is asked to assist with an IAQ complaint, it is likely that individuals are already very unhappy with management. It is therefore extremely important that any discussions with affected employees be two-way communications and must be done as soon as possible. See Chapter 11 for a discussion of risk communication. On the positive side, an IAQ investigation sends a message to the employees that the healthcare facility is concerned about their welfare, and this alone can reduce some of the stress and anxiety associated with poor IAQ.

MOLD

Molds and fungi are found both indoors and outdoors; they grow almost everywhere as long as sufficient moisture, food, and oxygen are all present. Problems with mold growth indoors have increased due to building changes since the 1970s: buildings are now built to be airtight and the construction schedules are year-round. Exposure to molds or their spores can cause allergic reactions in certain sensitive individuals or worsen preexisting conditions (ACOEM 2002; Shoemaker and House 2006). A rare but serious health effect is *hypersensitivity pneumonitis* (HP), which is recurrent and characterized by fever, cough, and shortness of breath. Chronic exposure can lead to lung fibrosis (scarring). In addition, certain types of mold are known to produce toxins and irritants. Examples include *Aspergillus, Cladosporium, Penicillium, Stachybotrys,* and *Trichoderma.* Some individuals have expressed concern that these toxins are the cause of BRS (Shoemaker and House 2006). While it is known that these species produce toxins, there is limited, conflicting evidence for health effects due to inhalation. Mold infections are extremely rare and are usually limited to individuals with severely compromised immune systems. However, since hospitals are generally caring for patients with lower immunity, prevention of mold exposure is important.

Sources of Mold

Water or moisture intrusion can be the result of building design flaws, construction or material defects, mechanical breakdowns, loss of system integrity, process failures, the degree of use, and the level of housekeeping or maintenance. Failure to identify or respond to equipment malfunctions or lack of maintenance may result in chronic water or moisture intrusion problems, which can lead to material damage and provide conditions for the mold growth. Common sites for mold growth are typically associated with moisture and include damp wallboard or ceiling tiles, humidification system drip pans, ventilation duct linings, wet walls near leaky fountains or sinks, and other places where condensation is a problem. Since many hospitals have flat roofs, leaks can cause a serious problem with water intrusion and mold growth. Carpeting that is saturated from a sewage backup can present a major source of mold or other microbial growth. As a precaution, carpeting or other porous building materials affected by a sewage backup should be removed and properly disposed. Non-porous materials, such as vinyl floor tile, can be cleaned and disinfected.

Recognition of Mold

From a diagnostic perspective, it is usually neither necessary nor advisable to sample for mold in air. Visible mold growth should obviously be cleaned and removed. In all cases, removing the source of moisture supporting the mold growth is more important than sampling for airborne mold levels. The sight of mold suggests a problem with moisture that must be addressed. However, there are limited instances when sampling for mold is indicated. If verification of the quality of a remediation project is desired, both pre-remediation and post-remediation sampling may be appropriate. Additionally, in order to conduct sampling that is statistically significant, multiple samples should be collected of both the indoor and outdoor environment, which is both time consuming and often costly. Air sampling may also be appropriate as part of an infection control environmental monitoring program in institutions serving bone marrow, stem cell, or solid organ transplants, burns, and other patients at risk for opportunistic environmental fungal infections.

Unfortunately, one of the major reasons for air sampling is to confirm the presence of mold for litigation or insurance claims. It is important to remember that not all laboratories have expertise in mold analysis. It is best to use a lab that is certified through the American Industrial Hygiene Association Environmental Microbiology Laboratory Accreditation Program (AIHA EMLAP) or an equivalent program. If sampling is to be conducted, it is important to contact the laboratory that is to do the analysis first, to determine the sample and media types they are able to analyze. In all cases, sampling must be conducted by trained individuals with experience in sampling for biological agents.

Tools for Sampling Mold

As discussed above, there are a wide variety of tools that can be used for sampling. If there is interest in air sampling for viable (culturable) mold, the *multiple-holed impact sampler* is considered the gold standard. It is normally used with either one stage to capture all particle sizes or in two stages to separate particles into respirable and non-respirable sizes. Some other viable air sampling methods are the *portable impactor*, the *slit-to-agar impactor*, the *button sampler* (which is a small multiple-hole impactor that could be used as a personal sampler), and the *impinger* (in which air is bubbled through a collection liquid).

The *spore trap* is a non-viable (non-culturable) method that draws an air sample through a small slit and deposits airborne particles on an adhesive-treated slide. The slide is then viewed with a microscope. Sticky tape is used to collect surface samples for microbial analysis. Additionally, real-time polymerase chain reaction (PCR) DNA analysis of bulk dust or particulates accumulated on air sampling filters can be used to identify whether a specific species of mold is present, but not whether the mold is viable. *PCR mold air sampling*, while more costly, has the advantage of allowing for full-shift collection periods, whereas the multi-holed impact samplers or spore trap samplers take samples over a matter of seconds to minutes.

If moisture may be accumulating behind wallboard, using a *moisture meter* can be very helpful. These come in non-invasive versions and in models that have pins that are inserted into the wallboard. In some cases, a *borescope* (similar to an endoscope) may be useful. To use a borescope, you must drill a hole and then attempt to visualize mold growth behind walls or in hard-to-reach places.

Evaluating Mold Data

Evaluating mold sampling data is challenging. First, not all mold or spores can be cultured in the laboratory after sampling. Second, there are no standards of comparison for the results to determine the existence of unsafe exposures. Third, the results of viable versus non-viable sampling are not comparable. Fourth, different viable sampling methods may have variable results; even duplicate sampling with the same method often produces widely varying results. Finally, it is important to remember that problematic biological species may be relatively few in number and can easily be missed with sampling (ACGIH 1999), particularly when attempting to collect viable samples. Culture-based samples tend to underestimate total viable concentrations because of the difficulty in achieving growth on the selected media.

If air sampling is conducted, it is important to sample both outdoor and indoor environments to compare total counts and types of mold species. Before sampling, it is important to develop sampling objectives. Is the sampling meant to count the number and type of culturable microorganisms, or biological particles, or both? No single method of sampling will determine both culturable and countable particles. In general, indoor concentrations should be significantly lower than outdoor concentrations and contain the same types of species. However, weather conditions (rain, fog, snow cover, wind velocity, and on) and indoor activity (vacuuming, foot traffic, and so on) can cause extreme fluctuations in the type and concentrations of spores indoors and outdoors. High indoor counts or significantly different species usually suggest a local source of contamination that must be located and eliminated. It can also represent "normal" conditions and only reflect weather or indoor activity. Other risk factors, such as the location of the problem (a bone marrow transplant unit versus an office), must be considered. Given these limitations, air sampling is only one investigation tool. Identifying wet building materials and conducting thorough physical inspections is of primary importance.

Prevention and Control of Mold

The most obvious approach to controlling mold and fungi should be to prevent moisture accumulations inside the building. If wallboard or carpeting becomes saturated, fast and effective drying is important to preventing mold growth. Carpet can be an excellent host for bacteria, dust mites, pollen, and fungi due to poor maintenance. Carpet should be antibacterial, soil-resistant, and have a short nylon nap with neoprene backing. It is recommended to restrict carpet use to low-risk, non-patient areas (Noskin and Peterson 2001).

Hospital construction activities can generate airborne dust particles contaminated with mold or mycotoxins; therefore, such construction activities need to be isolated from the hospital environment by installing separation barriers and negative pressure ventilation to capture and remove air contaminants. If possible, containments should be monitored to insure that they are effective in containing dust and other contaminants. Direct reading particle monitors are useful in detecting potential concerns with containments. Any monitoring should be performed by a trained individual. See Chapter 13 for more information on building construction.

Household plants can become a source of fungi and mold contamination if not controlled. Certain high-risk areas should be off-limits for houseplants. When mold growth is present, cleaning the surface or removal of the material and growth is appropriate. HVAC systems require preventive maintenance, especially to prevent condensation inside ventilation ducts or on filter beds. Cleaning of ventilation ducts is controversial as a means of controlling mold. It should only be done by experienced HVAC contractors using EPA-registered and -approved duct-cleaning compounds. Phenolic germicides should never be used to "fog" the inside of ventilation ducts.

Protecting the HVAC from Airborne Chemical, Biological, or Radiological Attacks

A relatively new issue is the protection of a health care facility's HVAC from chemical, biological, or radiological (CBR) threats (NIOSH 2002). Hospitals may be considered as potential "soft targets" of a CBR attack because such an attack would cause significant disruption to a community, and an effective means of disseminating CBR agents would be through a facility's HVAC system. Therefore, one essential component of a healthcare facility's emergency preparedness program is a plan to protect the HVAC from airborne CBR attack. This plan should have two elements:

1. Modifications to the buildings to decrease the likelihood or effects of a CBR incident; and
2. A method of responding quickly and appropriately should a CBR incident occur.

The first step in protecting the HVAC is to conduct a walk-through of the building to become thoroughly acquainted with the design and operations of the HVAC fire protection, and life-safety systems. This requires cooperation between the health and safety manager and the building plant engineer. NIOSH recommends that these items be considered during a walk-through (NIOSH 2002):

- What is the mechanical condition of the equipment?
- What filtration systems are in place? What are their efficiencies?
- Is all equipment appropriately connected and controlled? Are equipment access doors and panels in place and appropriately sealed?
- Are all dampers (outdoor air, return air, bypass, fire and smoke) functioning? Check the effectiveness of the seal when the dampers are closed.
- How does the HVAC system respond to manual fire alarm, fire detection, or fire-suppression device activation?
- Are all supply and return ducts completely connected to their grilles and registers?
- Are the variable air volume (VAV) boxes functioning?
- How is the HVAC system controlled? How quickly does it respond?
- How is the building zoned? Where are the air handlers for each zone? Is the system designed for smoke control?
- How does air flow through the building? What are the pressure relationships between zones? Which building entryways are positively or negatively pressurized? Is the building connected to other buildings by tunnels or passageways?
- Are utility chases and penetrations, elevator shafts, and fire stairs significant airflow pathways?
- Is there obvious air infiltration? Is it localized?
- Does the system provide adequate ventilation given the building's current occupancy and functions?
- Where are the outdoor air louvers? Are they easily observable? Are they or other mechanical equipment accessible to the public?
- Do adjacent structures or landscaping allow access to the building roof?

The answers to the above questions will determine the types of modifications that must be made to the building HVAC to limit attacks and specific elements that must be a part of the written response plan. Figure 8.2 demonstrates a vulnerable fresh air intake that has been improved by building an enclosure around it, and the best option (locating the louver three stories above the ground). Figure 8.3 shows some examples of modifications to vulnerable intake louvers.

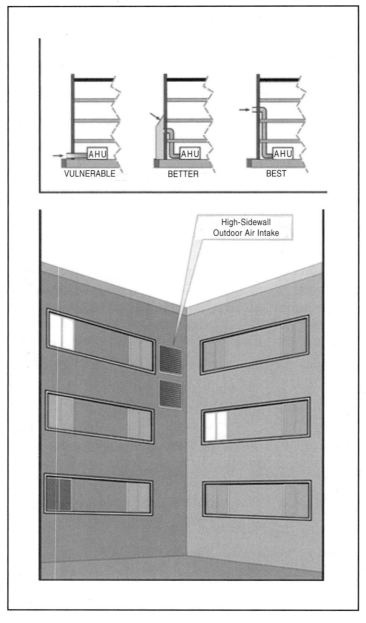

Figure 8.2 Protecting outdoor air intakes. (NIOSH 2002)

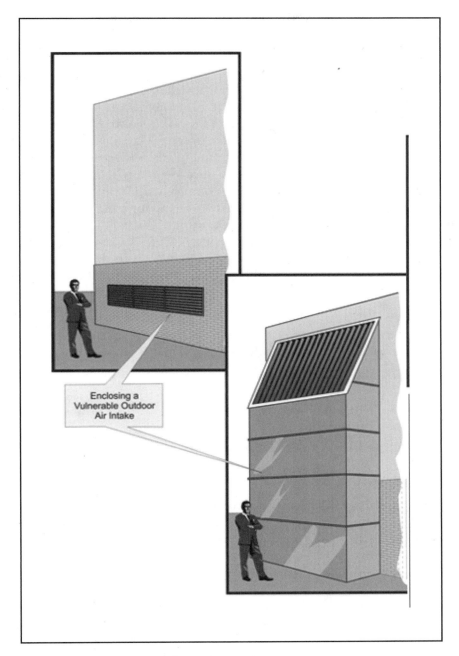

Figure 8.3 Examples of intake enclosures. (NIOSH 2002)

SUMMARY AND CONCLUSIONS

IAQ continues to receive considerable attention in the press and from the public. Some of the problems in IAQ are the result of building construction changes in the 1970s, poor building maintenance, and the fact that we spend so much time indoors. When assessing an IAQ problem, there are four factors to consider: the source of contaminants, the HVAC system, potential pathways of exposure, and the building occupants. The most common IAQ problem is *building-related symptoms* (BRS) also called *sick-building syndrome.* The second type of problem, *building-related illness* (BRI) means that the health complaint can be directly attributed to a problem with the building. Occupational asthma is an example of BRI that has been described as "out of control." There are over 350 biological, chemical, and physical agents that have been associated with occupational asthma. Exposure to mold and fungi can present adverse health effects under certain circumstances. While exposure to mold is unlikely to cause an infection, except in the case of an immuno-compromised individual, it may cause an allergic sensitivity in some individuals. Air sampling for mold is generally not advisable because the results are difficult to interpret. The best approach is to prevent moisture accumulations inside of buildings. If there is a large spill or other problem, a quick response is the key to avoiding mold growth. A recent concern is the need to protect a healthcare facility's HVAC from a terrorist attack. A thorough assessment can identify and allow the correction of any vulnerability to the system.

Review

1. Explain why IAQ problems have been so often cited in the press.
2. What are the four key elements to consider when investigating an IAQ problem?
3. Compare general or dilution ventilation to LEV for removal of air contaminants.
4. Why are RH and CO_2 measurements made when investigating IAQ complaints?
5. What is MCS, and why is it controversial?
6. What are some of the issues involved in sampling for indoor mold?
7. Describe the two main elements that must be addressed in a plan dealing with a terrorist attack of the building's HVAC system.

Reference List

American College of Occupational and Environmental Medicine (ACOEM). 2002. "Adverse Human Health Effects Associated with Molds in the Indoor Environment." (ACOEM Evidence-Based Statement 1–10). Elk Grove Village, IL: American College of Occupational and Environmental Medicine.

American Conference of Governmental Industrial Hygienists (ACGIH). 1999. *Bioaerosols: Assessment and Control.* Cincinnati, OH: American Conference of Governmental Industrial Hygienists.

American Industrial Hygiene Association (AIHA). 2003. *The Occupational Environment: Its Evaluation, Control, and Management.* 2d ed. Fairfax, VA: American Industrial Hygiene Association.

American Institute of Architects (AIA). 2006. *Guidelines for Design and Construction of Hospital and Health Care Facilities.* Washington, D.C.: American Institute of Architects.

American Lung Association (ALA), Environmental Protection Agency (EPA), Consumer Product Safety Commission (CPSC), and the American Medical Association (AMA). 1994. "Indoor Air Pollution: An Introduction for Health Professionals." Rep #1994-523-217/81322. Washington, D.C.: Government Printing Office.

American National Standards Institute (ANSI) and American Society of Heating, Refrigerating, and Air-Conditioning Engineers (ASHRAE). 2007. *Standard 62.1-2007, Ventilation for Acceptable Indoor Air Quality.* Atlanta, GA: American Society of Heating, Refrigerating, and Air-Conditioning Engineers.

Bartha, L., W. Baumzwiger, and D. S. Buscher. 1999. "Multiple Chemical Sensitivity: A 1999 Consensus." *Arch.Environ.Health.* 54:147–149.

Byrns, G. E., K. H. Palatianos, L. A. Shands, K. P. Fennelly, C. S. McCammon, and A. Y. Boudreau. 2000. "Chemical Hazards in Radiology." *Applied Occupational and Environmental Hygiene* 15:203–208.

Caress, S. M. and A. C. Steinmann. 2004. "A National Population Study of the Prevalence of Multiple Chemical Sensitivity." *Arch.Environ.Health.* 59:300–305.

Centers for Disease Control and Prevention (CDC). 1994. "Surveillance for Occupational Asthma—Michigan and New Jersey, 1988–1992." *MMWR* 43:9–17.

Environmental Protection Agency (EPA). 1995. "The Inside Story: A Guide to Indoor Air Quality." EPA #402-K-93-007. Washington, D.C.: Environmental Protection Agency.

Environmental Protection Agency (EPA) and National Institute for Occupational Safety and Health (NIOSH). 1991. "Building Air Quality: A Guide for Building Owners." EPA Publication No. 400/1-91-003/NIOSH Publication No. 91–114. Washington, D.C.: Environmental Protection Agency.

Health Care Without Harm (HCWH). 2006. *Risks to Asthma Posed by Indoor Health Care Environments: A Guide to Identifying and Reducing Problematic Exposures.* Lowell, MA: Lowell Center for Sustainable Production, School of Health and Environment, University of Massachusetts.

National Institute for Occupational Health and Safety (NIOSH). 2002. "Guidance for Protecting Building Environments from Airborne Chemical, Biological, or Radiological Attacks." Publication No. 2002-139. Cincinnati, OH: NIOSH-Publications Dissemination.

Noskin, G. A. and L. R. Peterson. 2001. "Engineering Infection Control Through Facility Design." *Emerg.Infec.Dis.* 7:354–357.

Occupational Safety and Health Administration (OSHA). "Indoor Air Quality Investigation." From *OSHA Technical Manual,* Section III, Chapter 2. Washington, D.C.: Occupational Safety and Health Administration.

Shoemaker, R. C. and D. E. House. 2006. "Sick Building Syndrome (SBS) and Exposure to Water-Damaged Buildings: Time Series Study, Clinical Trials and Mechanisms." *Neurotoxicol.Teratol.* 28:573–588.

Wheeler, S., L. Rosenstock, and S. Barnhard. 1998. "A Case Series of 71 Patients Referred to a Hospital-based Occupational and Environmental Medicine Clinic for Occupational Asthma." *West.J.Med.* 168:98–104.

CLASSROOM ACTIVITY

Indoor Air Quality Case Study

(NOTE: This case study is loosely based on an actual case study of an office building conducted by NIOSH.)

Scenario: You have just been hired as the environmental health and safety (EH&S) manager for Charity Hospital, an 800-bed, teaching hospital in Chicago, IL. During the interview, you were informed of a continuing IAQ problem in the administration office building. Among the occupants of this building are the hospital administrator, the human resources department, the risk manager, and doctors' offices. Your healthcare organization moved to this location in 2002, and the offices are located on two stories of a three-story building that had been renovated just prior to occupancy. The bottom story contains an outpatient pharmacy and a deli. There are 36 employees, 12 males and 24 females. The heating, ventilating, and air conditioning (HVAC) system is maintained by hospital facilities management and is serviced by a contractor. Air handling units are located on the roof of the building. Smoking is currently not permitted in the building.

Employee complaints started approximately six months ago, following roof leaks that resulted in damp carpeting on the third floor. The carpet was allowed to remain damp for approximately two weeks before being cleaned and treated. Ceiling tiles still show signs of moisture damage and some have a greenish-gray appearance. Approximately four months ago, your predecessor conducted a survey of the building. According to his report, there were carbon dioxide (CO_2) levels above 1000 ppm throughout the building and a strong odor of onions, which appeared to emanate from the deli on the first floor. He also discovered that since the onset of cooler weather, all fresh air inlets had been shut to save energy. It was the understanding of building facilities management that there would be at least 10% outside air provided to the building due to infiltration around the old leaky windows and doors. The former EH&S manager recommended that the fresh air inlets be opened to provide a minimum of 10% fresh air at all times. Facilities management agreed to have the outlets set at a minimum of 10% fresh air, and this resulted in a decrease in CO_2 levels. After these changes were made, the EH&S manager stated that it was his opinion that there were no significant problems with the building and that those who were complaining were, in his words, "a bunch of malcontents."

During your first visit to the office building, you found that many of the workers complained that they were feeling sleepy and that the air was "stuffy." The stuffiness was primarily a problem among the eighteen employees on the third floor.

Four employees (and reportedly one former employee) filed workers' compensation claims due to their experience of severe asthma-like conditions when they were in the building. An occupational medicine physician at the University of Illinois at Chicago evaluated three of the employees shortly after the leak. In the physician's report, she stated that, "there are problems with indoor air pollution in the facility." She recommended that air samples be taken and that the three employees be transferred to another office. At the time of your survey, the symptoms of the three employees had improved after their change in work locations to another building.

Exercises:

1. How do you proceed? (What should be your first step?)

2. 26 of 36 workers reported experiencing one or more of the following symptoms:

- 19 with nasal congestion or irritation
- 18 with headaches
- 18 with eye irritation
- 12 with severe fatigue
- 10 with impaired ability to concentrate
- 7 with shortness of breath
- 6 with lightheadedness
- 3 with throat irritation
- 2 with nausea

The symptoms were the most severe and frequent for occupants of third floor, west wing. However, there were individuals with complaints throughout the building.

What should be your next step?

3. There was evidence of damage around the window frames on the north side of the west wing of the second floor (possibly due to moisture), and evidence of water leaks through the ceiling tiles on the third floor on both wings. You noticed that some of the carpeting is still damp and there is also evidence of continued leakage in the roof slab above the false ceiling. The area of the leak above the false ceiling shows some evidence of mold growth.

Air Handling System. The HVAC system for the second and third floors of the building consists of four constant air volume air handlers, supply and return ductwork, and thermostatic controls (one thermostat per unit). Air handlers are made up of a fan and condenser-coil unit located on the roof. There are two air handlers serving each floor, one for the eastern half and one for the western half of the building. Each unit is designed to have outside air and returned air filtered using 30% dust spot filters. According to the design specifications, the units in the eastern portion of the building are designed to provide 250 cfm of outside air, and units in the western portion of the building provide 200 cfm of outside air.

Observations Regarding the HVAC. The outside air intake for the third floor west unit is eighteen inches horizontally from the exhaust duct outlet of the deli. An inspection of the inside of the HVAC air handler for the third floor west unit revealed that the condensation drip pan was plugged and overflowing.

Would you recommend taking air samples at this time and if so, what kind?

4. CO_2 monitoring rose from a mean of 422.5 at the time of employees' arrival to a mean of 830 ppm at 4 p.m. The highest readings were 900 ppm at 4 p.m. on the west wing of the third floor. See Table 1.

The CO_2 levels were below the 1000 ppm limit suggested by some authorities as a measure of poor air circulation. Are these levels acceptable?

5. **Relative Humidity and Temperature Results.** You measured temperature and relative humidity (RH) levels in several locations throughout the building. Temperatures ranged from 68°F to 76°F, with a mean of 72°F. RH measurements ranged from 50% to 88%, with a mean RH of 69%. See Table 2.

Are these temperatures and RH levels acceptable? If they are not, do you think this will contribute to overall satisfaction with building air quality?

Do you recommend that other types of sampling be conducted at this time? If yes, what types of samples or tests do you recommend?

6. **Microbial Sampling Results.** Wipe samples for viable fungi were conducted on some of the water-damaged ceiling tiles. Levels of fungi in wipe samples were low or undetectable. However, a bulk sample of damaged ceiling tile provided over 1,000,000 CFUs/gram. Both mold and yeast cells were isolated. This does provide evidence of sufficient moisture to promote microbial growth.

Air sample results collected during three consecutive days showed no evidence of significant indoor reservoirs of fungi. Outdoor samples were conducted at three different times, resulting in a mean fungal count of 430 CFU/m^3. *Cladosporium* is the most common species found outdoors, and this was also the species found in the indoor samples, along with smaller numbers of *Penicillium*. The outdoors samples also contained significant numbers of yeasts. In general, these results were typical for outdoor samples.

Indoor fungal counts were low compared to outdoor samples. (The mean inside level was less than one half of the outside level.) The highest fungal results were found in the aggressive samples taken in the third floor, west office with the water-stained carpet; however, the species were qualitatively similar to the outdoor samples. The significance of these results is difficult to determine, since in terms of absolute numbers they are still low.

Provide an overview of this case study. In your answer:

- Highlight the magnitude of the problem, e.g., the significance of physical, chemical, biological, or medical results.
- If you believe there is a problem, describe contributing factors.
- Make recommendations for improvement.

TABLE 1 Carbon Dioxide Concentrations

Location	Carbon Dioxide Concentration in ppm					Number of Occupants Present				
Sample Time	8 am	10 am	12 noon	2 pm	4 pm	8 am	10 am	12 noon	2 pm	4 pm
2 E	400	460	440	600	680	7	6	4	6	6
2 W	430	470	480	590	670	5	5	4	5	5
3 E	420	520	510	670	730	8	8	6	8	8
3 W	440	600	580	770	900	6	6	4	6	6
Outside	360	300	320	300	340	—	—	—	—	—

TABLE 2 Temperature and Relative Humidity (RH)

Location	Temperature in °F					Relative Humidity (RH)				
Sample time	8 am	10 am	12 noon	2 pm	4 pm	8 am	10 am	12 noon	2 pm	4 pm
2 E	70	72	72	73	75	50	56	58	64	64
2 W	69	70	71	74	76	62	76	78	78	79
3 E	68	70	70	73	74	52	60	65	68	70
3 W	68	71	71	72	74	66	78	84	85	88
Outside	80	82	84	87	88	64	61	56	54	52

CHAPTER **9**

Waste Management

Lee Shands and George Byrns

Learning Objectives

1. Distinguish the differences among the types of waste categories.

2. Discuss special concerns related to wastes generated in a healthcare facility.

3. Describe the various agencies that regulate waste generated in an institutional facility.

4. Discuss merits of various methods of medical waste disposal.

5. Discuss the importance of pollution prevention and sustainability as they relate to waste management.

6. Describe minimum elements of an effective waste management program.

WASTE CATEGORIES

Waste management deals with a variety of types of wastes. Wastes streams are generally broken into four broad categories: general refuse, hazardous waste, radioactive waste and special waste. *General refuse* or *municipal solid waste* consists of the solid materials that are discarded by a community. Any material that does not fall in one of the other categories is considered general refuse. Hazardous waste is often a confusing and misused term. *Hazardous waste* is defined by the degree of ignitibility, corrosivity, reactivity, or toxicity of the material by the Resource Conservation and Recovery Act (RCRA 1976). Items that would be included in this definition include acids, toxic chemicals, explosives and other potentially harmful wastes. Radioactive wastes, although hazardous, are generally categorized and discussed separately from other hazardous wastes because the types of hazards, as well as the handling and treatment of radioactive wastes, are distinctly different from other hazardous wastes. *Special wastes* are waste streams that require special handling and may pose some risks, but are not considered hazardous waste. Asbestos-containing materials are generally considered special wastes. Medical waste is usually classified as a special waste stream in regulations. *Medical wastes* are those potentially infectious materials generated in the course of patient care. The strict definition of medical waste varies among regulatory agencies and advisory bodies and will be discussed in more detail later in this chapter. *Mixed waste* streams are a combination of medical, chemical, radioactive, or general refuse. Mixed waste streams are difficult to handle and treat because of the differing regulations, hazards, and treatment requirements for each type of waste. The best solution for mixed waste streams is to keep the various types of wastes separate so that handling and treatment is simplified. Additionally, keeping the various waste streams separate will also reduce costs associated with treatment and disposal.

General Refuse

Waste management in a healthcare facility needs to be a multifaceted program. Healthcare facilities generate a number of differing waste streams. By far, the largest portion of waste generated in an institutional facility is general refuse. It has been estimated that 15 pounds per patient per day of general refuse is produced in an inpatient treatment facility (Rutala et al. 1989). The general refuse generated in a healthcare facility poses no specific hazards other than those in any general waste stream. The general refuse in a healthcare facility may vary in composition compared to other waste streams due to the quantity of plastics and disposables used in modern healthcare facilities. The largest issue with general refuse in a healthcare facility is that it finds its way into other waste streams; thereby dramatically increasing the volume and cost of disposal of medical, hazardous or radiological wastes. The same considerations given to proper collection and disposal of any municipal waste need to be given to general refuse generated in an institutional facility. Waste needs to be collected, stored and disposed of in a manner that does not attract or allow the breeding of vermin or generation of odors.

Hazardous Waste

Hazardous waste can be generated in various healthcare locations, including:

- Laboratories
- Dental clinics
- Radiology and nuclear medicine areas
- Pharmacies
- Maintenance and biomedical engineering
- Physical therapy

- Underground storage tanks
- Laundry
- Morgue
- Operating rooms
- Nursing units (especially in the course of chemotherapy)
- Hazardous waste storage areas
- Construction areas

Hazardous waste must be properly managed from the cradle-to-the-grave because workers can be exposed from the point of entry into the facility, during use, and at the point of disposal. Hazardous waste management is challenging because chemicals have a wide variety of risks, based on toxicity and potential exposure routes. See Chapter 2, "Health Care Hazards" for examples of chemicals that may become hazardous wastes. Some chemicals may be hazardous to both humans and the environment. In addition, there may be overlapping federal, state, and local regulations on these chemicals. Efforts should be made to substitute those chemicals with human or environmental risks with safer products. See the section entitled, "Pollution Prevention and Sustainability," below for more information on selection of alternatives.

Radioactive Waste

Radioactive wastes are generated in the process of diagnosis and treatment of various cancers. See Chapter 2 for hazards associated with ionizing radiation. One special concern is the treatment of the excreta of patients who have received radioactive therapy, since this would be considered a mixed waste. The primary federal agency with jurisdiction over radiological waste is the Nuclear Regulatory Commission (NRC). However, the Environmental Protection Agency (EPA) has jurisdiction over the release of radioactive substances to the outside air or into the sewage system. One frequently used method of dealing with radioactive substances with short half-lives is to store them in a secure area and hold them for at least ten half-lives. At this point, the radioactivity should be near background levels, and the waste may be handled as general refuse. Substances with longer half-lives require special handling and shipment to long-term storage sites. Shipment of these wastes must comply with all aspects of EPA's RCRA requirements.

Medical Waste

Medical waste management can be difficult for a number of reasons. First, there is no consensus on the definition of medical waste, and definitions of medical waste mandated under regulations vary between agencies. Second, the fear concerning the perceived potential to transmit human immunodeficiency virus (HIV) via medical waste has resulted in states and federal agencies adopting stringent regulations to placate public concerns. Third, the disposal method chosen for medical waste can have a significant impact on the environment, whether the disposal method is via land, air, water, or some combination of methods.

Some of the more frequently used definitions for medical waste include:

The EPA's definition of medical waste is unnecessarily broad while still being vague in some areas. According to the EPA, medical waste is generally defined under state regulations (EPA 2006). The Medical Waste Tracking Act of 1988 defines medical wastes as "any solid waste that is generated in the diagnosis, treatment, or immunization of human beings or animals, in research pertaining thereto, or in the production or testing of biologicals" (EPA 2006). According to the EPA, "this definition includes, but not limited to:

- blood-soaked bandages
- culture dishes and other glassware
- discarded surgical gloves
- discarded surgical instruments
- discarded needles used to give shots or draw blood (e.g., medical sharps)
- cultures, stocks, swabs used to inoculate cultures
- removed body organs (e.g., tonsils, appendices, limbs).
- discarded lancets" (EPA 2006)

The Occupational Safety and Health Administration (OSHA) defined regulated medical waste in the *Bloodborne Pathogens Standard* (OSHA 2006) as:

> . . . liquid or semi-liquid blood or other potentially infectious materials; contaminated items that would release blood or other potentially infectious materials in a liquid or semi-liquid state if compressed; items that are caked with dried blood or other potentially infectious materials and are capable of releasing these materials during handling; contaminated sharps; and pathological and microbiological wastes containing blood or other potentially infectious materials.
>
> Other Potentially Infectious Materials means (1) The following human body fluids: semen, vaginal secretions, cerebrospinal fluid, synovial fluid, pleural fluid, pericardial fluid, peritoneal fluid, amniotic fluid, saliva in dental procedures, any body fluid that is visibly contaminated with blood, and all body fluids in situations where it is difficult or impossible to differentiate between body fluids; (2) Any unfixed tissue or organ (other than intact skin) from a human (living or dead); and (3) HIV-containing cell or tissue cultures, organ cultures, and HIV- or HBV-containing culture medium or other solutions; and blood, organs, or other tissues from experimental animals infected with HIV or HBV.

The OSHA definition is significant because it is used by the regulatory agency to determine compliance with the waste handling portion of the *Bloodborne Pathogen Standard* (OSHA 2006). Rather than relying on listing all contaminated and potentially infectious wastes, it defines the characteristics of a waste that cause it to be potentially infectious. This allows the user to determine which items require special handling and should enter the medical waste stream. There was a potential concern with the definition because the user makes a judgment regarding the contamination of the item, and potentially infectious items might not be placed in the medical waste stream. In practice, the reverse is generally the problem; usually far greater quantities of non-infectious materials are put into the medical waste stream. Staff training is critical in managing the medical waste stream.

The Agency for Toxic Substances and Disease Registry (ATSDR) has separated medical waste into seven categories (ATSDR 1990). These are listed below, along with some examples of items that would be included in the categories:

- **Cultures and stocks:** Lab specimens
- **Pathological wastes:** Materials from autopsy, pathology laboratories
- **Blood and blood products:** Blood and materials saturated with blood
- **Sharps:** Discarded syringes, needles, and attached tubing, pasture pipettes
- **Animal waste:** Animal research with infectious agents
- **Selected isolation waste:** Materials used on patients with highly communicable diseases (CDC Class 4, for example, Lassa Fever)
- **Unused discarded sharps:** Because it is impossible to differentiate between "clean" sharps and infected ones

Other regulatory agencies and advisory organizations have varying definitions of medical waste. Medical waste is also defined by state regulatory agencies. These definitions can vary widely among the states, and between state and federal regulations. Healthcare facilities need to be aware of the definition of medical waste adopted by the state where the facility is located. State agencies often classify medical waste as a special waste or as other waste to differentiate among medical, hazardous and municipal wastes.

Medical Waste Regulations

Medical waste is regulated by a myriad of federal and state agencies. Each agency regulates the waste stream during specific portion of time during the cradle-to-grave process, or regulates items used in the handling or decontamination of medical waste. These overlapping regulatory environments, coupled with the varying definitions of medical waste, contribute to the daunting task of properly handling medical waste in compliance with all regulations while protecting employees and patients from the potential hazards. Below is a discussion of which federal agency is in charge of what type of medical waste:

- **OSHA:** OSHA regulates medical waste in the workplace. This includes the defining what constitutes medical waste, proper handling, labeling, and storage of medical waste, and employee training. Additionally, OSHA defines the labeling that is required on all medical waste containers, including sharps containers.

- **NRC:** The NRC regulates some types of radioactive medical waste.
- **FDA:** The Food and Drug Administration (FDA) regulates medical devices. Sharps containers, which are designed to provide a safe method of disposing used needles and other sharps, are considered a medical device and subject to FDA regulations.
- **DOT:** The Department of Transportation, Office of Hazardous Materials Safety regulates the transportation of medical waste across state lines (49 CFR 172 and 173).
- **U.S. Postal Service:** The U.S. Postal Service regulates medical waste that is shipped in the postal system.

Finally, and perhaps most importantly, the state governmental agencies, such as the health department and environmental protection department, regulate medical waste. State regulations address the categories of medical waste, required treatment or decontamination, consolidation, packaging and on-site storage requirements, how the waste is to be transported and disposed. State agencies will also regulate medical waste treatment centers operating in the state and define the types of onsite treatment permitted in healthcare facilities (Sehulster 2005).

Medical Waste Hazards

The main concern during the handling and disposal of medical waste is the potential for the transmission of blood-borne diseases, although airborne disease transmission may also occur (Sehulster 2005). The diseases of primary concern are the HIV, hepatitis B virus (HBV), and hepatitis C virus (HCV). There are other diseases that also have the potential for blood-borne transmission, such as Creutzfeldt–Jakob.

Occupational Exposure. The main pathway for blood-borne disease transmission is via direct exposure. The risk for disease transmission varies with the type and severity of the exposure. Studies of disease transmission to healthcare workers show the relative risk of contracting a disease after exposure. These rates are for all healthcare workers, and are not specific for waste handling. Prospective studies of healthcare providers showed the average risk for HIV transmission after a percutaneous exposure to HIV-infected blood to be about 0.3%. The transmission rate drops to approximately 0.09% for a mucous membrane exposure. HIV transmission after non-intact skin exposure has occurred with rates estimated to be lower than mucous membrane exposure (CDC 2005). Studies of healthcare workers exposed to HBV-contaminated blood via needle injuries have shown disease transmission rates as high as 37-62%, depending on the antigen status of the source patient (CDC 2001). Additionally, the potential for transmission of HBV via non-intact skin contact with contaminated environmental surfaces has been demonstrated. HBV has been shown to survive at least one week in dried blood at room temperature on environmental surfaces (CDC 2005). Conversely, HCV is as not easily transmitted through occupational exposures to blood as HBV. The incidence of seroconversion after percutaneous exposure to HCV is approximately 1.8% and transmission to healthcare workers has rarely occurred from mucous membrane exposure.

Another potential pathway for exposure is inhalation. Infective aerosols may be produced during the compacting or grinding of medical waste. One reported cluster of three tuberculosis cases occurred in a medical waste treatment facility that shredded the medical waste prior to decontamination (Sehulster 2005; Johnson et al. 2000).

The potential for disease transmission occurs during the handling of all wastes, including medical waste. Although few cases of disease transmission have been documented from the handling of medical waste, care and proper procedures must be followed to insure disease transmission does not occur.

Public Health Concerns. A major part of the public fear of medical waste is the assumption that it is highly contaminated with dangerous microbes such as HIV and HBV. The ATSDR report, "Public Health Implications of Medical Waste—Report to Congress" (ATSDR 1990) states: "Medical waste does not contain any greater quantity or different types of microbiological agents that does residential waste." The other mistake made regarding the potential for disease transmission from medical waste is that it is forgotten that certain steps are necessary for the *chain of transmission* to take place. The infectious agent must be present in sufficient quantity to produce infection, a susceptible host must be available, and an appropriate portal of entry for that agent must be provided into the susceptible host. Unless the entire chain is complete, no potential exists for disease transmission. In reality, medical waste poses a very low health risk to the general public. Human pathogens have poor survivability outside of the human host. Medical waste is contained in plastic sacks and then buried in trenches in sanitary landfills. Finally, for the general public, a portal of entry for the pathogen to enter the human body is unlikely.

Environmental Impact of Medical Waste. There are multiple ways medical waste can have an adverse impact on the environment. Indiscriminate dumping can result in contamination of land or water. However, it has been estimated that medical waste constitutes only 0.3% of the total refuse generated in a community, in which case, general refuse may be more of a problem (ATSDR 1990). Also, it has been shown that the quantity and types of microorganisms in medical waste do not differ from those found in residential wastes. Therefore, if medical waste is properly handled, it should pose no more significant environmental impact than that posed by any solid waste stream.

Incineration of medical waste leads to the release of toxic chemicals into the air (Franchini et al. 2004). Incinerator plumes may contain hydrogen chloride gas, carbon monoxide, dioxins, furans and other toxins. Older incineration units were once a significant source of air pollution, but the implementation of state and federal regulations resulted in severe reduction of the number of medical incinerators still in use in this country. In the past, it was estimated that over 25% of medical waste incinerators released air pollution above acceptable standards. Many states are prohibiting incinerators because of the problems associated with them resulting from poor operation. Reasons why incinerators emitted pollution included:

- The initial specifications for the design of the unit were faulty;
- Poor maintenance of units after they were put into service;
- Training of operators was absent or inadequate;
- There was improper sorting of the incoming waste streams; and
- The unit was overloaded.

Sewage disposal of medical wastes can affect the quality of water downstream, and significant quantities of organic wastes could overwhelm the sewage treatment facility. Therefore, industries, such as meat packing, must pre-treat their sewage discharge. Another potential problem is the disposal of toxic waste into the sewage system, which could result in upsetting or damaging the biological flora in the sewage treatment plant. This could present a concern especially with the use of ortho-phthaldehyde, a high-level disinfectant. Currently, the state of California requires that this germicide be neutralized before it is discharged to the sewer due to its aquatic toxicity. See the section on "Pollution Prevention and Sustainability" later in this chapter for more information on managing liquid wastes.

Potentially infectious wastes are often treated to render them non-infectious prior to disposal. Since medical wastes streams have been shown to contain no significant difference in the type and number of microorganisms than general municipal waste, this treatment is for public perception, rather than a real need to reduce the hazards of the waste. Proper steam sterilization of medical wastes results in refuse that is devoid of pathogenic microorganisms while still posing the same hazards and disposal problems as general refuse. However, complete sterilization of the incoming infectious waste streams may be difficult. Complete sterilization of items requires prior knowledge of the composition and make-up of items to be sterilized. Items with higher liquid content, more densely packed items or other unique factors can require longer processing times to result in complete sterilization. Quite often, this type of knowledge of the incoming infectious waste stream is lacking. Sterilization of wastes also poses a perception problem. Sterilized waste is often hard to visually differentiate from untreated waste. This is a problem when the waste reaches the final disposal site. The receiving facility, as well as public perception, may be that the healthcare facility is disposing of infectious waste inappropriately when sending sterilized waste. Because of the perception problem, sterilized infectious waste is often ground to render it unrecognizable prior to disposal. Currently, relatively few hospitals use this method of treating medical waste (Sehulster 2005). This became an issue when hospitals were inadvertently sent a dangerous strain of influenza virus as a part of a laboratory proficiency testing program. The Centers for Disease Control and Prevention (CDC) recommended that the dangerous strains be destroyed onsite by using steam sterilization or by incineration. Unfortunately, few had autoclaves in their laboratories or incinerators. As a result, some facilities used instrument-reprocessing steam sterilizers in the central services department to decontaminate the sample. This was a potential violation of infection control policy because contaminated items were brought into clean areas.

Other treatment methods for infectious waste include chemical decontamination of the waste stream. However, this may result in water or land contamination by the chemical used for decontamination. Chemical decontamination may also expose workers to the disinfecting agent. Other treatment methods, such as radioactive or microwave decontamination, also present potential hazards.

Medical Waste Management Recommendations

The following are recommendations are to improve medical waste management, (Byrns and Burke 1992):

1. The ATSDR definition of medical waste should be used. This definition is the clearest while still being inclusive in its scope.

2. Training in waste handling should be improved. Although medical waste is no more infectious than general refuse, proper handling procedures must still be followed. All staff members must be trained in proper disposal methods to insure potentially infectious wastes are segregated and placed in the appropriate containers. Paramount in this is the proper disposal of sharps. Sharps that are not properly disposed in puncture-proof containers pose a risk to housekeeping staff during the collection and disposal of the waste. Additionally, the staff needs to be trained to place only potentially contaminated items in the medical waste stream. Disposing of other items in the medical waste stream can dramatically increase the costs associated with medical waste disposal.

3. The public, and quite often the healthcare workers, need to be informed of the *true* risks associated with medical waste. Continued education of the public concerning the low risks associated with medical waste could lead to the implementation of more rational and realistic medical waste regulations.

4. Use of disposable items in the healthcare setting should be reduced whenever feasible. As the use of disposables increases, so does the quantity of medical waste.

5. All appropriate options for the treatment and disposal medical waste should be investigated and pursued. Most healthcare facilities no longer operate medical incinerators. However, those that still utilize incinerators, such as mortuaries, may generate hazardous waste in the form of incinerator ash.

Medical Waste Contract Monitoring

When medical waste is disposed of via a contract with an outside provider, the contract and all disposal steps need to be monitored. Monitoring needs to begin before the contract is awarded, to assure that the contractor is capable of disposing of the medical waste in accordance with all regulatory requirements.

The first step in contractor evaluation would be to review documents that are required to be submitted with the bid. Such documents should include: all permits and licenses required by the state or states through which the waste is to be transported, as well as the state where the waste will finally be disposed; and detailed information as to what is to be included in the contract. Questions that should be addressed in the contract include:

- Is the contractor supplying disposable or re-usable containers for collection of the medical waste? If reusable containers are to be used, who is responsible for the washing and sanitizing of the containers? What method is to be used to sanitize the containers? Disposable containers that the red-bagged medical waste is placed in eliminate the need for washing and decontamination, but can increase the cost of the contract.

- What method or methods will be used for disposal of the waste? If the waste is to be decontaminated, what method is used and how is efficacy determined? Will the waste be ground prior to disposal?

- What is the site of final disposal?

- How frequently will the contractor collect the waste?

- Will the contractor submit copies of the company's blood-borne pathogen and hazard communication programs for review? Will copies of the contractor's spill handling procedures also be submitted? These should be made available to the healthcare facility in order to make an informed decision regarding selection of a contractor.

- Will the contractor provide training to the healthcare staff on medical waste segregation and handling? Providing the contractor is knowledgeable and competent, training from an outside source can have a bigger impact on staff behavior.

- Will the waste disposal be billed on a per-pound basis? If so, consider onsite weighing of the waste prior to removal. This allows the generating facility to oversee the weighing and track the accuracy of the billing.

- Is there an option for an on-site visit of the contractor's disposal operation prior to and after the contract is awarded?

- Will the contractor provide copies of the regulatory agencies' review of the contractor's operation?

POLLUTION PREVENTION AND SUSTAINABILITY

The need to prevent the release of pollution and operate in a sustainable manner is relatively recent concern in health care. The approaches to pollution prevention (P2) and sustainability in healthcare are similar to those in industry, including reduction (or substitution), reuse, and recycling. Healthcare facilities do not manufacture a product, and this limits some of the P2 options that are available to manufacturing operations (Allen 2005). Nevertheless, as in other industries, the *precautionary principle* should be applied when wastes are released to the environment, which means that a waste product should be assumed to be hazardous until proven otherwise (Kaiser et al. 2001). Some waste products and byproducts are known to be significant toxins, such as mercury and dioxins because they bioaccumulate in the environment (Kaiser et al. 2001). In the past, cleaning and disinfecting products were assumed to be safe for sewage disposal. This assumption was incorrect because these toxic pollutants are not fully removed or neutralized by traditional municipal wastewater treatment plants (Allen 2005). Once they are discharged into natural water systems, these toxins may affect all levels of aquatic and marine food webs, and some may have carcinogenic, mutagenic, teratogenic, estrogenic, and other toxic effects. Other wastes discharged into the environment may have more subtle effects, such as elevated levels of phthalates from the extensive use of plastics in health care (Allen 2005). The discharge of antibiotics into municipal waste systems is another, and potentially even more important, waste stream that has received little attention. Antibiotics have been found in the environment long after they have been used in patient treatment (Levy 2002). They have been found in sewage plants, surface waters, and in river sediments. The release of these antibiotics in hospital waste contributes to the problem of antibiotic resistance (Kummerer and Henninger 2003).

While healthcare operations should be motivated to prevent pollution and achieve sustainability, there are financial incentives as well. When lifecycle costs (such as distribution, use, and disposal) are considered, it is often more cost effective to use so-called "green" products (Kaiser et al. 2001). Some hospitals have implemented cost-effective P2 interventions, such as substituting aliphatic fixatives for xylene and replacing formaldehyde with glyoxal in histology laboratories (Quinn et al. 2006). Other examples include mercury reduction plans, replacing wet chemistry film processing with digital imaging, and switching to microfiber mopping. Microfiber mops clean hospital floors more effectively, while using less water and disinfecting solution. While the individual mop head costs twice as much as conventional mops, there is a significant cost savings because of the reduced labor time, as well as the reduced use of water and chemicals. The service life of microfiber mops is also approximately ten times longer than conventional mops. In another example of P2, a hospital in Minnesota was able to substantially reduce solid waste volume and recover some direct costs by purchasing reusable dietary supplies and linen products (Minnesota OEA 1992). Hospitals are able to substantially reduce the volume and cost of disposal of waste paper and plastic products (70% of the waste stream) through recycling efforts.

Implementing P2 initiatives also helps avoid fines associated with environmental discharges, and can be an effective public relations opportunity. The healthcare organization can market their P2 activities to the general community giving them a completive edge over other healthcare organizations that have not yet discovered the benefits of "going green." The American Industrial Hygiene Association (AIHA) has recently formed a Healthcare Working Group. One of the work group's project teams is focusing on P2 and sustainability in health care, and their mission is to increase the awareness of these approaches.

SUMMARY AND CONCLUSIONS

Healthcare facilities generate large quantities of general refuse. In addition, hazardous and special wastes may be released to the environment. An effective waste management program is challenging because of the wide range of waste types, potential risks, and confusing and overlapping regulations.

There are known and potential hazards associated with improper disposal of waste products. These include both human and environmental risks. However, there may be significant economic and other benefits of implementing P2 programs and "going green." The primary obstacle in implementing these environmentally friendly programs is the limited amount of information currently available to assist the institutional environmental health and safety professional in program development. The American Industrial Hygiene Association (AIHA) has recently formed a Healthcare Working Group to focus on P2 and sustainability in health care.

Review

1. What is a mixed waste, and why is it a problem?
2. What are some of the major concerns in reducing the volume of general refuse?
3. What is a special concern involving radiological waste disposal in hospitals?
4. Is medical waste the same as hazardous waste, and why were unused needles and other sharp objects included in the category medical waste?
5. What is a lifecycle cost, and why is it important?
6. Why is it unsafe to dump cleaning supplies and solvents into the sewage system?

Reference List

Agency for Toxic Substances and Disease Registry (ATSDR). 1990. *The Public Health Implications of Medical Waste: A Report to Congress* (Rep. No. PB91-100271). Atlanta, GA: Department of Health and Human Services.

Allen, M. R. 2005. "Effective Pollution Prevention in Healthcare Environments." *Journal of Cleaner Production* 14:610–615.

Byrns, G. E. and T. Burke. 1992. "Medical Waste Management Implications for Small Medical Facilities." *Journal of Environmental Health* 55:12–15.

Centers for Disease Control and Prevention (CDC). 2001. "Updated U.S. Public Health Service Guidelines for the Management of Occupational Exposures to HBV, HCV, and HIV and Recommendation for Postexposure Prophylaxis." *MMWR*, 50:1–52.

———. 2005. "Updated U.S. Public Health Service Guidelines for the Management of Occupational Exposures to HIV and Recommendations for Postexposure Prophylaxis—2005." *MMWR* 54:1–17.

Environmental Protection Agency (EPA). 2006. "Medical Waste" (retrieved August 12, 2008) (http://www.epa.gov/epaoswer/other/medical/basic/html).

Franchini, M., M. Rial, E. Buiatti, and F. Bianchi. 2004. "Health Effects of Exposure to Waste Incinerator Emissions: A Review of Epidemiological Studies." *Ann.Ist.Super.Sanita.* 40:101–115.

Johnson, K. R., C. R. Braden, K. L. Cairns, K. W. Field, A. C. Colombel, and Z. Yang. 2000. "Transmission of Mycobacterium Tuberculosis from Medical Waste." *JAMA* 284:1683–1688.

Kaiser, B., P. D. Eagan, and H. Shaner. 2001. "Solutions to Health Care Waste: Life-cycle Thinking and "Green" Purchasing." *Environ.Health Perspect.* 109:205–207.

Kummerer, K. and A. Henninger. 2003. "Promoting Resistance by the Emission of Antibiotics from Hospitals and Households into Effluent." *Clinical Microbiology and Infection* 9:1203–1214.

Levy, S. B. 2002. "The 2000 Garrod Lecture: Factors Impacting on the Problem of Antibiotic Resistance." *J.Antimicrob.Chemother.* 49:25–30.

Minnesota Office of Environmental Assistance (OEA). 1992. *Waste Source Reduction: Hospital Case Study.* St. Paul, MN: Minnesota Office of Environmental Assistance.

Occupational Health and Safety Administration (OSHA). 2006. 29 CFR 1910.1030, *Bloodborne pathogens.* (retrieved August 12, 2008) (http://www.osha.gov/pls/oshaweb/owadisp.show_document?p_table=STANDARDS&p_id=10051).

Quinn, M. M., Fuller, T. P., Bello, A., & Galligan, C. J. 2006. "Pollution Prevention—Occupational Safety and Health in Hospitals: Alternatives and Interventions." *J.Occup.Environ.Hyg.* 3:182–193.

Rutala, W. A., R. L. Odette, and G. P. Samsa. 1989. "Management of Infectious Waste by U.S. Hospitals." *JAMA* 262:1635–1640.

Sehulster, L. 2005. "Medical Waste Management in the Bioterrorism Era" (retrieved August 12, 2008) (http://emergency.cdc.gov/coca/summaries/medicalwastemanagement_082305.asp).

CLASSROOM ACTIVITY

Medical Waste Management Scenario

Scenario: The BroJoe Hospital is a 150–bed, acute care facility that currently uses an outdated incinerator to treat all medical waste. The hospital generates 5000 lbs of general refuse per day and 550 lbs of medical waste. All general refuse is hauled to the local landfill at a cost of $0.05 per lb. The cost of burning waste in the incinerator is currently unknown, but is estimated to be no more than $0.04 per lb. for fuel costs.

The Illinois Department of Health has repeatedly cited you for air pollution. You have been informed by the state that you have six months to stop the pollution or face heavy fines ($5000 per day). What do you recommend to the CEO? So far, there are four options on the table. For each option, what are potential benefits or costs associated with this choice? What are some other options that have not been considered so far?

Some of the options suggested so far are listed in the table below.

Options to Reduce Air Pollution at BroJoe Hospital

Option	Benefit	Cost
1. Pay the fines.		
2. Contract with Fred's Waste Company, which will haul to a microwave treatment facility for a cost of $0.15 per lb.		
3. Build a large steam sterilizer on site for a cost of $350,000.		
4. Enter into a contract with Mega Hospital and use their incinerator for a cost of $0.10 per lb.		
5. Other options (What other strategies could help solve this problem?)		

CHAPTER 10

Occupational and Environmental Health Surveys and Surveillance

George Byrns

Learning Objectives

1. Distinguish between the terms survey and surveillance.

2. Identify and explain the major types of surveys.

3. Describe the characteristics of a good surveyor.

4. Discuss the importance of doing a high quality survey, including the written report.

5. Implement an approach to identify the top priority concerns found in a survey.

Health and safety programs can expect increased workload from emerging disease threats, such as avian influenza; unforeseen risks of new technology, such as new types of chemotherapy; and regulatory pressures due to new Occupational Safety and Health Administration (OSHA) or Joint Commission on Accreditation of Healthcare Organization (Joint Commission or JCAHO) standards. At the same time, tighter budgets and competing programs may result in decreased resources. Therefore, it is critical that health and safety professionals target the highest priority problems areas, assure that accreditation is maintained, and avoid liability due to failure to address known hazards. Under the Federal Tort Claims Act, an employee who is found negligent may be sued as an individual. In this chapter, you will learn about ways of improving how to conduct hazard surveys and how to prioritize the relative importance of the findings.

An important task of environmental and occupational health and safety professionals is monitoring for the presence of hazards. In order to monitor for these hazards, two similar sounding approaches are used, surveys and surveillance. *Surveys* are ways of collecting data for limited, specific purposes, and *surveillance* is a long-term activity that involves the collection of data and much more.

SURVEILLANCE

Surveillance is defined as the "ongoing systematic collection, analysis, and interpretation of data on specific health problem and in addition, the timely dissemination of these data to those responsible for prevention and control" (Thacker and Stroup 1994). Therefore, surveillance goes beyond simple data collection and includes evaluation and the use of such data. Later in this chapter, we will discuss a methodology for analyzing data to determine the top priority programs.

In the past, the term surveillance was applied solely to health outcomes, such as communicable diseases. This concept can also be applied to monitoring occupational or environmental exposures or hazards (Thacker et al. 1996). In order to promote this expanded use of surveillance, the Centers for Disease Control and Prevention (CDC) released the *National Environmental Public Health Tracking Program: National Network Implementation Plan* (NNIP) (CDC 2006). This CDC initiative is an attempt to better integrate data on exposure to hazards and health outcomes, with a goal of providing this information to a large number of local, state, and federal stakeholders. The process is described in Figure 10.1 below.

This same approach of integrating hazard, exposure and outcome health data should also be applied at the institutional level. According to the National Institute for Occupational Safety and Health (NIOSH), surveillance of occupational exposures has improved but it is still insufficient (CDC 2007). In the past, exposure or hazard data was collected for compliance or other purposes, but these data were not shared with the occupational health physicians or nurses. Clearly, there is a need to integrate exposure data and health outcome data (Ritz et al. 2005). In the new CDC model, hazard, exposure, and health effect data are linked to better establish cause-and-effect relationships. In addition, this national data tracking system will share results with stakeholders, such as governmental officials, academicians, healthcare providers, and nongovernmental organizations. When health and safety professionals work as a team with clinical personnel, there will be greater benefits to those we are protecting.

SURVEYS

Surveys are the most common way that a health and safety professional can anticipate or recognize hazards in a healthcare environment. Surveys can be conducted to identify biological, chemical, physical, or even psychological

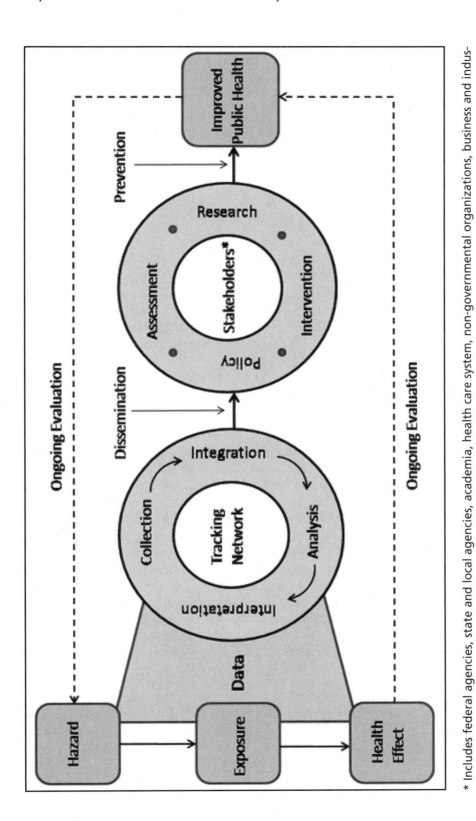

* Includes federal agencies, state and local agencies, academia, health care system, non-governmental organizations, business and industry, policymakers, media, public.

Figure 10.1 Environmental public health tracking. (Source: CDC 2006)

hazards. There are several types of survey approaches, and the choice of approach depends on a number of factors. The four major types of surveys are (Aday 2006a):

- Interviewer;
- Telephone;
- Self-administered; and
- Computer-assisted.

These will all be discussed below.

Interviewer Surveys

The interviewer survey is most commonly used in a healthcare setting for data collection. It consists of one or more individuals gathering information from respondents and making observations of conditions. It is the type of survey that is most time consuming, but it also allows the surveyor to ask the most complex questions because the interviewer is present to provide explanations (Fink 1993; Aday 2006a). Also, this type of survey tends to provide the most complete results.

Telephone Surveys

Telemarketers and telephone surveys are familiar to most people and are the fastest and cheapest means of gathering information (Aday 2006a). For example, the telephone survey is an efficient way to contact all individuals who may have been affected by a food poisoning outbreak. However, there are drawbacks to this type of survey. At present, it is not possible to use visual cues to help the respondent understand the question being asked, and the interviewer can not make visual observations of the physical environment. This situation may improve with the advent of camera phones and other technological changes, but these will not substitute for having the interviewer on the scene. Another limitation of telephone surveys is the growth of cellular phones. Individuals with cell phones may not be reachable using a telephone directory. In a formal investigation, this limitation could result in significantly biased results because of the potential for missing a large number of individuals.

Self-Administered Surveys

Self-administered surveys are useful for conducting screening surveys of employees or others. Some examples of this approach include low back pain prevalence surveys or an employee questionnaire on perceptions of workplace security from violence. These surveys should be used in gathering less complex information because of the reliance on the respondent to interpret the meaning of the questions (Fink 1993; Aday 2006a). Also, these types of surveys tend to have the lowest response rates because they tend to get lost. To be effective when using self-administered surveys, it is essential to send the target audience frequent, timely reminders to complete and return the form.

Computer-Assisted Surveys

A computer-assisted survey is relatively new and growing approach in data collection. This approach is used in conjunction with one of the other types of survey methods. It gathers the information, directing it into a notebook or palm-type computer for collection and tabulation (Aday 2006a). The computer-assisted method offers great promise, with built-in glossaries, help menus, and so on. For example, there may be a complete set of policies that the interviewer could review when confronted with an unusual situation. The most important advantage is that the computer may be able to do an analysis of the data and provide immediate feedback to the respondent. Ultimately, computer-assisted surveys will benefit all types of surveys. Unfortunately, the technology is still not widely available.

In this chapter, the focus will be on interviewer surveys.

Quality Assurance in Personal Interviews

In order to conduct a quality survey, the individual collecting the information should posses certain desirable characteristics (Aday 2006d). The first and most important characteristic is that the surveyor must have a sufficient level of expertise or education in the subject matter. Later in this chapter, we will discuss methods of improving expertise and standardizing surveyors.

With the exception of telephone interviews, surveyors should be well groomed and be professional in appearance. Surveyors should not do a "hard sell" but should be motivated, adaptable, and flexible. Frequently, when gathering survey information, the surveyor will encounter unexpected situations. One major advantage of computer-assisted surveys is that, in these instances, it may be possible to do some on-the-spot research with the computer to clarify the situation. The best defense against these unexpected situations is simply having experience as a surveyor.

Quality Assurance in Survey Questions

Occupational and environmental health surveys may be conducted using standard forms or just a clipboard and a pad of paper. If you plan to develop your own survey form, there are some basic guidelines for asking the right questions. Before embarking on the time-consuming process of developing a new survey form, check to see if others have developed questionnaires that could be adapted to meet your needs (Aday 2006c). In forming survey questions, particular care should be taken in selecting the right words. Word clarity is essential. Select words that express the concept and can be easily understood. Obviously, the educational level and language skills of the respondent must be taken into consideration. A common mistake of inexperienced surveyors is failure to be balanced when asking a question. Avoid asking leading questions. In other words, when in asking a question, the surveyor should not give the impression that one answer is preferred over another. For example, when I was surveying a radiology department, an early mistake I made was saying to the technician, "I am sure that you do . . . ." This type of loaded question makes it difficult for the respondent to give an honest answer.

Another common mistake is asking *double-barreled questions*, which ask for two different responses at the same time. An example of a double-barreled question would be asking one of the housekeepers, "Do you know what an MSDS is, and do you follow it?" This question is vague and makes it hard for the respondent to know which part of the question to answer. She may know what an MSDS is but be unable to read it.

What about question length? If a question is too short, the respondent may not fully understand what has been asked. However, if the question is too long, the respondent may get lost and forget the purpose of the question.

What about open-ended versus closed-ended questions? Open-ended questions are useful in the early data-gathering stages, when the surveyor is unsure which issues will be most important (Aday 2006c). These questions give the respondents the opportunity to elaborate in their responses, which may yield important clues of factors that may have been omitted. The major drawback is that qualitative analysis of responses from open-ended questions is difficult and time-consuming. Closed-ended questions allow a limited range of responses, such as nominal (yes/no or male/female, and so on), ordinal (high, medium, low), or numeric. Their obvious advantage is the ease of analysis, and these questions tend to be more reliable. The disadvantage is that the response options may not fully reflect the views of the respondent. It is usually best to start with general questions and move on to more specific questions on a given topic. This makes it easier to skip a section if it does not pertain to the respondent.

The survey questions are then assembled into a questionnaire. The final steps before administering the questionnaire are pre-testing and pilot-testing the questions. *Pre-testing* means that you try the questions on your health and safety colleagues to get their feedback, and *pilot-testing* occurs when you administer the questionnaire on a limited group of respondents for their feedback. The questionnaire is then modified, based on the feedback, and administered.

Assuring Quality in Administering Questions

Types of errors that can occur when administering the questions include over-reporting and yea-saying. *Over-reporting* refers to respondents exaggerating an issue or a problem, and *yea-saying* is the tendency of respondents to answer yes to every question, if they believe that yes is the socially correct answer. Controlling for over-reporting can be done if there are objective records to confirm or refute a respondent's claim. A solution for yea-saying is to include both positive and negative statements about the same issue within a battery of questions (Aday 2006b).

Another concern is that surveys occur in a *point in time;* conditions may have been different before the survey and may change after the survey. Thus, surveys cannot be relied upon as the sole source of information. Frequent, open communication with all departments is essential to assure that safety and health management is notified when conditions do change for the worse. It is important that the surveyor be considered "part of the solution" for a problem. The least effective survey is one that points out problems that the staff is already aware of and for which the surveyor offers no suggestions for improvement.

Improving the Quality of the Surveyor

It is also important to recognize that surveyors have varying degrees of expertise in any given area. In some cases, it may be necessary to use outside consultants when dealing with highly specialized and technical problems. One effective means of improving the performance of facility surveyors is through standardization; an inexperienced surveyor and a more experienced, standardized surveyor conduct joint surveys of the same installation. The Food and Drug Administration (FDA) has had a formal program to standardize and certify retail food inspectors for many years (FDA 2003). Standardization could also be applied to health and safety professionals working in healthcare facilities by hiring a recognized expert to do joint surveys with the local individuals and comparing results for consistency.

Another approach to improving the interviewing skills of a surveyor is through training using mock questions and role playing using standard case scenarios. Large health corporations can prepare self-study manuals for their surveyors to assist them in improving their skills. In addition, detailed surveyor manuals can be prepared that describe the frequency, scope and specific issues found in various departments. The manual may also contain standard survey forms, glossaries, and other types of useful guidance for the surveyor.

There are significant advantages of using a team approach, particularly when conducting health and safety surveys. When visiting patient care units, it is very important to include nurses or physicians during the survey because they are more likely to identify a procedural problem than a non-clinician. The health and safety professional brings expertise in hazard and exposure assessment. Plant engineering or facilities management personnel can help pinpoint utilities-related problems, such as malfunctioning ventilation equipment. See Chapter 5 for more information on hazard surveys using a team concept.

Survey Collection Forms

Checklists are commonly used to collect environmental health or safety data. They provide clues to potential hazards, and organize the data. The disadvantages are that such checklists often provide limited space to describe conditions, and they can be prone to inaccuracies and conflicts in interpretation. For example, if the surveyor rates a condition as a 3 on scale of 1 to 5, another surveyor may rate the same condition higher or lower based on personal preference. A better option would be to fully describe the condition, including information on the code that is being violated.

Conducting the Survey

One approach is to show up for a survey unannounced in hopes of catching building occupants doing something wrong. While there may be some benefits of unannounced surveys due to the element of surprise, there is also a strong likelihood that certain key facility contacts will be unavailable. Therefore, these personnel should be contacted in advance before doing the survey. One common mistake in doing safety audits is not inviting a member of the union to participate in the survey. If a facility has a local bargaining unit, an employee representative has the right to be present during facility safety audits.

The format of the survey will vary depending on the type and scope of the evaluation. A food service survey can use a relatively standardized format. On the other hand, an industrial hygiene survey must be modified, depending on circumstances. For example, a noise survey tends to collect very different information than a survey of waste anesthetic gas emissions. Some useful tools have been developed to assist in indoor air quality (IAQ) surveys. See "Tools for Collecting Information" in Chapter 8 for more information. If you are using an instrument, you must be aware of its accuracy, status of calibration, and limitations of use. The use of an uncalibrated instrument can invalidate the results of a survey.

All surveys should begin by giving affected staff and management a brief introduction of the purpose and scope of the survey and should conclude with an out-briefing with supervisors and managers. The out-briefing is an opportunity to alert them of major findings and to correct any misconceptions you may have.

Report Writing

Once data collected from the survey is tabulated and analyzed, it is time to write the report. However, before you begin, first consider who the intended audience is for the report. Is the report intended as a technical document for the plant engineer, or an executive summary for the hospital administrator? Even if the report is more technical in nature, avoid including laundry lists of complaints. It is important to describe any emerging trends that suggest a worsening in overall conditions. Often such reports serve multiple audiences. In this case, prepare the report with a cover that only contains summary data for administration and the governing board, and attach a detailed report that is intended for engineering or department heads.

When writing technical reports, recommendations may come from codes, standards, or guidelines. To assure accuracy and completeness in reporting, the source of the recommendation should be cited. Often such recommendations will cost money to implement, and as a result, questions may be raised. Explicit code citations eliminate gray areas, or at a minimum provide the opportunity to discuss differing interpretations of the codes or standards. Occasionally, a situation arises that is not covered by a code, standard or guideline but presents a potential risk in the opinion of the safety and health professional. In this situation, it should be made it clear that this is a matter of opinion, and the reason that the situation is important.

Assigning Priorities

Surveys may identify numerous deficiencies in program operations or in the physical plant or utilities. It is important to highlight the most significant findings that need immediate attention. The question is how to determine which of the findings are most significant. The answer is to use a formal system of weighing risks. A possible priority setting system is described below.

Weighing Risk

Each concern that was identified in the survey should be assessed for four risk factors:

1. Injury or illness severity potential;
2. Frequency of occurrence;
3. Cost of corrections; and
4. Other negative outcomes.

Injury or Illness Severity Potential. If an adverse situation is allowed to continue, what potential injury or illnesses may result? Situations may have:

a) Life-threatening potential
b) Severe injury or illness potential
c) Minor injury or illness potential
d) No injury or illness potential

Frequency of Occurrence. How likely is it that the situation to occur? Situations may be:

a) Continuously present
b) Frequently present
c) Occasionally present
d) Rare events

Cost of Correction. What is the cost of implementing your recommendations to eliminate the situation? The cost for capital improvements will vary with the size and scope of the operation. Obviously, the cost of correction of a minor capital improvement will differ in a large medical center compared to a small nursing home. Situations may be corrected:

a) Without cost
b) Within operating budgets
c) As a minor capital improvement (e.g., $200,000 or less (in hospitals))
d) As a major capital improvement (e.g., more than $200,000)

Other Negative Outcomes. What other negative outcomes may occur if the situation is allowed to continue? Situations may result in:

a) Loss of accreditation, major fine or litigation
b) Major Joint Commission citations; moderate risk of fine or litigation
c) Minor Joint Commission recommendation; low risk of fine or litigation
d) No negative outcomes

The next step is to review each of the four factors and to assign a priority for the finding. The rating for each of the factors is based on knowledge of codes, standards, guidelines, or professional experience. It is important to remember that the four risk factors do not have the same weight. Cost or loss of accreditation should not be weighed as heavily as severity and likelihood of occurrence.

Priorities can then be assigned as:

- Class A - Highest priority
- Class B - Medium priority
- Class C - Lowest priority

OSHA uses the terms *imminent, serious* and *other than serious* when describing the priority of a hazard.

Examples of Priority Analysis

An example of a Class A hazard would be a required fire exit is blocked with a desk. This situation has the potential to cause the loss of life during an evacuation, is continuously present, has minimal cost to fix, and may result in citation or fine from the local fire marshal.

An example of a Class B hazard would be a nitrous oxide leak in a dental clinic. This situation presents an unknown injury or illness potential, depending on the amount of gas released and the potential for exposure to women of child-bearing age. (Remember that nitrous oxide has been identified as a reproductive toxin.) The leak will be continuously present until biomedical personnel make repairs. The cost to fix the leak should be relatively minor, and there is a possibility of litigation if one of the dental personnel exposed to the gas has reproductive problems.

An example of a Class C hazard would be the emergency trauma room has only 220 square feet of floor area, and the American Institute of Architects (AIA) recommends that emergency trauma rooms have 250 square feet of floor area (AIA 2006). This situation presents no injury potential unless the lack of space results in tripping or other hazards. It will be continuously present unless there is a major capital improvement, and it would likely result in either a minor or no Joint Commission recommendation. In this example, the cost is so high, relative to any potential benefit, that it is unlikely that funds would be available until the next major facility renovation.

The above examples demonstrate one possible approach to priority setting. There may be others that are equally useful. The main point is that surveyors must be systematic in determining the most serious conditions because they may be asked to justify their positions.

SUMMARY AND CONCLUSIONS

One of the most important tasks of a health and safety professional is the collection and use of data. Surveys are one useful way to collect data. A similar sounding term, *surveillance* involves the systematic collection, analysis, and interpretation of data on specific health problem and its timely dissemination to those who need it. It is important to integrate environmental and occupation surveillance of hazards and exposures with traditional health outcome-based surveillance. There are a variety of survey approaches for data collection. Surveyor interviews are the most common approach used in healthcare institutions. To be effective in data gathering, there is a need for better survey instruments and improved staff expertise. One effective means of improving expertise is through surveyor standardization. After completing data collection, tabulation, and analysis, a report is prepared. It is critical to know the target audience and tailor the report to that audience. Finally, using a systematic method of determining the top priorities for correction is essential.

Review

1. What are the differences between surveys and surveillance?
2. What are the advantages and disadvantages of personal interviews versus self-administered questionnaires?
3. How can the quality of surveyors be improved?
4. Why is it important to cite the codes or other references in a technical report?
5. What are some important factors to consider when identifying high-priority issues?

Reference List

Aday, L. A. 2006a. "Choosing the Methods of Data Collection." In *Designing and Conducting Health Surveys* (2d ed., pp. 100–123). San Francisco, CA: Jossey-Bass Publishers.

Aday, L. A. 2006b. "Formulating Questions about Knowledge and Attitudes." In *Designing and Conducting Health Surveys* (2d ed., pp. 268–287). San Francisco, CA: Jossey-Bass Publishers.

Aday, L. A. 2006c. "General Principles for Formulating Questions." In *Designing and Conducting Health Surveys* (2 ed., pp. 194–220). San Francisco, CA: Jossey-Bass Publishers.

Aday, L. A. 2006d. "Monitoring and Carrying Out the Survey." In *Designing and Conducting Health Surveys* (2 ed., pp. 311–339). San Francisco, CA: Jossey-Bass Publishers.

American Institute of Architects (AIA) 2006. *Guidelines for Design and Construction of Hospital and Health Care Facilities.* Washington, D.C.: The American Institute of Architects.

Centers for Disease Control and Prevention (CDC). 2006. *CDC's National Environmental Public Health Tracking Program: National Network Implementation Plan (NNIP)* (retrieved August 19, 2008) (http://www.cdc.gov/nceh/tracking/pdfs/nnip/pdf)

———. 2007. "Indicators for Occupational Health Surveillance." *MMWR* 45:1–7.

Fink, A. 1993. "Collecting Information: The Right Data Sources." In *Evaluation Fundamentals: Guiding Health Programs, Research, and Policy* (pp. 87–109). Newbury Park: Sage Publications.

Food and Drug Administration (FDA). 2003. "FDA Procedures for Standardization and Certification of Retail Food Inspections/Training Officers" (retrieved August 19, 2008) (http://www.cfsan.fda.gov/~ear/rfi-toc.html).

Ritz, B., I. Tager, and J. Balmes. 2005. "Can Lessons from Public Health Disease Surveillance Be Applied to Environmental Public Health Tracking?" *Environ.Health Perspect.* 113:243–249.

Thacker, S. B. and D.F. Stroup. 1994. "Future Directions for Comprehensive Public Health Surveillance and Health Information Systems in the United States." *Am.J.Epidemiol.* 140:383–397.

Thacker, S. B., D.F. Stroup, R.G. Parrish, and H.A. Anderson. 1996. "Surveillance in Environmental Public Health: Issues, Systems, and Sources." *Am.J.Public Health.* 86:633–638.

CLASSROOM ACTIVITY

Program Evaluation Exercise

Purpose: To acquaint the student with the importance of weighing risk factors to identify those items with the highest priority for correction.

Procedure: Divide into groups as directed and review the list of environmental health hazards. Using the format presented in the lecture, rank the ten hazards from highest to lowest. Be prepared to defend your choices. For each hazard, recommend a corrective action. Use the formal hazard ranking system included at the end of this exercise to determine risk rankings.

Scenario: This Happy Valley Day Care Center has a staff of fourteen and serves approximately 70 children, from age six months to five years. The following hazards have been identified during your survey:

1. The kitchen has only a two-compartment sink for manual washing of eating utensils. (The code states that there should be a three-compartment sink.)

2. Hot water temperature at hand-washing sinks was measured to be 150°F. (The code states that the maximum temperature at the tap should be no higher than 110°F.)

3. The width of exit doors is only 35". (The code states that these doors should be 36".)

4. The measured concentration of bleach solution used to disinfect the diaper-changing area was only 450 ppm. (The code states that the bleach solution should be between 500–800 ppm. In food contact areas, it should be 100–200 ppm.)

5. The center does not have a written policy on exclusion of sick children. (While this is required by code, according to the Director, she does not accept sick children.)

6. The playground area is littered with rocks, broken glass, and other debris.

7. The daycare center vehicle does not have a posted "No Smoking" sign inside the vehicle.

8. The closest hand-washing sink to the diaper-changing area is located in the kitchen, approximately 15 ft away. (The code states that there should be a hand-washing sink in the immediate vicinity of the diaper-changing area.)

9. The cook did not have a thermometer to check the internal temperatures of foods.

10. There was no soap at the hand-washing sink in the staff restroom.

Assessing Hazard Priority in a Day Care Center

Describe the use of **disease or injury severity potential** as a means of defining risk. Situations may have:

a) Life-threatening potential

b) Severe injury or illness potential

c) Minor injury or illness potential

d) No injury or illness potential

Describe the use of **frequency of occurrence** as a means of defining risk. Situations may be:

a) Continuously present

b) Frequently present

c) Occasionally present

d) Rare events

Describe the use of **cost of correction** as a means of defining risk. Situations may be corrected:

a) With no cost

b) Within operating budgets

c) As a minor capital improvement (Less than or equal to $1,000)

d) As a major capital improvement (More than $1,000)

Describe the use of **other negative outcomes** as a means of defining risk. Situations may result in:

a) Loss of accreditation/license, major fine or litigation

b) Moderate finding (inspector will return in 60 days); moderate risk of fine or litigation

c) Minor finding; low risk of fine or litigation

d) No risk

CHAPTER **11**

Hazard Communication, Risk Communication and Social Marketing

George Byrns

Learning Objectives

1. Explain the difference between a hazard and a risk.

2. List five steps in conducting a hazard assessment.

3. Define the terms *hazard communication*, *risk communication*, and *social marketing*.

4. Compare and contrast these different methods of communication.

5. Understand when to use a particular form of communications and under what conditions.

6. Explain the importance of uncertainty on risk perception.

In this chapter, we will discuss hazards and risks. We will also describe effective strategies for communication and training about these hazards and risks. Anticipating emerging problems is one of the most challenging elements of a comprehensive institutional environmental health and safety (IEHS) program in a healthcare institution. In Chapter 5, we discussed the importance of maintaining good communications with employees to learn of potential hazards before an injury or illness occurs. Good communication is also important in implementing a control strategy. When we attempt to control a problem, we may select engineering changes, change work practices, or use personnel protective equipment (PPE). Engineering changes require the least amount of employee training; convincing employees to use PPE requires the most amount of training. All three types of controls involve persuading employees to feel ownership for the solution. Unfortunately, the best way to communicate or to train is open to debate. The three diverse approaches available are:

- Hazard communication
- Risk communication
- Social marketing

HAZARD AND HAZARD COMMUNICATION

A *hazard* is something with the potential to do harm. For example, a hazardous substance may be flammable, explosive, radioactive, or toxic.

Hazard communication, also called the workers' right-to-know, is a program to inform workers about hazards and how to protect themselves. The Occupational Safety and Health Administration (OSHA) *Hazard Communication Standard* (OSHA 1996) requires that all chemicals produced or imported be evaluated for their hazard potential. This standard was promulgated because chemical manufacturers refused to inform employees about hazards, claiming they were trade secrets. While these companies may still withhold certain trade secrets if it is justified to OSHA, this information must be divulged in an emergency. There are five key elements in this program:

1. Chemical inventory list
2. Material safety data sheets (MSDSs)
3. Labeling
4. Training
5. Written hazard communications plan

Clinical laboratories are not covered by the standard; they are regulated under a similar standard called *Occupational Exposure to Hazardous Chemicals in Laboratories* (OSHA 2006).

Chemical Inventory List

Each employer must compile a master list of hazardous chemicals used in the facility. In Chapter 2, we described just a few of the hazardous materials that may be found in a healthcare facility. A chemical is considered to be hazardous based on its potential physical or health hazards. Some examples of chemical physical hazards are flammability, explosiveness, or reactivity. One physical hazard often found in healthcare facilities is oxidizing agents like oxygen, nitrous oxide, organic peroxides, and others. These chemicals are not flammable, but they cause other substances to burn more easily and more intensely. Another example of a major physical hazard is compressed gas cylinders. These must be properly secured because if they fall and damage their regulators, it can cause them to act like torpedoes. Health hazards may be more subjective than physical hazards. Chemical toxicity is one example of a health hazard. However, all chemicals may be toxic, given a sufficient dose. Also the route of exposure and individual susceptibility can affect the degree of toxicity of a chemical. It is important to understand the relationship between toxicity and dose. For example, a chemical that has high toxicity but exposure results in very low doses may have only a moderate hazard potential; similarly, a chemical with very low toxicity in high doses would also have a moderate hazard potential. This concept must be used with caution because it does not account for routes of exposure nor individual differences in susceptibility. Also, employees may be exposed to several, similar acting chemicals at the same time.

Another important issue is whether exposure to a chemical will have acute or chronic effects. For some chemicals, a low-dose exposure over a long period of time will result in chronic effects. Federal agencies, such as OSHA, and non-profit organizations, such as the American Conference of Governmental Industrial Hygienists (ACGIH), have determined the safe exposure levels based on a time-weighted average (TWA) for a number of chemicals. The major classes of health hazards are:

- **Corrosives:** Cause tissue damage and burns on contact with the skin and eyes.
- **Primary irritants:** Cause inflammation of the skin or eyes on contact but with no permanent tissue damage.
- **Sensitizers:** Cause an allergic reaction.
- **Acutely toxic materials:** Cause an adverse effect, even at a very low dose.
- **Carcinogens:** May cause cancer.
- **Teratogens:** May cause birth defects.
- **Organ-specific hazards:** May cause damage to specific organ systems, such as the blood, liver, lungs, or reproductive system.

The most effective means of organizing and maintaining an up-to-date inventory of hazardous chemicals in a facility is to work with the purchasing department. The purchasing agent should request that each bulk shipment of hazardous chemicals contain a copy of an MSDS in order to be certain of having the most current version of a chemical's MSDS. Some departments bypass the purchasing department and directly order chemical supplies. In such instances, the department managers should forward a copy of MSDSs for their chemicals. Otherwise, chemicals that are not in the healthcare facility's master inventory must be identified during environmental rounds.

Material Safety Data Sheets (MSDSs)

A *material data safety sheet* (MSDS) is a form containing detailed information prepared by the manufacturer or importer of a chemical. OSHA requires that certain types of information be provided in all MSDSs, but do not mandate a particular format for an MSDS. The topics that OSHA requires on all MSDSs are as follows:

- Identity (name of substance)
- Physical hazards
- Health hazards
- Routes of body entry
- Permissible exposure limits (PELs)
- Carcinogenic factors (cancer-causing)
- Safe handling procedures
- Date of sheet preparation
- Control measures (personal protective equipment (PPE))
- Emergency first aid procedures (emergency telephone number)
- Contact information (for the preparer of the sheet)
- Special instructions

For mixtures, hazardous chemicals comprising one percent or greater of the composition of the mixture must be listed. If the hazardous chemical is a carcinogen, it must be listed if it is present in the mixture at levels of 0.1 percent or greater.

A current MSDS must be available to all employees who come in contact with a particular hazardous chemical. Employees must have access to a chemical's MSDS during their shift. Some companies use computer-based systems that allow their employees to view copies of MSDSs at their work-stations. One particular problem is assuring that employees have access to MSDSs when working in sites that are remote from the main campus such as satellite clinics. An automated computer-based system is an effective means of providing this access. However, it is necessary to have a back-up system in the event that the automated system fails. Under OSHA's 1910.1020, *Access to employee exposure and medical records*, employers shall keep MSDSs for a period of at least 30 years, in addition to any other record that reveals the identity of the chemical and where and when a potentially hazardous chemical was used.

Labeling

All hazardous materials must have a label on the container itself, the batch ticket, the placard, or the process sheets. One exception to this labeling rule is a chemical in a portable container that is immediately used by the employee. OSHA does not specify the exact type of labeling that is required; it simply must convey the appropriate warnings and the identity of the hazardous chemical(s). One popular approach to labeling is the use of the hazard diamond shown in Figure 11.1. Using this system, each colored diamond represents a type of hazard. For example, blue indicates health

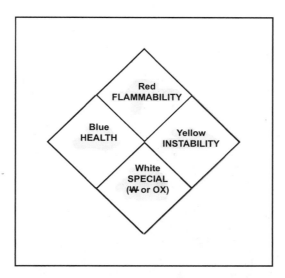

Figure 11.1 NFPA 704. (©2007,
National Fire Protection Association.)

hazard, red is for flammability, and yellow is reactivity. Each of these dia-
monds is rated from 0 to 4. A 0 means that the chemical does not present
that type of hazard, and a 4 indicates an extreme hazard. The white diamond is reserved for special hazards, such as radioactive substances, oxidiz-
ers, bases, and so on.

According to the NFPA:

> This warning system is intended to be interpreted and applied only by prop-
> erly trained individuals to identify fire, health , and reactivity hazards of chem-
> icals. The user is referred to certain limited number of chemicals with
> recommended classifications in NFPA 49 and NFPA 325 contained within the
> *Fire Protection Guide to Hazardous Materials,* which should be used as a guideline
> only. Whether the chemicals are classified by NFPA or not, individuals using
> the 704 system to classify chemicals do so at their own risk.

Another approach to chemical hazard warning is the Hazardous Materials
Identification System (HMIS III) shown in Figure 11.2. HMIS is a registered
mark of the National Paint and Coatings Association (NPCA). According to
NPCA:

> HMIS ratings are based on a 0–4 rating scale, with 0 representing minimal
> hazards or risk, and 4 representing significant hazards or risks. Although
> HMIS ratings are not required on MSDSs (OSHA 1996), the preparer may
> choose to provide them. HMIS ratings are to be used with a fully implemented
> HMIS program.

This system also identifies the types of PPE that should be used. For example,
an A in the PPE box indicates the need for safety glasses, whereas a K requires a

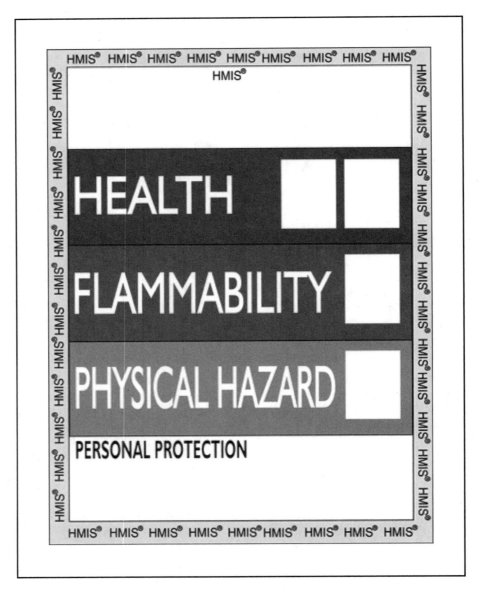

Figure 11.2 HMIS® III. (Used with permission from NCPA)

combination of PPE methods. Anything rated higher than a K involves special guidance from the supervisor or health and safety professional.

Written Hazard Communication Plan

OSHA requires that there be a written hazard communications program that describes how the program will be managed. The written plan must clearly state how chemical hazards will be communicated to employees through the use of warning labels, signs, and training programs. The first step is to identify the person(s) responsible for the program. Generally, the facility's IEHS manager has overall responsibility for managing the program. However, responsibility for implementing training of employees falls on individual supervisors. The role of the IEHS manager is to assist these supervisors so they are capable of training their employees. In terms of training, the standard only requires that employees be trained once about a particular hazardous chemical, unless there is new information about the chemical or the workers' exposure has changed. The key issue is whether the workers sufficiently understand the hazards and are able to protect themselves.

The written plan should describe how the chemical inventory will be maintained and how MSDSs will be organized and made available to all employees. The plan must also explain how contractors will be informed of hazards when they are working in the facility. In remodeling projects, it is important to specify in the contract that contractors provide copies of MSDSs for hazardous chemicals that they bring to the facility. Access to these MSDSs could be important in an emergency.

There are a number of sources that offer model hazard communication plan templates. While they may be useful, these plans must be modified to meet local conditions. An example is the online training program from Oregon OSHA (OR-OSHA) on the basics of the *Hazard Communication Standard*. See "Additional Resources" section for information on this program

At some point, the *Hazard Communication Standard* will be replaced with a new international approach for labeling and hazard notification called the *globally harmonized system* (GHS). GHS evolved because of the growth in international trade and lack of uniformity among countries regarding labeling and hazard identification (UN 2007). A comparison between OSHA's standard and GHS is found on the OSHA Web site (see "Reference List" section at the end of the chapter).

RISK ASSESSMENT, COMMUNICATION AND MANAGEMENT

Risk is the probability of some harmful event occurring. There may be no consensus regarding the likelihood or severity of the possible event. Also, something may be extremely hazardous, but it may not present a risk if there is no potential for exposure to it.

Risk Assessment

Risk assessment is the process of determining the likelihood and potential severity of a risk. One approach to workplace risk assessment includes the following five steps (HSE 2006):

Step 1: Identify the hazards.
Step 2: Decide who might be harmed and how.

Table 11.1 Risk Determination Phase Table

Item No.	Threat Name	Vulnerability Name	Risk Description	Existing Controls	Likelihood of Occurrence	Impact Severity	Risk Level

Step 3: Evaluate the risks and decide on precautions.

Step 4: Record your findings and implement them.

Step 5: Review your assessment and update if necessary.

The Centers for Medicare & Medicaid Services (CMS) offer a risk assessment approach for healthcare operations (CMS 2002). Table 11.1 demonstrates the CMS approach to risk assessment.

The headings in Table 11.1 are described as follows:

- **Item number:** The item number is used as a means of tracking a potential risk. The threat may be environmental/physical, human, natural, or technical.
- **Vulnerability:** Vulnerability refers to those systems or operations that may be affected by the threat.
- **Risk description:** The risk description provides more detail how the vulnerability creates a risk to the facility operation.
- **Existing controls:** Existing controls are those that currently are in place to minimize severity or likelihood of the risk.
- **Likelihood of occurrence:** How likely is it that the threat will create a vulnerability to one or more system or process? According to CMS, likelihood is based on factors such as the system environment, existing controls; the presence, motivation, tenacity, strength and nature of the threat; and the presence of vulnerabilities. Likelihood ranges from negligible to extreme.
- **Impact severity:** Impact severity is ranked from insignificant to critical.
- **Risk level:** Defined after the threat is then accessed for both likelihood of occurrence and impact severity. The risk level may be defined as low, moderate, or high.

The CMS approach is discussed in the CMS Information Security Risk Assessment (RA) Methodology (CMS 2002).

The Joint Commission offers a similar approach to risk assessment called the Strategic Surveillance System (S3). For more information on the Joint Commission model, visit their Web site (see "Reference List" at the end of the chapter).

Risk assessment is a complex process that is beyond the scope of this book. Interested readers are referred to *Risk Assessment for Environmental Health* for more information on this complex and challenging topic (Robson and Toscano 2007).

Risk Management

Risk management is the process of weighing the political, social, and economic implications of the different approaches to controlling the risk and determining the best strategy.

Some examples of risk management concerns in a healthcare facility include the need to manage workers' compensation claims and to identify and control hazards. One major difference in health care from many other industries is the possible effects of catastrophic failure (Carroll and Norris 2007). When risks are not properly managed in any industry, there will be economic loss. In health care, there is also a likelihood of fatalities.

A traditional healthcare risk management program focuses on specific types of risks, but it does not consider the interactive effects of risks on one another. As discussed in Chapter 5, patient injuries may result in employee injuries. The current approach is called *enterprise risk management* which is broader in focus and attempts to explore the effects of multiple risks on the total organization (Carroll and Norris 2007). Thus, the effects of a single risk can have consequences on insurance rates, employee morale and retention, recruitment, and public relations. The goal is to identify the highest priority risks and to manage risks that may fall within more than one risk category, such as bioterrorism. In the past, the mailroom was never considered as a potential risk for terrorist attack; however, today we know that terrorists may transmit biological agents through the mail system.

Risk management is the natural outcome of risk assessment. Once a risk is identified, assessed, and assigned a priority, the next step is to select a risk solution. Potential options in managing a risk are: avoiding it, accepting it, reducing it, or sharing it with another entity such as the insurance company. Each of these options involves the expenditure of resources, such as building structure, operations, and human capital.

The key to successful risk management is monitoring all steps in the process (Carroll and Norris 2007), such as:

- Did solution strategy achieve objectives?
- Is the strategy being properly implemented?
- Is information appropriately communicated to senior management? Failure to communicate and document continues to be one of the most important sources of liability claims facing the health care industry.

Risk Communication

The term *risk communication* has different meanings to different groups (NRC 1989). The National Research Council (NRC) defines it "as an interactive process of exchange of information and opinion among individuals, groups,

Table 11.2 Differences in perception of risk. (Adapted from *Communicating in a Crisis: Risk Communication Guidelines for Public Officials* (DHHS 2002))

Risks are More Acceptable if they are Perceived as:	Risks are Less Acceptable if they are Perceived as:
Voluntary	Imposed
Under an individual's control	Controlled by others
Having clear benefits	Having little or no benefit
Distributed fairly	Unfairly distributed
Natural	Manmade
Statistically within the normal range	Catastrophic
Generated by a trusted source	Generated by an untrusted source
Familiar	Exotic
Affecting only adults	Affecting children

and institutions" (NRC 1989). They further state that "it involves multiple messages about the nature of risk and other messages, not strictly about risk that express concerns, opinions, or reactions to risk messages or to legal and institutional arrangements for risk management."

Risk Perception of Environmental Hazards

A key issue in risk communications is determining an individual or group's perceptions about a risk. Table 11.2 lists factors that increase or decrease the perceptions of risk.

It is important to remember that scientists and lay people do not view risk the same way (DHHS 2002). Scientists examine the probability of a risk and would consider something with greater than a one in a million likelihood of occurrence as low risk. Lay people tend to personalize risk information. For example, they may have known someone who developed cancer from exposure to a hazardous chemical; thus, they tend to be less influenced by probability or rates than scientists.

The level of uncertainty about the severity of a risk greatly influences individual perceptions of that risk. If there is strong consensus of the negative consequences of exposure to a hazard and the goal is to inform individuals of that risk, *hazard communication* should be used as described above. If there is strong consensus of the risk of a hazard, and the desired outcome is to motivate individuals to take action to avoid the risk, *social marketing* should be employed (discussed below under "Persuasion and Social Marketing). Risk communications methods should be used when a situation is perceived to be risky by one of the parties, and there is no consensus on the degree of risk. In addition, risk communications is often needed when one party will benefit economically if the situation is permitted to exist.

When is risk communication successful? If the level of understanding of all parties is increased, and all parties are satisfied that they have been informed within the limits of understanding, the risk communications process was successful. What is the ultimate goal of risk communication? The goal is to make the target group(s) a partner in finding an equitable solution. Is it likely that all parties will be satisfied in every case? The answer is obviously no, especially in a situation with high uncertainty and unequal risks and benefits.

What happens if there is a failure to communicate? If the target audience believes their concerns are being ignored, and they perceive that the situation is placing them at risk, then there will be unrest, which is termed *outrage* (Covello and Sandman 2001).

The steps in risk communication are:

1. Set realistic goals. Before risk communication is attempted, the specific communication goals must be understood. According to the Department of Health and Human Services' *Communicating in a Crisis: Risk Communication Guidelines for Public Officials,* "educating the public on the complexities of bioterrorism and preparing them for any eventuality" is not realistic (DHHS 2002). Providing them with a general overview of the problem, some examples of specific dangers, and providing some guidance on an appropriate response is a realistic goal.

2. Assure that openness in communications comes early in the process and is sustained throughout the process.

3. Maintain balance in interactions between competing parties by holding each side accountable for statements. It is important to separate opinions and perceptions from objective information that is supported with facts.

4. Select a risk communicator who is both technically competent and a competent public speaker. A technically competent speaker who uses acronyms and jargon, talks over the heads of laypersons, or talks down to them will not be an effective communicator. It is also a bad idea to use polished speakers who are ignorant of the subject matter because it will likely cause a loss of public trust. The goal of the communicator should be to deliver a message that is brief, clear, and effective (DHHS 2002). It is most important to acknowledge uncertainty and build public trust and confidence.

It is also important to work with the media. Failure to do so can result in unwanted, inaccurate publicity. It is best to provide the reporter covering the story a written statement, which helps the reporter write the story, but also decreases the possibility of being misquoted.

PERSUASION AND SOCIAL MARKETING

When a safety and health issue arises that has more than one possible solution, but the need to control it is without doubt, the only question becomes which solution is the best. Under the hierarchy of controls, an engineering control is best because it eliminates the problem and requires the least amount of training to implement the change. Unfortunately, there are situations where engineering controls are not possible, and other less desirable controls, such as persuading individuals to use personal protective equipment (PPE), must be considered. This can be challenging because once people develop unsafe behaviors, the habits are formed, and it is difficult to change them.

While it may be difficult to get people to change behaviors, it is not impossible. Marketing personnel and politicians can be very effective in getting us to buy their product or cast our vote their way by being persuasive. These same persuasive messages can be used by IEHS professionals to change behaviors. This use of marketing principles to promote ideas, issues, or practices is called *social marketing* (Perloff 1993).

Before discussing social marketing, there must first be a definition for the term *persuasion*. Unfortunately, there are many conflicting definitions. Basically, it is an attempt by one person to change the mental or emotional state of another person (Perloff 1993). Is this the same as coercion? There are subtle differences between the two. *Coercion* is a negative term that implies that the target audience has no choice but to accept or reject the message. Unfortunately, in some instances of persuasion, there may also be a question of whether there is a true choice. For instance, if a maintenance worker refuses to wear a respirator when removing asbestos-containing materials and this person is told to either wear the respirator or be fired, the worker does have a choice. Nevertheless, many would consider this example as coercive. (However, because of potential for adverse health effects and liability concerns, it may be appropriate to be coercive in this example.)

The goal in persuasion is to promote a change in beliefs, attitudes, or behaviors in the target audience. So, how do we persuade people to change? There are many techniques ranging from simple to complex. A few examples are described below.

Simple Persuasion Techniques

Two simple persuasion techniques are *foot-in-the-door* and *mere exposure*. The idea behind the foot-in-the-door technique is that people are more likely to comply with a second, larger request after they have been convinced to perform a small request (Perloff 1993). The expression gets its name from the notion that getting the target person to listen a short, simple request, it will be easier to succeed later on when asking for a more time-consuming, challenging request. This approach is discussed under "Social Judgment Theory" later in this chapter.

The second simple persuasive technique is *mere exposure*. People tend to react unfavorably to things that are new or unfamiliar. Instead of "familiarity breeds contempt," what this theory has shown is that "familiarity breeds liking," and repeated exposure to a message increases the favorable response to this message. Everyone has experienced this phenomenon at some point in our lives. The practical use of this technique is that before attempting to implement a new policy in a healthcare facility, it is important to get the message out in flyers, posters, email messages, and short briefing sessions before beginning full implementation.

Modeling

Modeling is a slightly more complex persuasion technique. It has been known for years that people learn new behaviors by observing role models. However, for this behavior change to occur, several steps must take place (Perloff 1993). Obviously, the audience must notice the behavior being modeled; therefore, step one in modeling is for the role model to get the audience's attention. It is also necessary for the audience to retain what is being modeled. Thus, the next step is to promote message retention by asking the audience to describe what they have been observing. The audience must be able to act on the message. This means that our target audience must have the ability to physically perform the action, or they must have the supplies or equipment readily available to perform the desired activity. Lastly, the audience must be motivated to act. What are the consequences associated with acting or failing to act? If the issue is serious enough, the consequences for failing to act may be termination of employment.

Modeling theory is an extremely effective means of changing behaviors. Not surprisingly, the key player in modeling safe behavior is the departmental supervisor. It will be very difficult to get employees to adopt safe behaviors unless their supervisors are serving as role models for these behaviors.

Social Judgment Theory

Social judgment theory reminds us that any attempt at communication must begin with the receiver (Perloff 1993). Before attempting to change a person's behavior, it is important to understand the person's beliefs and biases. What is at issue is that receivers do not judge a message purely on merit but analyze the message, comparing it to their initial attitude before they determine whether to accept it. If a person's "latitude of rejection" is high, strong persuasive arguments will not be effective. Forcing a policy change on a person with strong objections may result in a boomerang effect; the person may actively work against the proposal. When instituting a major change, it is best to do a survey of employees to determine their attitudes. If they are generally supportive or neutral to the proposal, it can be implemented. If they are opposed, it is better to gradually attempt to establish the credibility of the proposal first. Using the foot-in-the-door technique, minor, less controversial changes would be made first; once these are in place and accepted, the more comprehensive changes would be put in place.

Cognitive Dissonance Theory

People tend to be uncomfortable when they engage in behavior that is in conflict with their beliefs. The idea behind *cognitive dissonance theory* is the human need to rationalize behaviors that cause this psychological discomfort (Perloff 1993). For example, it is OK for me to smoke because, unlike others, I will not get cancer. To counter this false rationalization, people must be convinced that an alternate (safe) behavior will benefit them in some way. For smokers, it can be argued that, in addition to the health benefits of cessation, they will smell better, they will look better, and they will save lots of money. In the case of people refusing to wear PPE when required, the argument could be made that people who follow the procedure and wear them are more knowledgeable than those who do not use PPE. The challenge is to identify benefits of the changed behavior that exceed the value of continuing in the negative behavior.

Attribution Theory

Attribution theory is a natural human tendency to search for patterns in order to understand why things happen and to predict future outcomes (Weiner 1986). This is a complex theory, with major elements including: locus of causality, stability, and controllability. *Locus of causality* refers to assigning blame for an injury or other incident, either internally, e.g., to an unsafe behavior, or externally, e.g., to an unsafe condition. *Stability* refers to whether the hazard is permanent or temporary, and *controllability* refers to whether you can direct the situation. This theory has major relevance in preventing injuries and illnesses in the workplace (DeJoy 1994). If workers blame their own behaviors for injuries, there is an opportunity to work with them to change the behavior and prevent an injury in the future. On the other hand, if the worker attributes the injury to bad luck or as just a part of the job, it may be more difficult to change behaviors. By conducting a thorough investigation of an incident, the locus of causality, stability, and controllability may be established. If the cause of the injury is a permanent condition that is not controllable by the worker, only a solution that changes the condition (like an engineering control) will succeed.

Social Marketing

Social marketing has been defined as "the design, implementation, and control of programs seeking to increase the acceptability of a social idea or practice in a target group(s)" (Kotler 1975). The components of social marketing include: market segmentation, consumer research, idea configuration, communication, facilitation, incentives, and exchange theory. *Market segmentation* means defining the target audience. It is important to identify a small homogeneous group to be the target of the program because one approach directed at all employees in a healthcare facility may not be successful. In the consumer research stage, the attitudes and habits of the target group must be determined in order to predict the possible amount of rejection. One way to do this is to form an employee advisory panel before trying a new strategy. Next, in the *idea configuration* stage the message structure and style should be selected that will be most likely to get the attention of, and response by, the target audience. In the *communication* stage, the structure of the message will determine whether it will be a one-sided or two-sided message (Perloff 1993). Two-sided messages consist of giving both sides of the argument; this approach works best when the latitude for rejection is high. The two most common message styles are fear and modeling. Fear tactics may get people's attention, but they may not achieve lasting results. A message based on modeling safe behaviors may take longer to implement but the results may be last longer. As was discussed in the section on "Modeling," above, the target group must be able to act on the message. Therefore, *facilitation* means that everything possible is done to make it easy for the target group to perform as required. Incentives and exchange theory address the "what's in it for me" concept. *Incentives* may be a pen or a coffee cup containing a logo of the message. In *exchange theory*, if employees are expected to change their behaviors, it should be made clear to them that the benefits of making this change exceed the costs of failing to take the recommended action.

How does social marketing differ from business marketing? The major difference is the criteria for success. Business marketing is considered a success if sales of the marketed product increase. It is more difficult to evaluate results of social marketing. In both social and business marketing, the objective is eliciting a behavior. In health and safety social marketing, success would ideally be determined by a decrease in the incidence of a disease or type of injury. Unfortunately, this is not always possible to determine, so success might be measured based on process measures. For example, success might be a significant increase in the percentage of employees who can demonstrate how to do a respirator fit check after participating in a new training program on respiratory protection.

PROPERTIES OF A COMPETENT COMMUNICATOR

As discussed earlier in this chapter, an effective message is given by someone who is both technically competent and is a skilled public speaker. What are the properties of a skilled communicator? A competent communicator speaks moderately fast, using powerful, forceful language. He or she speaks loud enough to be heard and varies pitch levels. In addition, to be most effective, a competent communicator use a conversational style of speech, speaks in standard English and uses no jargon. What about humor? Humor can be very effective in making a message more memorable (Perloff 1993). However, it must be used with caution. Humor can interfere with the listeners' comprehension of the message. If the goal of humor is to increase attention to the message, it is appropriate, but if the goal is to increase comprehension, it may do more harm than good. Also, beware of humor that pokes fun at or belittles individuals or groups, as this may be offensive to the audience. The safest type of humor is self-deprecating because this is less likely to offend someone.

MATCHING THE PROBLEM WITH A COMMUNICATION STYLE

We have described three very diverse methods of communicating with our target audiences: hazard communication, risk communication, and social marketing. The question is, which communication style works best in a particular situation?

Hazard Communication. In hazard communication, we are simply conveying information about the hazards associated with a chemical and the means to protect the worker. This is information that is not controversial, and no attempt is made to motivate anyone. It is just the statement of the facts. The key issue in hazard communication is whether the target audience understands the hazard and the means to protect themselves. It is usually not sufficient to simply give employees an MSDS and ask them to read it or show them a twenty-minute video and assume that they can protect themselves. Following each hazard communications training session, employees should be given a short quiz to test their level of understanding. If the employee achieves a passing score, the training was effective.

Risk Communication. When dealing with a controversial issue, especially where there is significant uncertainty regarding the potential for exposure and the potential for harm from that exposure, risk communication is used. In risk communication, the goal is to increase the level of understanding of all parties involved to the extent possible. The IEHS professional's role in risk communication is as a mediator; parties must be held accountable and avoid exaggerating or underestimating the risks.

Social Marketing. When no uncertainty exists regarding the risks associated with a product or a behavior, social marketing is employed. The goal is to go beyond simple conveyance of information and to motivate the target audience to avoid a risky product or risky behavior. There are a variety of persuasive approaches to use in a social marketing campaign, ranging from simple foot-in-the-door techniques to more complex psychological approaches, such as social judgment theory.

SUMMARY AND CONCLUSIONS

Communicating and training are important tasks of any environmental and occupational IEHS program. Depending on the goal, there are several approaches that may be taken. The goal of hazard communication is simply to increase the level of understanding of employees so that they can protect themselves from exposure to hazardous chemicals. Having access to MSDSs and using appropriate container labels or warning signs are important components of this program. Risk communication techniques should be used if an issue is controversial, and the level of uncertainty regarding the severity or likelihood of a risk is high, especially if one group benefits from a situation more than other groups. The goal of risk communications is to increase the level of understanding of all parties and to assure that all parties are satisfied that they have been informed within the limits of understanding. When there is little uncertainty about the risks of a hazard and the goal is to increase acceptance of a control strategy, social marketing should be employed, using one or more persuasion theories. Simple persuasion strategies, such as the foot-in-the-door technique, or more complex theories, such as modeling, may be used. While there are several distinct approaches to communication, they share common elements. They all require a messenger who is technically competent and is a skilled public speaker.

Review

1. Explain the difference between a hazard and a risk.
2. Describe the basis behind OSHA's concept of hazard potential.
3. What are five steps in conducting a hazard assessment?
4. Why do scientists and lay people have differing views on risk?
5. How does our level of scientific certainty influence our methods of communication?
6. What happens when there is a failure to adequately communicate a risk to the public?
7. Are social marketing and persuasion the same as coercion?
8. How does business marketing differ from social marketing?

Reference List

Carroll, R. L. and G. A. Norris. 2007. "Enterprise Risk Management in Health Care: The Basics." In P. Nakamura and R. L. Carroll, eds., *The Essentials*, 5th ed., pp. 1–12. San Francisco, CA: Jossey-Bass.

Centers for Medicare and Medicaid Services (CMS). 2002. *CMS Information Security Risk Assessment (RA) Methodology* (Version #1.1) (retrieved August 12, 2008) (http://www.csrc.nist.gov/groups/SMA/fasp/documents/risk_mgmt/RA_meth.pdf).

Covello, V. T. and P. M. Sandman. 2001. "Risk Communication: Evolution and Revolution." In A. Wolbarst, ed., *Solutions to an Environment in Peril*, pp. 164–178. Baltimore: Johns Hopkins University Press.

DeJoy, D. M. 1994. "Managing Safety in the Workplace: An Attribution Theory Analysis and Model." *Journal of Safety Research* 25:3–17.

Department of Health and Human Services (DHHS). 2002. *Communicating in a Crisis: Risk Communication Guidelines for Public Officials* (Rep. No. 02NLM: WM 401 C734 2002). Washington, DC: Department of Health and Human Services.

Health and Safety Executive (HSE). 2006. *Five Steps to Risk Assessment* (Rep. No. INDG163(rev2)). Sudbury, UK: HSE Books.

Kotler, P. 1975. *Marketing for Nonprofit Organizations*. Englewood Cliffs, NJ: Prentice-Hall.

National Research Council (NRC). 1989. *Improving Risk Communication*. Washington, D.C.: National Academy Press.

Occupational Safety and Health Administration (OSHA). 1996. 29 CFR 1910.1200, *Hazard Communication* (retrieved August 12, 2008) (http://www.osha.gov/pls/oshaweb/owadispo.show_document?p_table=STANDARDS&p_id=10099).

————. 2006. 29 CFR 1910.1450, *Occupational Exposure to Hazardous Chemicals in Laboratories* (retrieved August 12, 2008) (http://www.osha.gov/pls/oshaweb/owadispo.show_document?p_table=STANDARDS&p_id=10106).

Perloff, R. M. 1993. *The Dynamics of Persuasion.* Hillsdale, NJ: Lawrence Erlbaum Associates.

Robson, M. G. and W. A. Toscano. 2007. *Risk Assessment for Environmental Health.* San Francisco: Jossey-Bass.

Weiner, B. 1986. "The Structure of Perceived Causality." In *An Attribution Theory of Motivation and Emotion*, pp. 43–78. New York: Springer-Verlag.

CLASSROOM ACTIVITY

Communication Approaches

Given the following three issues, select: hazard communication, risk communication, or social marketing as a communication approach. In each case, defend your approach.

Scenario: You are the safety officer at Happy Valley Hospital and have been asked to deal with the following issues:

1. The average number of reported needlestick injuries has risen from two to six this year. (Assume the increase is result of nurses recapping needles and not due to better reporting.) Develop a plan to address the problem of nurses who recap needles after use.

2. The Central Services Department supervisor decided to switch from glutaraldehyde to ortho-phthalaldehyde as a new high-level germicide. However, she and her staff are uncertain about the hazards associated with this product. You have been asked to explain the hazards and safe handling methods.

3. There are plans to decommission the existing medical waste incinerator and haul the waste to a microwave treatment unit in the next county. Members of the community are concerned about the dangers associated with traffic accidents and spillage of the medical waste. You have been asked by the hospital's chief executive officer to discuss this plan with the community.

4. You have noticed that members of the plant engineering department are failing to use hearing protection when they perform noisy tasks, such as leaf blowing. Recent audiograms reveal significant threshold shifts (hearing loss) in two of these workers. In addition, a survey with a noise level meter demonstrated peak levels above 150 dB, and dosimetry reports showed an average daily dose of 92% and 114%, respectively (based on an 80 dB threshold, 85 dB criterion, and 5 dB exchange rate). The department supervisor does not share your views that this is a major concern.

5. A new antineoplastic agent is being used for the treatment of Hodgkin's Lymphoma. The pharmaceutical company's MSDS mentions that there is evidence that the drug is teratogenic in mice, and that caregivers are required to avoid respiratory and dermal contact. The Director of Nursing is asking for your assistance in training her staff in methods of safely administering the product.

CHAPTER **12**

Prevention of Workplace Violence

George Byrns

Learning Objectives

1. Define the term violence.

2. Identify the most prevalent type of violence affecting healthcare workers.

3. Identify the factors contributing to workplace violence.

4. Describe an approach to the evaluation of the potential for violence.

5. Discuss violence prevention and control measures.

Since the 1980s, workplace violence (WPV) has been a significant source of morbidity and mortality for workers (Forster et al., 2005; NIOSH 2006). According to the Bureau of Labor Statistics (BLS), there were 69 homicides in healthcare workers from 1996 to 2000 (OSHA 2004). While these deaths due to WPV are worrisome, the healthcare and social assistance industries lead all other industries in the numbers of WPV nonfatal lost-time injuries. The incident rate was 8.4 assault-related injuries per 10,000 workers in hospitals, compared to 2.4 per 10,000 workers in all industries, and the injury rate for nursing and personal care facilities was nearly 22 per 10,000. See Table 12.1 below.

The rates are probably much higher, due to severe underreporting and because the BLS reports only injuries that were severe enough to result in lost time from work (OSHA 2004; McPhaul and Lipscomb 2004). One problem in reporting violent incidents is that there are several definitions for WPV. NIOSH defines *workplace violence* as "violent acts, including physical assaults and threats of assault, directed toward persons at work or on duty" (NIOSH 2002). OSHA uses a broader definition, including violent or threatening behavior and verbal violence (e.g., threats, verbal abuse, hostility, or harassment)

Table 12.1 Incidence Rates for Nonfatal Assaults per 10,000 Full-Time Workers, 2006. (Source: Adapted from BLS 2006)

Private Sector Overall	2.4
Health Care & Social Assistance	8.8
Hospitals	8.4
Nursing Home & Residential Care	21.8

(OSHA 2004). These and other forms of violence, such as stalking, may not be reported until there is an actual physical assault.

VIOLENCE RISK FACTORS

OSHA identified some of the major risk factors that increase the risk of violence in healthcare facilities (OSHA 2004):

- The prevalence of handguns and other weapons among patients, their families or friends;
- The increasing use of hospitals by police and the criminal justice system for criminal holds and the care of acutely disturbed, violent individuals;
- The increasing number of acute and chronic mentally ill patients released from hospitals without follow-up care (these patients have the right to refuse medicine and can no longer be hospitalized involuntarily unless they pose an immediate threat to themselves or others);
- The availability of drugs or money at hospitals, clinics and pharmacies, making them likely robbery targets;
- Factors such as the unrestricted movement of the public in clinics and hospitals and long waits in emergency or clinic areas that lead to client frustration over the inability to obtain needed services promptly;
- The increasing presence in facilities of gang members, drug or alcohol abusers, trauma patients or distraught family members;
- Low staffing levels during times of increased activity, such as mealtimes, visiting times and times when staff are transporting patients;
- Isolated work with clients during examinations or treatment;
- Solo work, often in remote locations with no backup or way to get assistance, such as communication devices or alarm systems (this is particularly true in high-crime settings);
- Lack of staff training in recognizing and managing escalating hostile and assaultive behavior; and
- Poorly lit parking areas.

TYPES OF VIOLENCE

Another problem in the prevention and control of violence is that there are different types of WPV. Table 12.2 shows the four types of WPV that may occur in a healthcare setting.

As the OSHA Guidelines point out, the availability of drugs, needles and syringes, and money at healthcare facilities make healthcare facilities candidates for type I violence (OSHA 2004). Also, as in any other workplace, there is the potential for worker-on-worker (type III) or personal relationship violence (type IV). While these other types of violence do occur, type II violence (customer/client) is by far the most likely form of WPV in healthcare settings (Gerberich et al. 2004; McPhaul and Lipscomb 2004). According to NIOSH, WPV is likely to occur during times of high activity and interaction with patients (NIOSH 2002). Some of the higher risk times are during meals, visiting hours, and patient transportation. WPV may occur anywhere in a hospital, but NIOSH identified the following areas as high risk:

- Psychiatric wards
- Emergency rooms
- Waiting rooms
- Geriatric units

Table 12.2 Typology of Workplace Violence. (NIOSH, 2006; California State Department of Industrial Relations 1995)

Type	Description
I. Criminal intent	The perpetrator has no legitimate relationship to the business or its employee, and is usually committing a crime in conjunction with the violence. These crimes can include robbery, shoplifting, trespassing, and terrorism. The vast majority of workplace homicides (85%) fall into this category.
II. Customer/client	The perpetrator has a legitimate relationship with the business and becomes violent while being served by the business. This category includes customers, clients, patients, students, inmates, and any other group for which the business provides services. It is believed that a large portion of customer/client incidents occur in the health care industry, in settings such as nursing homes or psychiatric facilities; the victims are often patient caregivers. Police officers, prison staff, flight attendants, and teachers are some other examples of workers who may be exposed to this kind of WPV, which accounts for approximately 3% of all workplace homicides.
III. Worker-on-worker	The perpetrator is an employee or past employee of the business who attacks or threatens another employee(s) or past employee(s) in the workplace. Worker-on-worker fatalities account for approximately 7% of all workplace homicides.
IV. Personal relationship	The perpetrator usually does not have a relationship with the business but has a personal relationship with the intended victim. This category includes victims of domestic violence assaulted or threatened while at work, and accounts for about 5% of all workplace homicides.

Mentally unstable patients present an assault risk to healthcare workers in psychiatric units. In addition, homes for mentally handicapped individuals were considered high-risk sites for nurse's aides (Eriksen 2006). A study of violence in a Vancouver hospital found that, during a one-year period, 57% of emergency room staff reported that they had been physically assaulted (Fernandes et al. 1999). Furthermore, 68% of respondents believed that the frequency of violence was on the increase. The emergency services (ES) area may have several reasons for the increased risk of violence. Some examples include patients or visitors who become angry because service is denied or a patient who is involuntarily admitted. Also, if a gang member is receiving treatment after an attack, opposing gang members may enter the ES to "finish the job." Long waiting times in some facilities may increase stress and anger for patients and visitors, and patients or residents of geriatric units may be confused or agitated due to undiagnosed Alzheimer's Disease, dementia or aftereffects of stroke.

ELEMENTS OF A VIOLENCE PREVENTION PROGRAM

All healthcare organizations must have a written WPV prevention program that is appropriate for the size and complexity of the establishment and which is adaptable enough to handle a variety of situations. This comprehensive program must make it clear to all employees, patients, and visitors that there is a zero tolerance for violence (OSHA 2004). All employees should be aware of this policy and encouraged to promptly report incidents and suggest ways to reduce or eliminate risks. A key issue is the need to maintain security in the workplace. This will require written agreements with local law enforcement agencies and others to prevent and mitigate workplace violence. The policy should assign responsibility and authority for the program to one individual (generally the facility's health and safety manager). However, to be effective, management must ensure that adequate resources are available to implement the program.

OSHA lists five main elements of an effective WPV prevention program (OSHA 2004):

- Management commitment and employee involvement;
- Worksite analysis;
- Hazard prevention and control;
- Safety and health training; and
- Recordkeeping and program evaluation.

Management Commitment and Employee Involvement

As in any safety program, management's commitment to and employee involvement in the WPV prevention effort are essential for success. In most cases, a team or committee should be set up to assist in the development, implementation, and evaluation of this program.

Management Commitment

Managers must make it clear that they support and promote a proactive safety culture, which includes ensuring that department heads and supervisors understand and comply with the WPV prevention plan. Management must prepare a written authority statement to empower the individuals implementing the plan and allocate sufficient resources to assure the success of the plan. A comprehensive medical and psychological program must be established to care for any employee who is affected by a WPV. Finally, management must support and implement recommendations from the health and safety committee regarding the WPV plan.

Employee Involvement

Promoting employee involvement and feedback to the WPV plan assures that they will have a sense of ownership for the plan. Employees must be trained to fully understand the plan, including procedures for prompt reporting of incidents or suggestions to improve the program. Finally, they must participate in committees or teams that assess the status of the program, and an employee representative should be a member of inspection teams.

Worksite Analysis

Worksite analysis is a systematic method of anticipating, recognizing, and evaluating existing or potential hazards for WPV. This analysis consists of records review, employee screening surveys, and worksite inspections. Once the extent of the WPV problems are identified, control strategies may be considered.

Records Review

There are a number of important records that may be reviewed to identify existing or potential hazards, including employee medical records, safety reports, workers' compensation records, and insurance claims. Safety records may include the OSHA Form 300 (OSHA 2004b), police reports, incident (or near-miss) reports, and safety surveillance reports (as described in Chapter 5).

The following records must be tabulated to identify any possible trends relating to potential at–risk situations:

- Departments, units, or workstations
- Job titles
- Activities
- Day of the week or time of day

The tabulation is intended first to develop a baseline, and second to monitor trends in terms of frequency and severity of incidents. The development of a baseline for comparison will require the collection of several years of data. It may also be possible to contact other similarly sized institutions to compare WPV experiences and use these institutions as a benchmark.

Employee Screening Surveys

Employee questionnaires or surveys are one effective means to anticipate vulnerabilities in the WPV plan. The surveys should be conducted at least annually or whenever there is a change in the WPV plan or in incident rates. Employees should be given the option of anonymity when they identify their perceptions of the adequacy of the security plan. These surveys can serve two important functions; they can identify unanticipated risk factors, and they can assess the effects of changes in the WPV program. They can also provide some reassurance to employees that management is concerned about their welfare and cares about improving the facility's safety culture. Another means of strengthening the program is to have surveys by independent reviewers, such as health and safety consultants, law enforcement officials or insurance representatives.

Worksite Inspections

Worksite inspections may be assigned to the security department or may be one element of routine safety surveys. Ideally, both sources of information are used. Worksite inspections should target those areas, such as the emergency department, that are expected to be high risk. Particular attention should be paid to building layout or design, especially to isolated locations and job activities. Surveyors should identify lighting problems or lack of communication devices, as well as any unsecured areas that may harbor a potential assault perpetrator. In addition to identifying physical problems, the surveyors should also question employees regarding their knowledge of the WPV plan. For example, is the employee familiar with the incident reporting system? Does this employee know how to de-escalate a potentially violent incident?

Hazard Prevention and Control

Once the above information is compiled and tabulated, the health and safety manager should be in a position to determine what if any prevention or control strategies are needed to improve the program. A comprehensive program should include three strategies:

- **Primary prevention:** preventing the incident,
- **Secondary prevention:** reducing the severity of an incident, and
- **Tertiary prevention:** providing counseling and treatment for those affected by an incident.

Engineering controls strategies are generally most effective in achieving primary prevention. Administrative or work practice changes may have limited effect in preventing the incident but should be effective in secondary prevention. An appropriate post-incident response is essential for tertiary prevention.

Engineering Controls

Engineering controls are preferred for WPV because they remove the hazard from the environment and require the least amount of employee training once they are in place (AIHA 2003). Some of the engineering control options recommended by OSHA include (OSHA 2004):

- Modifying new construction to reduce or eliminate security hazards
- Installing and maintaining alarm systems and other communications devices in high risk locations
- Providing metal detectors to restrict entry into emergency services areas
- Using closed-circuit video equipment to give security personnel the ability to monitor high-risk locations 24 hours per day
- Placing curved mirrors at hallway intersections or in concealed locations
- Using deep service counters or bullet-resistant glass in patient reception, triage, or admitting areas
- Having seclusion rooms to hold criminal or violent patients
- Providing comfortable waiting rooms for visitors
- Constructing all counseling or patient care rooms with two exits
- Providing locks on all employee bathrooms
- Locking all unused doors, in compliance with fire codes
- Installing bright, effective lighting both indoors and outdoors (especially in parking areas)

Administrative or Work Practice Controls

Administrative controls or changes in work practice are designed to reduce or minimize the potential for violence or the severity of the incident. Some options recommended by OSHA include (OSHA 2004):

- Developing and promoting the zero-tolerance for violence policy to patients, visitors, and employees
- Establishing a liaison with local law enforcement agencies to assure rapid response during an emergency
- Advising all employees of the procedures to respond to a WPV incident
- Requiring all employees to report WPV incidents to a supervisor or manager
- Ensuring that the security staff is adequate in number and properly trained
- Providing staff with identification badges, preferably without last names, to readily identify employment

- Limiting access by visitors to all parts of the facility except the waiting areas. This may include instituting a sign-in procedure with passes for visitors, especially in the newborn nursery area.
- Establishing and posting a list of restricted visitors for individuals with a known history of violence
- Prohibiting staff from working alone, especially at night, and providing staff members with security escorts to parking areas at night

Post-incident Response

An essential component of the WPV plan is the post-incident response and evaluation policy, which should describe the program for comprehensive treatment of employees who were victimized personally or who were traumatized by witnessing a WPV incident. Victims of WPV suffer a variety of psychological effects following an assault. According to OSHA, these may include (OSHA 2004):

- Short- and long-term psychological trauma
- Fear of returning to work
- Changes in relationships with coworkers and family
- Feelings of incompetence, guilt, and powerlessness
- Fear of criticism by supervisors or managers

Therefore, several types of services should be made available to victims of WPV, including trauma-crisis counseling, critical-stress debriefing, or other forms of employee assistance. Counselors should be properly trained and qualified to handle these types of incidents.

SAFETY AND HEALTH TRAINING

OSHA recommends that all employees be aware of the concept of *universal precautions for violence*; in other words, violence can be expected but its effects can be avoided or minimized through proper preparation and training. All employees, including managers and supervisors, should receive training in the WPV plan, including initial orientation for all new staff, as well as annual training on key elements of the plan. At least annually, the training program should be evaluated to determine its effectiveness in preparing staff to implement the WPV prevention plan. The training program should be assessed for content, methods, and frequency.

OSHA recommends that *all* employees receive annual training covering:

- Risk factors for WPV
- Recognition of aggressive behavior and de-escalating or diffusing this behavior, and if necessary, the use of chemical or physical restraints

- The facility's violence response procedures
- The location and use of alarms or other communications systems
- Incident reporting systems
- The importance of multicultural diversity and staff sensitivity to racial and ethnic differences
- Procedures to obtain care after a violent incident

Training for Supervisors and Managers

In addition to the above, supervisors and managers should receive training in their roles in monitoring employee compliance with the program and information on specific WPV hazards in their respective departments.

Training for Security Personnel

Security personnel require additional training in proper handling of aggressive or abusive individuals and methods of defusing hostile situations. When security services are provided by others, the scope of work for the contract must be reviewed to assure that security personnel have received proper training.

RECORDKEEPING AND PROGRAM EVALUATION

Records must be kept for regulatory reasons and to provide information for continuous program improvement.

Recordkeeping

Some examples of records that should be kept are:

- OSHA Form 300, *Log of Work-Related Injury and Illness* (OSHA 2004b)
- Employee medical records that will provide information on any physical assaults and injuries that have been sustained. See Chapter 5 for more information on these records.
- Incident reports that are generated for any safety-related incident. OSHA provides an example of incident reporting (OSHA 2004).
- Safety committee minutes, hazard survey reports, or reports of corrective actions
- WPV training records, including the names of attendees and qualifications of trainers

Program Evaluation

At least annually, the WPV program should be reviewed to evaluate its success and point out items that need improvement. OSHA recommends that the results of the annual review be shared with all employees (OSHA 2004). It is important that reports protect employee confidentiality by either presenting only aggregate data or by removing any personal identifiers. The program evaluation should focus on the following:

- Reviewing reports and minutes from committee meetings dealing with WPV
- Analyzing injury, illness or fatality trends and comparing these to either an internal baseline, benchmarking these trends against national data, or comparing them to data from institutions of similar size
- Measuring improvements that are reflected by lowering the frequency and severity of WPV incidents
- Surveying employees periodically to determine their perceptions regarding workplace security
- Surveying employees before and after WPV prevention program changes
- Reviewing compliance with federal or state reporting requirements
- Requesting and reviewing the results of outside consultant reviews of the WPV program

SUMMARY AND CONCLUSIONS

WPV has been a growing threat to healthcare workers. Patient-to-worker violence has been the primary cause of this problem, and WPV injury rates to healthcare workers exceed that of any other industry. There should be a policy of zero tolerance for WPV, and this policy should be supported and enforced by top management. OSHA guidelines provide a comprehensive approach to implement an effective WPV prevention plan.

Review

1. Provide a reason why workplace violence (WPV) is underreported.
2. What are at least three reasons for the apparent increase in WPV incidents directed at healthcare workers?
3. What are the four types of WPV, and which one is most prevalent?
4. What are OSHA's five elements of an effective WPV plan?
5. What is meant by universal precautions for violence?

Reference List

American Industrial Hygiene Association (AIHA). 2003. *The Occupational Environment: Its Evaluation, Control, and Management.* 2d ed. Fairfax, VA: American Industrial Hygiene Association.

Bureau of Labor Statistics (BLS). 2007. *Fatal occupational injuries by selected worker characteristics and selected industry, All U.S., all ownerships, 2007.* (retrieved August 28, 2008) (http://data.bls.gov/iif/oshwc/cfoi/cftb0223.pdf)

————. 2006. *Incidence rates of nonfatal occupational injuries and illnesses involving days away from work by selected worker and case characteristics and industry, All U.S., private industry, 2006.* (retrieved May 13, 2008) (http://data.bls.gov/oshwc/cfoi/cftb0214.pdf).

California State Department of Industrial Relations (1995). *Cal/OSHA Guidelines for workplace security* Sacramento, CA: California State Department of Industrial Relations.

Eriksen, W. 2006. "Practice Area and Work Demands in Nurses' Aides: A Cross-sectional Study." *BMC.Public Health* 6:97.

Fernandes, C., M., F. Bouthillette, J. M. Raboud, L. Bullock, C. F. Moore, and J.M. Christenson. 1999. "Violence in the Emergency Department: A Survey of Health Care Workers." *CMAJ.* 161:1245–1248.

Forster, J. A., M. T. Petty, C. Schleiger, and H. C. Walters. 2005. "kNOw Workplace Violence: Developing Programs for Managing the Risk of Aggression in the Health Care Setting." *Med.J.Aust.* 183:357–361.

Gerberich, S. G., T. R. Church, P. M. McGovern, H. E. Hansen, N. M. Nachreiner, and M. S. Geisser et al. 2004. "An Epidemiological Study of the Magnitude and Consequences of Work Related Violence: The Minnesota Nurses' Study." *Occupational and Environmental Medicine* 61:495–503.

McPhaul, K. M. and J. A. Lipscomb. 2004. "Workplace Violence in Health Care: Recognized But Not Regulated." *Online.J.Issues Nurs.* 9:7.

National Institute for Occupational Safety and Health (NIOSH). 2002. *Violence: Occupational Hazards in Hospitals* (DHHS (NIOSH) Publication No. 2002-101). Cincinnati, OH: NIOSH-Publications Dissemination.

————. 2006. *Workplace Violence Prevention Strategies and Research Needs* (Publication No. 2006-144). Cincinnati, OH: NIOSH-Publications Dissemination.

Occupational Safety and Health Administration (OSHA). 2004. *Guidelines for Preventing Workplace Violence for Health Care & Social Service Workers* (OSHA 3148-01R 2004). Washington, DC: OSHA.

CLASSROOM ACTIVITY

Workplace Violence

Scenario: The hospital administrator at Happy Valley Hospital tells you that she thinks the incidence of patient-to-worker attacks has increased in the last year. Some examples of violent acts that have resulted in employee injuries included gang violence in the emergency room, assaults on employees in the parking lot during the evening shift, and attacks on nursing personnel in the psychiatric unit. Your task is to implement a workplace violence prevention and control program. How do your proceed? The tenets of industrial hygiene provide a useful framework in the development of a comprehensive approach. The tenets are as follows: anticipate, recognize, evaluate, and control the hazard.

In groups, prepare a plan to control violence in your hospital. Your plan should address these tenets:

- Anticipate
- Recognize
- Evaluate
- Control

In developing your control strategies, use Haddon's Matrix below.

Haddon's Matrix for Violence Prevention

	Human	Supplies or Equipment	Physical & Social Environment
Before the Incident			
During the Incident			
After the Incident			

CHAPTER 13

The Role of the Health and Safety Manager in Design and Construction Planning

George Byrns and Lee Shands

Learning Objectives

1. Discuss the importance of good design as it relates to health and safety concerns.

2. Review the steps in construction and demolition planning.

3. Discuss the role of the health and safety professional in construction planning.

4. Describe the effects of equipment on building requirements.

5. Describe the process of achieving sustainability in building design and operations.

Building physical environments may significantly affect the health and safety of occupants (Lundstrom et al. 2002). Good designs and operations are cost-effective, efficient and optimize patient care and employee performance. However, poor design and operations can contribute to injury or illnesses among healthcare providers and those served by them. There are three infectious agents of special concern: *Legionella pneumophilia*, *Aspergillus spp.*, and *Mycobacterium tuberculosis* (TB). One community outbreak of Legionnaire's disease was linked to a hospital's cooling towers, and another hospital's hot water plumbing system was determined to be the source of sporadic cases among its patients (Brown et al. 1999; Visca et al. 1999). A good source of information on *Legionella pneumophilia* is the Web site (http://www.legionella.org).

VENTILATION AND AIR QUALITY

Good ventilation is critical to protect patients and employees from microorganisms and chemical contaminants (Leung and Chan 2006). The American Institute of Architects (AIA) specifies the minimum numbers of air changes per hour (ACH) in a given area, pressure relationships, and filtration requirements (AIA 2006). For example, infectious patient isolation rooms should provide $\geq$ 6 ACH in existing facilities and $\geq$ 12 ACH in newly constructed facilities. Also, infectious isolation rooms should be under negative pressure relative to surrounding areas, whereas surgical suites should be under positive pressure. All ventilated areas within a hospital should be equipped with filters that are at least 30% efficient, and critical areas need final filters of at least 90% efficiency. In the operating room, placement of supply and exhaust grilles is critical. Air should be supplied through non-aspirating diffusers located near center of the work area, and exhaust ducts should be located both high and low to direct airborne contaminants away from the surgical area. Ideally, there should be at least 20 ACH in the operative suite. In addition, bone marrow transplant units and other protective environments should be equipped with a high efficiency particulate air (HEPA) final filter. HEPA filters are capable of removing 99.97% of particles that are 0.3μm in diameter.

The mold, *Aspergillus spp.*, is a particular problem because it is ubiquitous. Its spores are found in air, water, and dust, and they may be easily aerosolized, especially during demolition (Noskin and Peterson 2001; Bouza et al. 2002). Once inhaled, *Aspergillus* may cause serious and potentially fatal upper or lower respiratory, or systemic infections in susceptible individuals. Elimination of these fungi from the ventilation system is particularly important in the bone marrow transplant units. Patients undergoing these procedures are extremely susceptible to opportunistic infections. In one unusual case, hospital-acquired *Aspergillus* keratitis was traced to a hospital's demolition project (Burt et al. 2003).

Another microbe of concern is TB, since it may be highly prevalent in certain communities. While it is important to have properly ventilated patient isolation rooms, one study found that inadequate ventilation ($\leq$ 2 ACH) of general patient rooms was associated with tuberculin skin conversions among healthcare workers (Menzies et al. 2000). High rates of conversions were also found in personnel who performed bronchoscopes in poorly ventilated treatment rooms. It is essential that the diagnosis and treatment of patients suspected of having TB occur in rooms with proper dilution ventilation. However, this study also points out the need for good ventilation throughout the hospital because of the potential for healthcare worker exposure to undiagnosed TB patients. See Chapter 2 for more details on the control of TB.

Monitoring air quality and ventilation system performance are important components in assessing and controlling the risks from environmental contaminants within hospitals. This can include annual checks of the heating, ventilating, and air conditioning (HVAC) system to assure that minimum air exchange rates and pressure differences are being met, as well as more complex monitoring. One relatively simple method of air monitoring is to verify filter efficiencies at the supply air diffuser. A particle counter measurement is collected outdoors for comparison indoors with respect to the predicted reduction of total particles indoors provided by the filters. Particle counters are also used to check for dust intrusion into occupied spaces from the construction zones. As discussed in Chapter 8, taking air samples for viable mold or other microorganisms is challenging and should only be performed by individuals with suitable expertise.

One common mistake in new construction or renovation projects is to assume that the project architect or mechanical engineer is fully aware of infection control or safety requirements. Another incorrect assumption is that the ventilation systems perform as designed. Ventilation drawings should be thoroughly reviewed to assure that critical areas, such as isolation rooms, are getting the required numbers of ACHs and that air movement and pressure relationships are appropriate. System and building performance also needs to be verified directly. For example, a patient infectious isolation room should be designed in such a way to provide at least 12 ACH under negative pressure, and the movement of air should be towards the patient and away from anyone entering the room. The ventilation exhaust duct should be located in the wall or ceiling directly above the patient's head, and the supply duct should enter the room above the door to the room. Furthermore, more air should be removed from the room than is supplied to provide a static pressure difference of at least 0.01 inches water gauge (AIA 2006). This is typically verified using a smoke test under the closed door or by permanently installing a static pressure monitor in the wall. Additional areas may require a specially designed ventilation system to control airborne contaminants such as biological agents, gases, fumes and dusts. These areas need to be designed to maintain appropriate pressure relationships, air exchange rates and filtration efficiencies. Some examples of areas requiring special ventilation systems include operating rooms, special procedure rooms, laboratories, sterile supply rooms, pharmacies, and clean and dirty work rooms.

OTHER DESIGN ISSUES FOR INFECTION CONTROL

There are other design issues that have implications for infection control. For example, floors with hard surfaces seldom present a problem in terms of harboring microorganisms, but carpeting is a different matter (Noskin and Peterson 2001). Since carpets are difficult to thoroughly clean, they may contain significant numbers of microorganisms. Therefore, carpeting should be avoided in high-risk areas because attempts at cleaning may release microbial aerosols. In general, any surface that is subject to contamination should be constructed of smooth, cleanable materials.

Except for vaccinations, hand washing is the single most effective means of preventing diseases. Therefore, sinks should be optimally placed to facilitate frequent hand washing. Recently, the Centers for Disease Control and Prevention (CDC) began stressing the importance of using alcohol rubs for routine hand hygiene (CDC 2002). Placement of wall-mounted dispensers for alcohol and other important devices, such as sharps containers, are vital parts of an infection prevention plan.

DESIGN ISSUES FOR SAFE WORKING ENVIRONMENTS

Building design and construction has an obvious role in providing a safe working environment. The final design must comply with fire codes and allow for safe egress during a fire or other emergency. During construction and demolition, fire safety must be a concern. According to the AIA, partitions and enclosures around renovated areas should be solid in nature and sealed at the floor and ceiling to limit the spread of smoke, fire or other contaminants (AIA 2006; Bartley 2000).

Building design may also affect health and safety during routine operations. For example, current healthcare design standards do not fully address ergonomic hazards. Certain locations where frequent patient lifting occurs should be equipped with ceiling-mounted lifting devices. Another example of how building design affects worker health is a dental clinic layout. In the past, these clinics were designed as *rear-delivery:* the hand-pieces and suction probe were located behind the head of the patient. This was done to accommodate either right-handed or left handed dentists or hygienists. The problem with this design is that dentists or hygienists were required to frequently bend and twist to reach their instruments. After years of twisting and working in awkward postures, many dental personnel developed severe musculoskeletal problems (Akesson et al. 1999). The solution to this design problem is to provide side- or front-delivery set-ups. Side-delivery systems are designed to swing to the right or left, depending on the preferences of the dental care provider.

From the above discussion, it should be clear that health and safety personnel should be involved in every step of the design and construction process. It is important to work with architects and engineers early in the project to identify and correct any facility design flaws prior to construction because changes later become extremely costly.

STEPS IN CONSTRUCTION OR DEMOLITION PLANNING

There are a series of sequential steps that must occur when building or demolishing a facility. Failure to follow these steps in the correct order can have serious consequences ranging from an inefficient design to environmental or occupational harm. The most important step is program planning, described below.

Program Planning

Prior to the start of any construction or demolition project, there must be a needs assessment. Thorough planning is necessary to determine the types of services to be provided, the scope of the project and other important considerations. Data sources used for planning must be accurate to determine program requirements. For example, it will be necessary to determine current and future inpatient and outpatient loads. In a remodeling project, this may not be too difficult; however, for a new facility, this information may not be readily available. What will be the scope of operations? Will surgical, obstetric or emergency trauma services be needed? What is the prevalence of infectious diseases like TB? This information is necessary to determine how many isolation rooms will be needed. Unfortunately, it may be difficult to predict the emergence of other types of infectious diseases, such as severe acute respiratory syndrome (SARS) or avian influenza.

Planning is also important in demolition. Often, buildings must be demolished before new construction can begin. A key issue in planning is to anticipate the presence of hazardous materials, such as lead-based-paint or asbestos. Failure to anticipate these hazardous materials can result in unnecessary occupational exposures and environmental contamination, as well as also significantly increasing the cost of the project.

Selection of the Appropriate Site

There are a number of location factors that affect the desirability of a site (Brauer 2006). Some factors, such as climate and natural conditions, are unavoidable when building a healthcare facility. Others, including avoidance of flood plains and the availability of fire protection and utilities, are essential. There should be good access via roads, accessibility for emergency vehicles, and adequate parking for staff, patients and visitors. The types of neighborhoods and the need for special security arrangements should also be considered when selecting a site.

Often when a facility is expanding, the site selection is limited to the adjacent properties. Although this generally makes the expansion more feasible, it can raise concerns over the dust and soil microbes that will be generated during construction in a location near an existing healthcare facility. Major construction next to existing air intake structures and building openings, such as doors and windows may require special considerations. For example, the air intakes may need to be re-ducted to another location, or more frequent monitoring of dust intrusion may be necessary.

A recent concern is the need to comply with environmental regulations in the design, construction, renovation, expansion, equipment, and operation of all healthcare facilities (AIA 2006). There may be special concerns, such as air quality restrictions, that limit emissions from incinerators and other flue-fired equipment. Other concerns include: underground storage tank requirements, hazardous and medical waste storage and disposal, stormwater management, and asbestos in buildings. See Chapter 6, "Environmental Management," for additional details.

Design Standards

There are literally dozens of different design standards used in the construction or renovation of a healthcare facility. A few of the most important standards are listed below:

- Design, construction, and equipment: AIA's *Guidelines for Design and Construction of Hospital and Health Care Facilities* (AIA 2006).
- Fire and building egress and many others: National Fire Protection Association (NFPA) Standards, including the *Uniform Fire Code* (NFPA 2006a) and *Building Construction and Safety Code* (NFPA 2006b).
- Mechanical and plumbing: *International Mechanical Code®* (ICC 2006) and *National Standard Plumbing Code®* (PHCC 2006).

Infection Control Risk Assessment (ICRA)

According to the AIA, the CDC and the Joint Commission on Accreditation of Healthcare Organizations (Joint Committee or JCAHO), an infection control risk assessment (ICRA) must be conducted prior to the start of any construction or renovation project (AIA 2006; CDC 2003; JCAHO 2009). The primary focus of the ICRA is to identify the potential for exposures of susceptible patients to dust and moisture, and determine the need for dust and moisture containment measures (CDC 2003). Therefore, infection control must be one of the major considerations in the construction or demolition planning process. This means that infection control, employee health, health and safety, and environmental services (housekeeping) personnel should meet with the architectural design team early in the design process. Some of the goals of the healthcare team should be to (CDC 2003):

- Conduct a risk assessment of the project to determine potential hazards to susceptible patients.
- Prevent unnecessary exposures of patients, visitors, and staff to infectious agents.
- Oversee all infection-control aspects of construction activities.
- Establish site-specific infection-control protocols for specialized areas.
- Provide education about the infection-control impact of construction to staff and construction workers.
- Ensure compliance with technical standards, contract provisions, and regulations.

- ▨ Establish a mechanism to address and correct problems quickly.
- ▨ Develop contingency plans for emergency response to power failures, water supply disruptions, and fires.
- ▨ Provide a water-damage management plan (including drying protocols) for handling water intrusion from floods, leaks, and condensation.

Key to the success of the ICRA is for the healthcare team to maintain frequent, open lines of communications with the design team and to make sure that construction workers are educated about the critical nature of infection control. As discussed earlier, a particular concern is the potential for contamination of the HVAC system and the spread of infectious agents due to construction activities. The control of airborne contaminants is often accomplished by using a portable air handler, equipped with HEPA filters, to create negative pressure within the construction area. The CDC also recommends that members of the health and safety team monitor construction worker adherence to infection control protocols on a daily basis until the completion of the project. In addition, infection control personnel should closely monitor nosocomial infection rates during and immediately after construction, renovation, or demolition projects to observe any patterns.

Air Sampling

An important role of the institutional environmental health and safety officer in the ICRA is to conduct air sampling. This can include checks of the HVAC system to assure that minimum air exchange rates and pressure differences are met, as well as more complex monitoring. As previously mentioned, a particle counter may be used to check for dust intrusion into occupied spaces from the construction zones. This device will give a rough qualitative indication of a potential problem. Taking air samples for viable mold or other microorganisms is challenging and should only be performed by individuals with suitable expertise. See Chapter 8 for more information on air monitoring techniques. In addition, the American Conference of Governmental Industrial Hygienist's *Bioaerosols: Assessment and Control* is a useful guide on the appropriate uses and limitations of microbial air sampling (ACGIH 1999).

Construction Phases

Once the initial planning is completed and there is a decision to proceed, the design also follows some sequential steps. The architectural team starts with simple design sketches that become increasing more detailed and complete over time.

Early Design Phase

After the needs assessment is completed and a site is selected, the planning team begins the early design phase. During this phase, efforts are made to group departments that share services together. Figure 13.1 is a bubble diagram

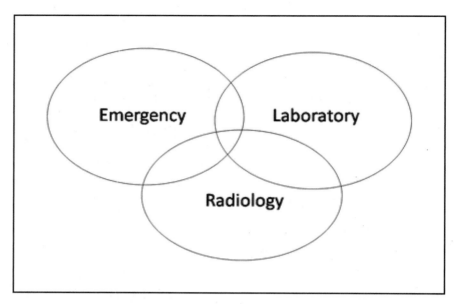

Figure 13.1 Bubble diagram.

showing the need for shared services between the emergency department (ED), radiology, and the laboratory. The idea is that a patient, who presents in the ED, may need lab diagnostic services or an x-ray; therefore, having these three departments in close proximity makes the process more efficient.

The early design phase is also the time that schematics or simple line drawings are prepared to lay out each department planned for this facility. Other concerns during the early design phase include such as things as acoustical and electromagnetic field (EMF) shielding. For example, if the facility plans to have a helicopter pad, it should be accessible to the emergency room, but the design should avoid elevated noise levels in patient care units. Another example is that the magnetic resonance imaging (MRI) unit should be located away from equipment that is sensitive to electromagnetic emissions. If the physical therapy (PT) department plans to do electromyography (a technique for measuring muscle activity), PT should not be located in the vicinity of the MRI unit. Failure to account for these incompatible operations can result in additional expenses later in attempting to shield patients and staff from the noise or EMF emissions.

Middle Design Phase

During the middle design phase, construction drawings contain only site plans and floor plans. The design is considered to be 25-50% complete at this point. This is also the time when in-depth discussion of equipment needs must occur, including a complete list of all equipment that will be required for each room. This discussion is necessary because the footprint of each piece of equipment must be determined to assure that it will fit in the allotted space. This is also the time to make major changes if needed.

Late Design Phase

The project design is considered to be 75-100% complete during the late phase. At this time, mechanical plans (plumbing and ventilation) are prepared, as well as electrical drawings, details and elevations. Details and elevations provide top and side views of work stations and other areas to give the viewer a better idea of the layout.

Do not assume that the project architect or mechanical engineer is fully aware of infection control or safety requirements. Ventilation drawings should be thoroughly reviewed by the health and safety manager to assure that critical areas, such as infectious isolation rooms and surgical units, are getting the required numbers of ACHs and that pressure relationships and air movement are all appropriate. Some areas may require specially designed ventilation systems for controlling airborne contaminates, such as biological agents, gases, fumes and dusts. These areas should be designed to maintain appropriate pressure relationships, air exchange rates, and filtration efficiencies. Some examples of areas requiring special ventilation systems include special procedure rooms, laboratories, sterile supply rooms, pharmacies, and clean and dirty work rooms.

Any modifications to the design at this point may require a change order, which can significantly increase the cost of the project.

Specifications Book

The specifications book provides specific information on materials and equipment. This book is important because it describes the size of equipment and other useful details. One often overlooked detail is noise output from equipment. While one particular brand of equipment may be more expensive than others, it may also be quieter. As a result, it may be most cost effective in the long run to purchase the more expensive, but quieter, equipment. For example, the less expensive equipment may require acoustical noise shielding to avoid establishing a hearing conservation program; this would likely cost a good deal more than the difference between the two types of equipment.

Building Renovations

It is often too expensive to start from scratch, so renovating an outdated building is often the best option. However, like new construction projects, building renovations require consultation with infection control and safety programs (AIA 2006).

When renovating a portion of a building that is still in use, it is best to build a solid fire wall between the occupied and non-occupied spaces to prevent the migration of contaminants and limit the spread of fire (JCAHO 2009). Another important issue during renovations is the ventilation system. Will the renovated space contain ductwork that is connected to the system ventilating the occupied space? If the answer is yes, care must be exercised in addressing this issue. Simply blocking the duct will affect airflow in other areas of the facility. See the section, "Final Steps," below for a discussion regarding air balance.

It is important to remember that even small renovation projects can have an effect on infection control. There is a potential for the release of bacteria, fungi and mold during any project that stirs up dust from walls, ceilings or floor spaces. Additional risks may result if the project disturbs the flow of water or air in the heating or cooling systems. Some examples of projects that may be of concern include the demolition of existing walls or ceilings, removal of part or all of a ceiling, breeching walls, ceilings or floors, and the removal of uncovered or partially covered debris from construction areas.

Demolition

Renovation, new construction, or transfer of property may first require a demolition project. Demolition projects present a number of concerns. Frequently, the discovery of hazardous materials, such as asbestos and lead, can significantly increase cost of the entire project. In some cases, this will require a separate hazardous waste removal project that can exceed the total cost of the entire project. Therefore, prior to the start of a demolition project, it is essential that a thorough examination of the site be conducted to minimize later discovery of unpleasant surprises.

Demolition contractors are often anxious for the project to proceed quickly. As a result, dust and debris generated during the demolition may present fire safety and air contaminant control issues. A representative of the healthcare organization should be present during the demolition project. The demolition team should avoid cutting corners so that there are no major risks to the institution or surrounding community as a result of the project. Subpart T of OSHA's *Safety and Health Regulations for Construction* establishes the safety standards for employers engaged in demolition work (OSHA 2007). Requirements under these standards include: performing an engineering survey prior to work commencing; eliminating hazards associated with various utilities; housekeeping; removing debris; and eliminating hazards associated with falling materials and structural instability.

MINIMIZING RISKS

Whenever a construction project is undertaken in the vicinity of an existing healthcare facility, there is a risk of disease transmission. Actions that can be taken to minimize the risk include the following:

■ Developing infection containment standards to be followed by all construction contractors or in-house facility staff and including the standards in all construction contracts.

- Evaluating each project for necessary infection control measures.
- Developing and utilizing a checklist to evaluate compliance with containment standards.

All projects should be evaluated for the level of infection risk they may pose to patients, staff and any sterile environments. The infection control team should evaluate the project and rate the disease transmission risk and implement appropriate control measures. A project with high risk of disease transmission to patients, staff and sterile areas would require solid barrier dust partitions, negative pressure air machines with HEPA filters, sealing ventilation systems, use of sticky mats at exits, covering construction debris and use of coveralls and booties for workers. Some general measures that can be taken to minimize the risks associated with any project include scheduling work for after hours in outpatient areas and dust control via damp mopping or HEPA vacuuming in work areas. Other general measures would include re-routing foot traffic around the construction area, using "track rugs" to control dirt or debris, keeping construction refuse in covered containers with daily disposal, designating break areas, installing toilet and hand-washing facilities for the construction workers, and communicating the requirements to all contractors.

FINAL STEPS

Prior to taking occupancy of a new or renovated facility, certain final steps called *commissioning the building* must take place. Representatives of the healthcare organization use a punch-list to identify construction defects. The construction contractor must correct these defects before the building is accepted by the healthcare organization. A key issue that must be checked is the "balance" of the ventilation system. As discussed earlier, the AIA has design criteria for the number of ACHs, pressure relationships, and other details. *Air balance* means that each room is in compliance with the standard. For instance, if a room is designed to have 12 ACH under negative pressure, a hospital representative must verify that this criterion is met. Achieving proper air balance is difficult because a minor adjustment of a damper within one duct can affect airflow characteristics in many other rooms. Another final step is that certain equipment, such as x-ray units, should be tested by qualified personnel prior to accepting ownership.

GREEN DESIGN, CONSTRUCTION, AND OPERATION

In 2000, the U.S. Green Building Council (USGBC) developed the Leadership in Energy and Environmental Design (LEED) Green Building Rating System™ for commercial buildings (USGBC 2000). The LEED program promotes and certifies buildings that use environmentally friendly concepts in their design and non-toxic materials in their operation. There has been recent interest in addressing environmental sustainability in healthcare facilities. *The Green Guide for Health Care*™ (GGHC) is a self-certification program that is similar in approach to LEED (GGHC 2007). The GGHC gives a project points for using environmentally sustainable approaches in the following areas:

- **Construction Credits:**
  - Integrated design
  - Sustainable sites
  - Water efficiency
  - Energy and atmosphere
  - Materials and resources
  - Environmental quality
  - Innovation and design process

- **Operations Credits:**
  - Integrated operations
  - Transportation operations
  - Energy efficiency
  - Water conservation
  - Chemical management
  - Waste management
  - Environmental services
  - Environmentally preferable purchasing
  - Innovation in operations

Some examples of green construction include simple design changes, such as increasing the amount of insulation, using high efficiency HVAC systems, and increasing the amount of natural lighting (installing large windows on the south side of the building and using light wells and reflective surfaces) (Healthy Building Network 2005). These types of changes save energy, money and, in the case of using daylight, may improve work efficiency. Another simple improvement is installing photo-optic lighting sensors in restrooms, storerooms and other unoccupied spaces. Going green also involves the purchase of non-toxic supplies, low emissions equipment, and use of green building techniques. Some examples of non-toxic supplies include using finishes with low emissions of volatile organic compounds, but not using materials made with polyvinyl chloride (Healthy Building Network 2005). Healthcare facilities in some communities are required to properly manage storm water drainage from roofs and parking lots. One project involved restoring a wetland for filtering storm water, requiring the installation of an oil interceptor first.

Another resource for sustainability in health care is Hospitals for a Healthy Environment, now part of Practice Greenhealth, which started as a joint project between the Environmental Protection Agency (EPA), the American Hospital Association (AHA), Health Care Without Harm, and the American Nurses Association (ANA). Practice Greenhealth is a nonprofit membership organization bringing together Hospitals for a Healthy Environment, Green Guide for Health Care, and Healthcare Clean Energy Exchange. Practice Greenhealth educates healthcare professionals about pollution prevention opportunities and provides resources to healthcare organizations wishing to become sustainable (Practice Greenhealth 2008).

SUMMARY AND CONCLUSIONS

A well-organized construction plan can save money and provide an optimal work space.

Particular care must be taken during renovation to avoid creation of disease or fire hazards. Building and equipment design is important in the control of three infectious agents of special concern: *Legionella pneumophilia*, *Aspergillus spp.*, and *Mycobacterium tuberculosis*. A construction project progresses through distinct phases. Any major modifications to the design should occur prior to the final phase to avoid serious cost overruns. Any demolition projects require close scrutiny and contingency plans to avoid fire and infection control risks. Before accepting a newly constructed or renovated building, the building must be *commissioned*. This means that the building and its equipment have been verified to meet design criteria. There is a movement in health care toward green design, construction and operation, which promotes environmentally friendly design concepts and sustainability.

Review

1. Building design and construction can affect the health and safety of building occupants. What are three diseases that may be spread via the airborne or droplet routes?
2. What is the purpose of bubble diagrams?
3. Why is it important to consider equipment needs during the middle design phase?
4. What are some special health and safety concerns involving demolition projects?
5. What is a punch-list?
6. What does LEED certification mean?

Reference List

American Conference of Governmental Industrial Hygienists (ACGIH). 1999. *Bioaerosols: Assessment and Control.* Cincinnati, OH: American Conference of Governmental Industrial Hygienists.

American Institute of Architects (AIA). 2006. *Guidelines for Design and Construction of Hospital and Health Care Facilities.* Washington, D.C.: The American Institute of Architects.

Akesson, I., B. Johnsson, L. Rylander, U. Moritz, and S. Skerfving. 1999. "Musculoskeletal Disorders among Female Dental Personnel—Clinical Examination and a 5-year Follow-up Study of Symptoms." *Int.Arch. Occup.Environ.Health.* 72:395–403.

Bartley, J. M. 2000. "APIC State-of-the-art Report: The Role of Infection Control During Construction in Health Care Facilities." *Am.J. Infect.Control.* 28:156–169.

Bouza, E., T. Pelaez, J. Perez-Molina, M. Marin, L. Alcala, and B. Padilla. 2002. "Demolition of a Hospital Building by Controlled Explosion: The Impact on Filamentous Fungal Load in Internal and External Air." *J.Hosp.Infect.* 52:234–242.

Brauer, R. L. 2006. "Facility Planning and Design." In *Safety and Health for Engineers* (pp. 547–557). New York: Van Nostrand Reinhold.

Brown, C. M., P. J. Nuorti, R. F. Breiman, A. L. Hathcock, B. S. Fields, H. B. Lipman. 1999. "A Community Outbreak of Legionnaires' Disease Linked to Hospital Cooling Towers: An Epidemiological Method to Calculate Dose of Exposure." *Int.J.Epidemiol.* 28:353–359.

Burt, B., G. Pappas., and P. Simcock. 2003. "Hospital Acquired Aspergillus Keratitis." *Br.J.Ophthalmol.* 87:923.

Centers for Disease Control and Prevention (CDC). 2002. "Guideline for Hand Hygiene in Health-Care Settings: Recommendations of the Healthcare Infection Control Practices Advisory Committee and the HICPAC/SHEA/APIC/IDSA Hand Hygiene Task Force." *MMWR* (RR-16) 51:1–44.

————. 2003. "Guidelines for Environmental Infection Control in Health-Care Facilities: Recommendations of the CDC and the Healthcare Infection Control Practices Advisory Committee (HICPAC)" *MMWR* (RR-10) 52:1–42.

Green Guide for Health Care (GGHC). 2007. *The Green Guide for Health Care* (Version. 2.2). (retrieved September 2, 2008) (http://www.gghc.org).

Healthy Building Network. 2005. "Green Healthcare Construction Case Studies." (retrieved September 2, 2008) (http://www.healthybuilding.net/healthcare/Green_Healthcare_Case_Studies.pdf).

International Code Council (ICC). 2006. *International Mechanical Code.* Florence, KY: Delmar Cengage Learning.

Joint Commission on the Accreditation of Healthcare Organizations (JCAHO). 2009. *Hospital Accreditation Standards.* Oakbrook Terrace, Illinois: Joint Commission Resources.

Leung, M. and A. H. Chan. 2006. "Control and Management of Hospital Indoor Air Quality." *Med.Sci.Monit.* 12:SR17–SR23.

Lundstrom, T., G. Pugliese, J. Bartley, J. Cox, and C. Guither. 2002. "Organizational and Environmental Factors that Affect Worker Health and Safety and Patient Outcomes." *Am.J.Infect.Control.* 30:93–106.

Menzies, D., A. Fanning, L. Yuan, and J. M. FitzGerald. 2000. "Hospital Ventilation and Risk for Tuberculosis Infection in Canadian Health Care Workers." *Ann.Intern.Med.* 133:779–789.

National Fire Protection Association (NFPA). 2006. NFPA 5000, *Building Construction and Safety Code.* Quincy, MA: National Fire Protection Association.

Noskin, G. A. and L. R. Peterson. 2001. "Engineering Infection Control through Facility Design." *Emerg.Infect.Dis.* 7:354–357.

Occupational Safety and Health Administration (OSHA). 2007. 29 CFR 1926.850, *Safety and Health Regulations for Construction.* (retrieved March 11, 2008) (http://www.osha.gov/pls/oshaweb/owadisp.show_document?ptable+&STANDARD?p_id=10795).

Plumbing-Heating-Cooling Contractors Association (PHCC). 2006. *National Standard Plumbing Code—Illustrated.* Falls Church, VA: Plumbing-Heating-Cooling Contractors Association.

Visca, P., P. Goldoni, P. C. Luck, J. H. Helbig, L. Cattani, and G. Giltri. 1999. "Multiple Types of Legionella Pneumophila Serogroup 6 in a Hospital Heated-water System Associated with Sporadic Infections." *J.Clin.Microbiol.* 37:2189–2196.

CHAPTER **14**

Environmental Health and Safety Concerns in Nursing Homes

George Byrns

Learning Objectives

1. Describe the increased need for facilities to care for the elderly and some of the problems this growth has caused.

2. Use nursing homes to describe the importance of design in controlling the institutional environment.

3. Review some of the GAO findings regarding the nursing home industry.

4. Discuss unique health and safety concerns of the elderly.

5. Describe the differences between hospitals and nursing homes in establishing comprehensive infection control and safety programs.

Society has an obligation to protect those individuals who are most defenseless: children, the aged or infirm, and those who are incarcerated. Environmental health and safety concerns in nursing homes are important because the average age of citizens in the U.S. and other industrialized countries is increasing, and this will result in an increased need for facilities to care for the aged.

As of 2006, there were approximately 3.1 million U.S. residents housed in 16,100 nursing homes certified by the Centers for Medicare and Medicaid Services (CMS) (CMS 2007). According to CMS, this was a significant increase in the number of people residing in nursing homes, and the average age of a resident was slightly younger than previous years. They suspect that this was due to an increasing number of short-stay residents. Short-stay residents are those with a temporary infirmity, such as post-surgical patients who need some time to rehabilitate before returning to their homes. It was also reported that the number of nursing homes participating in the CMS program steadily decreased since 1997(CMS 2007). The reasons for this decrease in the number of nursing homes were not given but may be due in part to closer scrutiny by the Government Accounting Office (GAO), which is now called the Governmental Accountability Office.

Since 1998, GAO has been investigating abuses to residents in the nation's nursing homes (GAO 2002). In its 2002 report, the GAO found deficiencies in the quality of care provided to nursing home residents, including incidences of physical abuse. There was also concern expressed over weaknesses in complaint investigations, annual surveys, and enforcement actions by state enforcement agencies. In the 2005 report, the GAO found that the number of nursing homes with serious deficiencies had dropped from 29% in 1999 to 16% in 2005, but serious problems still remained (GAO 2005). One of the major concerns was an inconsistence in the quality of inspections by regulators. The GAO reported a need for regulatory agencies to hire and retain qualified inspectors to be able to cope with current demands and the expected increased workload from new facilities (GAO 2005). In 2007, GAO issued another report where they studied the effectiveness of monetary penalties on nursing home operators. They focused on those operations that continually harm nursing home residents (GAO 2007). Their analysis revealed that enforcement measures did not deter these nursing home operations from harming the residents. One of reason for the lack of effectiveness of enforcement was that penalties were not imposed during an appeal period and some of the appeals took years to resolve. Another concern was that these poor performing operations made temporary corrections but then reverted to the unsafe behaviors later on. The third and potentially most serious issue was that there was reluctance to revoke a nursing home's certification in the Medicare/Medicaid program because of concerns that this could create difficulties for some residents to find another home. The GAO's recommendation was that CMS revise its enforcement program in such a way that penalties are imposed immediately and that nursing home operators with a history of problems receive greater scrutiny (GAO 2007). In their most recent report, the GAO revisited the problem of unqualified surveyors and deficient surveys (GAO 2008). Federal inspectors re-surveyed homes that had been previously surveyed by state inspectors. Approximately, one third of state nursing home inspections missed violations that were judged as having the potential to cause more than minimal harm, and nearly twelve percent of surveys missed violations that were judged capable of actual harm or immediate jeopardy. Most of these violations involved the quality of care of residents, but safety concerns were also mentioned. Poor survey methodology and inexperienced state surveyors were listed as contributing causes (GAO 2008). The GAO acknowledged that the CMS has made some improvements in the quality of their surveillance program, but deficiencies remained. CMS agreed to take steps to improve the situation. The main point of these investigations is that society has an obligation to care for these vulnerable populations in a manner that does not violate their basic human rights.

In Chapter 5, we discussed the fact that the nursing home industry is one of the most hazardous places to work because of the high injury rates. OSHA's National Emphasis Program (NEP), which began in July 2002, focuses on ergonomic hazards related to resident handling in nursing homes and personal care facilities (OSHA 2002). Other hazards covered in NEP were exposure to blood and other potentially infectious materials, exposure to tuberculosis, and hazards that can lead to slips, trips, and falls. In this chapter, we will describe environmental health and safety concerns of both patients and staff at these facilities.

NURSING HOME STANDARDS

There are a number of regulations and standards that pertain to the nursing home industry. For example, the Joint Commission on Accreditation of Healthcare Organizations (Joint Commission) has a long-term care facility standard that is similar to that of hospitals (JCAHO 2008). Accreditation by the Joint Commission is considered to be acceptable for Medicare. Over 98% of nursing homes in the U.S. are certified, and most of these are evaluated with CMS standards by federal or state inspectors (CDC 2007; Harrington et al. 2006).

The National Fire Protection Association (NFPA) has a number of standards that pertain to nursing homes. One of the most important is NFPA 101, *Life Safety Code®* (NFPA 2006). Compliance with this code is complicated and depends on whether the facility is a newly constructed or existing facility and whether it is considered a healthcare or residential care facility.

AIA Standards

The American Institute of Architects (AIA) maintains design and construction standards for nursing homes (AIA 2006). Facilities traditionally identified as skilled or intermediate care facilities are covered under one section of the code, but assisted living nursing homes are covered under sections dealing with lodging or rooming houses or a section dealing with residential board and care. There are several types of extended care facilities covered in the AIA standard. Some examples are skilled care nursing, standard nursing (also called intermediate care), Alzheimer's units, and assisted living. These facilities may be either free standing or attached to an acute-care hospital. All of these facilities need to be designed to assure barrier-free access, since many of the residents will have limited mobility.

Residential Units

The AIA standard allows a maximum of four residents per room in existing facilities, and a maximum of two residents per room in new construction. The standards do not specify a minimum amount of space per room, but they do require that the rooms be large enough to use a wheelchair and to gain access to each side of the bed. Providing sufficient space to position mechanical lifting devices near the bed was not considered in the 2006 standards; however, this is proposed in the next version of the standards (in draft as of publication). A discussion the problems of worker back injuries due to resident lifting occurs later in this chapter.

Service Areas

There are also a variety of requirements for ancillary services, such as dietary facilities and linen and laundry. The design of nursing home dietary facilities must conform to food service sanitation codes and must provide for the unique needs of bed-ridden residents, such as the transport of hot and cold foods. Linen services may be provided through a contract or provided on-site. Some of the minimum features for either in-house or off-site linen processing include properly vented, soiled holding facilities and a laundry design that separates clean and soiled linen processing. A properly vented, soiled linen room should provide a minimum of ten room air changes per hour under negative pressure.

Details and Finishes

The issue of design details and finishes is particularly important in nursing homes because a fall may result in a life-threatening injury. Therefore, nursing home designs should avoid slippery surfaces and sharp corners. They should also avoid abrupt changes in floor surfaces to avoid tripping hazards. Some other important health and safety design features are providing operable windows with screens, as well as grab bars and handrails on both sides of corridors and in toilet rooms. In addition, the standards call for easily cleanable surfaces. This means that carpeting should be avoided in certain locations.

Mechanical Standards

The AIA mechanical standards are less rigorous than those of hospitals but do share some common features. For example, the heating ventilating and air conditioning (HVAC) system should prevent cross contamination by moving air from clean areas toward "less clean" areas. There are no requirements for mechanically vented isolation rooms; thus, nursing homes lacking proper isolation rooms should not house residents who are infected with airborne diseases. Infection control is covered later in this chapter. Proposed AIA standards for 2010 (in draft as of this edition) require air from an isolation room be exhausted directly to the outside. As in hospitals, fresh air inlets must be at least 25 feet from exhaust discharge openings. In resident care areas with central HVAC, the system must include final air filters with 80% efficiency. The standards do allow through-the-wall fan coil units that only have 68% efficient filters.

Plumbing and other piping systems must comply with the *National Standard Plumbing Code®* (PHCC 2006). Some important provisions are the requirement for wrist blades or other types of devices that allow staff to wash hands without touching the handle with their fingers. There should be sufficient hot water to meet the needs of the facility, but the temperature at sinks used by residents must be maintained between 95 and 110°F.

Electrical standards must meet NFPA 70 (the *National Electrical Code®*) and 99 (the *Standard for Health Care Facilities®*) (NFPA 2005a; NFPA 2005b). Lighting levels must meet the standards of the Illuminating Engineering Society of North America (IESNA 2006). Nurse call systems, emergency power systems, and fire alarm systems are all required in nursing homes the same as in hospitals.

Infection Control

Infections among nursing home residents are common and may affect the respiratory tract, urinary tract, skin and soft tissue, and gastrointestinal tract (Nicolle 2001). Infection control in nursing homes is complicated by the varying levels of nursing care provided, the size of the facility, and other factors (Smith and Rusnak 1997). While many nursing homes have developed infection control programs, due to fewer resources, these programs tend to be less extensive than those in hospitals. Complicating matters is that annual incidence rates range from 3% to as high as 15%, and many infected residents are asymptomatic (Jarvis 2001).

Special Host Factors
The elderly are at a greater risk of infection due to primary and secondary immune deficits (Smith and Rusnak 1997). Some primary deficits include a decreased production of gastric acid and decreased mucosa in the gastrointestinal tract. In the eyes, there is decreased tear and lysozyme production, and diminished blinking. With age, there is a decrease in lung vital capacity, a weakened cough, and a lower clearance mechanism due to mucociliary transport changes. Other primary deficits include a thinning of skin, a loss of connective tissue, and reduced blood flow due to atherosclerosis. Secondary immune deficits include a diminished function of polymorphonuclear leukocytes (PMNs), and diminished function of T and B lymphocytes, resulting in a delayed hypersensitivity response and a decrease in antibody production. These age-related changes increase the susceptibility of residents to a wide range of infectious organisms. In addition, elderly residents are more susceptible to disease because of underlying medical conditions, medications such as steroids and antibiotics, and impaired mental status which may result in aspiration pneumonia (Smith and Rusnak 1997). Other factors such as incontinence and indwelling catheters further increase the risk.

Sites of Infection
Long-term care facilities may serve as a reservoir for a number of important infectious agents such as methicillin-drug resistant *Staphylococcus aureus* (MSRA), tuberculosis, influenza, and gram negative bacteria (Stone et al. 2001;

Smith and Rusnak 1997). The most common nosocomial infections in nursing homes were urinary tract infections (UTIs), respiratory infections, skin infections, gastroenteritis, and conjunctivitis (Smith and Rusnak 1997). Heavy use of indwelling catheters contributes to high UTIs rates, and these infections tended to be due to antibiotic-resistant organisms. Control of UTIs involves limiting the use of indwelling catheters and assuring that when catheterization is performed, it is done by trained personnel using aseptic techniques.

Respiratory infections are common among the institutionalized elderly persons; due to their impaired immunity, they tend to be more serious (Smith and Rusnak 1997). Elderly residents with underlying health conditions, such as chronic obstructive pulmonary and heart disease, are at a significant risk of developing life-threatening cases of pneumonia. Aspiration pneumonia is also a potential problem. Some of the solutions to prevent respiratory infections include elevating the resident's head during feedings and administering the pneumococcal and influenza vaccines.

Skin infections are associated with pressure sores, also called *decubitus ulcers*. These also may be life threatening and require extensive medical intervention. Residents' lack of mobility is a major predisposing factor. However, other factors, such as incontinence, malnutrition, and treatment with steroids, may also be important. Prevention of bed sores requires a routine plan for repositioning and the use of special mattresses or foam protectors to reduce pressure and friction to the resident's skin.

One overlooked risk factor for infection is the quality of the linen service. Improper laundering procedures can present a risk to both the staff and to the residents. In one salmonella gastroenteritis outbreak, 32 residents and 8 employees became ill. While the cause of the residents' illness was foodborne, the nursing home laundry appeared to be the source of the employees' illness (Standaert et al. 1994). Employees ate in the laundry and did not wear personal protective clothing while handling the soiled linen. In order to assure the destruction of microorganisms such as salmonella, industrial laundry operations use high temperatures and high pH detergents (11 and above) (Byrns and Bland 1980). It is necessary to reduce the pH of the linen to the slightly acid side (approximately 5.5). Therefore, the last step in the laundry wash cycle is to add a neutralizing chemical called a *sour*. Failure to reduce the pH of the linen, combined with resident incontinence, creates serious skin irritation that may lead to bed sores.

The high prevalence of gastroenteritis infections is due to the impaired immunity of the elderly, problems with incontinence, and person-to-person spread due to group activities and reduced mental function (Smith and Rusnak 1997). Also as described above, foodborne outbreaks can be a problem. Food service inspections can help prevent major outbreaks, but prevention of cross-infection due to group activities can be challenging. Another type of infection, conjunctivitis, can also spread rapidly through a population of elderly persons; control involves glove use and hand washing during eye care.

The control of infections in extended care facilities is a major challenge. Studies have shown that assuring adequate staffing with skilled nurses, appropriate use of antibiotics, sufficient numbers of hand-washing sinks, and good hand hygiene were important infection control measures that should be applied (Loeb et al. 2003; CDC 2002). One study found two factors that decreased infection rates: smaller nursing homes and the provision of paid sick leave for staff (Li et al. 1996).

HEALTH AND SAFETY PROGRAMS IN NURSING HOMES

Figure 14.1 demonstrates some of the varied types of safety hazards found in a typical nursing home. The risks fall into the same categories (chemical, biological, physical, and psychological) that were discussed in Chapter 2.

Safety issues in nursing homes are similar to acute care but, there are higher percentages of less skilled workers, and there is a higher staff turnover. The annual turnover rate for the largest job category, certified nursing assistants (CNAs), is over 70% (AHCA 2003). Nursing homes are also having a hard time recruiting registered nurses and licensed practical nurses. According to the American Health Care Association (AHCA), there were about 96,000 nursing position vacancies in nursing homes throughout the U.S.; the majority of these vacancies, about 52,000, were for CNAs. As we discussed earlier, the percentage of elderly people in the U.S. continues to grow, so the demand for workers will also continue to increase. One major reason for this large staffing problem is that the work is hard and dangerous. In 2001, nursing and home care was the second most dangerous workplace for non-fatal injuries with an injury rate of 13.0 per 100 workers. In 2006, the total injury and illness rate dropped to 8.9 per 100 workers, but this is still about twice the national average injury rate (BLS 2006). The high incidence of injuries creates a downward spiral because as workers become disabled, they may no longer be able to work or may seek employment elsewhere, leaving the remaining workers short-handed. Ironically, one of the major risk factors for workplace injury was understaffing (Trinkoff et al. 2005).

The most common types of lost-time injuries to nursing home workers in 2006 were strains and sprains (51%). (BLS, 2006) While most injuries were associated with patient handling, other tasks, such as pushing and pulling heavy carts or maintaining awkward postures, were also risk factors. In my research, nursing home workers who used manual lifting techniques instead of mechanical lifts reported significantly more low back pain (Byrns et al. 2007). This information was analyzed using odds ratios (OR) and 95% confidence intervals (CIs). The most dangerous task was manually lifting a resident who had fallen to the floor (OR = 3.5, 95% CI = 1.2–9.8). These results mean we are 95% confident that the odds of having back pain were at least 1.2 times higher in those who lifted using just their backs compared to those who used mechanical lifting devices.

One key issue identified by GAO inspectors was fire safety (GAO 2005). As of 2003, all nursing homes must comply with the 2000 version of NFPA 101 *Life*

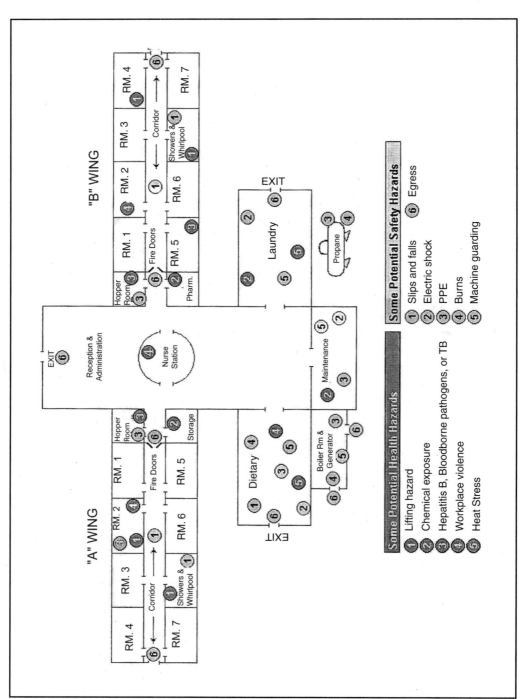

Figure 14.1 Nursing Home Hazards. (Courtesy of OSHA)

Safety Code for existing facilities (NFPA 2000). However, even under the 2000 Code, nursing homes were not required to have automatic sprinklers if they were constructed of non-combustible materials (NFPA 2000). In 2003, fires in two separate facilities claimed the lives of 31 nursing home residents. CMS is re-evaluating the need to install automatic sprinklers in older nursing homes to reduce the loss of life during a fire (GAO 2005).

Safety Program Management

The nursing home administrator should appoint a safety director to oversee the implementation of the facility-wide safety program. In most cases, this is a collateral duty assignment of the facility maintenance director. As in a hospital, there must be facility-wide and department-specific safety policies and procedures. One of the policies should be the requirement for performing hazard surveillance. Surveillance should focus on potential hazards, staff knowledge and compliance with safety policies, especially the restricted resident lifting and fire safety policies. See Chapters 5 and 10 for more information on surveys and surveillance.

Nursing homes should also create a facility health and safety committee. The committee size depends on the size and complexity of the nursing home. At a minimum, the committee should meet quarterly to discuss the workplace hazards and their means of control. Another important function of the safety committee is to oversee the safety education and data management aspects of the safety program.

Emergency Preparedness

Nursing homes should have an internal emergency preparedness plan that is similar to hospitals. For example, the fire alarm system must be directly connected to the fire department or by another reliable means. As in a hospital, there must be regularly scheduled fire drills. The need for emergency power is based on the size and complexity of the institution. At a minimum, there should be sufficient emergency lighting to assist staff and residents in evacuating the building if necessary. A nursing home's external emergency plan should be integrated into the community-wide plan. However, nursing homes generally play a supportive role in providing for the care of less severely injured patients in a disaster. See Chapter 7 for more information on emergency preparedness.

Hurricane Katrina revealed special emergency preparedness concerns regarding nursing home operations and the need to evacuate (GAO 2006b). A recent GAO investigation found that the ultimate decision to evacuate a facility was left to the nursing home administrator, not state or local governments. This decision was complicated and based in part on the ability of the home to shelter residents in place and the adequacy of their supply system. For some homes, there is a reluctance to evacuate too soon because of the dangers in moving large numbers of bed-ridden residents. On the other hand, evacuating too late also increases the risks of loss of life. One of the most serious issues identified in this investigation was that the demand for transportation services would exceed the supply in a major disaster. It was also noted that the National Disaster Medical System (NDMS), a federally coordinated program to support the nation's medical response capacity during emergencies, was not set up to assist nursing homes (GAO 2006b). This issue and the adequacy of resident transportation were addressed in a follow-up investigation by the GAO (GAO 2006a). In this report, the GAO urged the federal government to assist state and local governments in providing transportation and to address the need of nursing homes during evacuations.

Hazardous Materials and Wastes Management

Nursing homes must have a program for hazardous materials and wastes management; the approach would be similar to an acute care facility. In general, nursing homes would be expected to have fewer and less toxic materials than a hospital. Provisions must be made for the safe storage and disposal of contaminated sharps and other medical waste.

SAFETY DEVICES AND PRACTICES

As previously discussed, the fall of a nursing home resident may be a life-threatening event. Therefore, particular care is necessary regarding the placement of grab bars and handrails, as well as the importance of slip resistant, even floor surfaces.

Some other safety concerns include the use of portable heaters and extension cords. The elderly are susceptible to heat loss, and their family members may attempt to bring portable heaters or other devices into the facility. Because such heaters and other devices may present a fire or electrical safety concern, there must be a policy that addresses the inspection and approval of any personal devices before they may be used in the facility. Other concerns are storage areas and the placement of nurse call devices. Storage areas must be kept free of clutter and flammable materials, and nurse call devices must be placed within easy reach of the resident, including in bathrooms and near the toilet.

Ergonomics Case Study

Wyandot County Nursing Home is a 100–bed, county-run intermediate- to skilled-care facility in Ohio (OSHA 2003). Between 1995 and 1997, workers' compensation costs averaged almost $140,000 per year, and CNA turnover rate was below the national average, but was still about 55%. In order to address the problem of workers' compensation costs and the need to reduce CNA turnover, the nursing home administrator initiated a number of changes. He established a policy prohibiting single-person lifts of residents.

He also purchased two kinds of lifts, one for residents who could stand (called a sit-to-stand lift) and another for residents who could not (called a total body lift). Gait belts were purchased for residents who could walk with assistance. (These are devices that are strapped around the resident so that staff has some degree of control if the resident falls.) Some other changes were to replace the old hand-crank beds with electric beds making it easier to move and transfer residents to and from the bed. A final change was to install ceiling-mounted lifts in two double bedrooms. These devices are arranged on tracks that allow the resident to be lifted from the bed to a chair, stretcher, or into the toilet room. The administrator then arranged for staff to be trained in equipment use and in proper transfer techniques. The total cost of implementing these changes was $280,000. While this cost seems high, the facility's workers' compensation costs dropped to less than $4000 per year, and potentially even more significant, staff turnover decreased. The reduction in staff turnover is expected to save the nursing home $125,000 per year in recruiting and training costs. This case study clearly demonstrates the value of a proactive safety program that includes an investment in ergonomics. OSHA provides guidance in the means of preventing ergonomic disabilities (OSHA 2003). See Chapter 2 for more information on the importance of ergonomic interventions.

ENVIRONMENTAL CONCERNS

Nursing homes should maintain a high level of sanitation, not only for infection control reasons, but for the mental health of the residents. As previously discussed, it is best to avoid carpeting in residents' rooms because of the difficulty in keeping it clean.

In terms of environmental compliance, nursing homes are expected to comply with federal regulations the same as any other institution. See Chapter 6 for more information on environmental management. Other environmental concerns, such as food protection, are the same as in hospitals. Food sanitation must be maintained at a high level because a foodborne disease outbreak would have devastating consequences. Radiation protection is generally not a concern because diagnostic and treatment procedures are usually conducted off-site.

SURVEY PROCEDURES

As discussed in Chapter 10, the best survey uses a *team approach*. Members of the team should be knowledgeable of environmental health, safety, and clinical care. The format of a nursing home survey depends on the objectives: Is the survey conducted to determine compliance with Joint Commission standards or CMS regulations, or is the survey focusing on a particular issue, such as compliance with the OSHA *Bloodborne Pathogens Standard* (OSHA 2006)? Routine hazard surveys should review conditions, practices and staff knowledge of facility policies and procedures. The role of an institutional environmental health and safety (IEHS) professional may be as an advisor, team member, or regulator.

SUMMARY AND CONCLUSIONS

There has been a steady increase in the need for facilities to care for the elderly. Studies by the GAO have uncovered serious problems in some of these facilities, and the increasing percentage of elderly persons in the U.S. will only make this situation worse. Therefore, nursing homes should be designed and operated in such a manner as to protect the basic human rights of their residents. This is particularly important because the elderly have certain conditions, such as weakened immune systems and osteoporosis, which make them more susceptible to infections and injuries. The elderly may also have decreased mobility, which presents a risk in the event of fire or other evacuation. Since the aged are a highly vulnerable population, public health agencies need to monitor the quality of facilities and operations at nursing homes. The most effective survey is one that is conducted using a team of professionals who are knowledgeable of environmental health, safety, and clinical care. Environmental health and safety professionals play a key role on these teams.

Review

1. What were the major findings of the 2002, 2005, 2007 and 2008 GAO Reports on nursing homes?

2. Why is prevention of resident falls so important in nursing homes? Discuss design features that protect against these falls.

3. What are wrist blades?

4. What are some examples of primary immune system deficits among the elderly?

5. What is the most common type of infection among the elderly, and what is a contributing factor for these infections?

6. What is a decubitus ulcer, and what are some contributing factors for this condition?

7. Studies have shown that certain measures are important in preventing infections in nursing homes. What were these measures?

8. There are similarities between hospitals and nursing homes regarding occupational injuries and illnesses. What are some of the differences between them?

9. What was the most common type of occupational injury in nursing homes, and what was the likely cause?

Reference List

American Health Care Association (AHCA). 2003. *Results of the 2002 AHCA Survey of Nursing Staff Vacancy and Turnover in Nursing Homes.* Washington, D. C.: American Health Care Association.

American Institute of Architects (AIA). 2006. *Guidelines for Design and Construction of Hospital and Health Care Facilities.* Washington, D.C.: The American Institute of Architects.

Bureau of Labor Statistics (BLS). 2006. *Incidence rates of nonfatal occupational injuries and illnesses involving days away from work by selected worker and case characteristics and industry, All U.S., private industry, 2006.* Washington, D. C.: Bureau of Labor Statistics.

Byrns, G. E. and L. A. Bland. 1980. "Environmental Health Impact in the Hospital Laundry." *Journal of Environmental Health* 42:258–262.

Byrns, G. E., D. Knoblauch, and C. M. Mallory. 2007. "Are All "No-lift" Policies the Same?" *AOHP Journal* 28:19–23.

Centers for Disease Control and Prevention (CDC). 2002. "Guideline for Hand Hygiene in Health-Care Settings: Recommendations of the Healthcare Infection Control Practices Advisory Committee and the HICPAC/SHEA/APIC/IDSA Hand Hygiene Task Force." *MMWR* (RR-16) 51:. Atlanta: U.S. Government Printing Office.

———. 2007. National Nursing Home Survey (NNHS). National Health Care Surveys (retrieved September 2, 2008). (http://www.cdc.gov/nchs/about/major/nnhsd/Facilitytables.htm).

Centers for Medicare and Medicaid Services (CMS). 2007. *Nursing Home Data Compendium.* Baltimore, MD: Centers for Medicare and Medicaid Services.

General Accounting Office (GAO). 2002. *Nursing Homes: More Can Be Done to Protect Residents from Abuse* (Rep. No. GAO-02-312). Washington, D.C.: U.S. General Accounting Office.

———. 2005. *Nursing Homes: Despite Increased Oversight, Challenges Remain in Ensuring High-Quality Care and Resident Safety* (Rep. No. GAO-06-117). Washington, D.C.: U.S. General Accounting Office.

———. 2006a. *Disaster Preparedness: Limitations in Federal Evacuation Assistance for Health Facilities Should Be Addressed* (Rep. No. 06-826). Washington, D.C.: U.S. Government Accountability Office.

———. 2006b. *Disaster Preparedness: Preliminary Observations on the Evacuation of Hospitals and Nursing Homes Due to Hurricanes* (Rep. No. 06-443R). Washington, D.C.: U.S. Government Accountability Office.

———. 2007. *Nursing Homes: Efforts to Strengthen Federal Enforcement Have Not Deterred Some Homes from Repeatedly Harming Residents* (Rep. No. 07-241). Washington, D.C.: U.S. Government Accountability Office.

————. 2008. *Nursing Homes: Federal Monitoring Surveys Demonstrate Continued Understatement of Serious Care Problems and CMS Oversight Weaknesses* (Rep. No. 08-517). Washington, D.C.: U.S. Government Accountability Office.

Harrington, C., H. Carrillo, and C. LaCava. 2006. *Nursing Facilities, Staffing, Residents and Facility Deficiencies, 1999 Through 2005.* Department of Social and Behavioral Sciences, University of California.

Illuminating Engineering Society of North America (IESNA). 2006. *Lighting for Hospitals and Health Care Facilities* (Rep. No. RP-29-06). New York: Illuminating Engineering Society of North America.

Jarvis, W. R. 2001. "Infection Control and Changing Health-Care Delivery Systems." *Emerg.Infect.Dis.,* 7:170–173.

Joint Commission on Accreditation of Healthcare Organizations (JCAHO). 2008. Facts about Long Term Care Accreditation (retrieved September 5, 2008) (http://www.jointcommission.org/AccreditationPrograms/LongTermCare/AccreditationOptions/ltc_facts.htm).

Li, J., G. S. Birkhead, D. S. Strogatz, and F. B. Coles. 1996. "Impact of Institution Size, Staffing Patterns, and Infection Control Practices on Communicable Disease Outbreaks in New York State Nursing Homes." *Am.J.Epidemiol.* 143:1042–1049.

Loeb, M. B., S. Craven, A. J. McGeer, A. E. Simor, S. F. Bradley, D. E. Low. 2003. "Risk Factors for Resistance to Antimicrobial Agents among Nursing Home Residents." *Am.J.Epidemiol.* 157:40–47.

National Fire Protection Association (NFPA). 2005a. NFPA 70, *National Electrical Code.* Quincy, MA: National Fire Protection Association.

————. 2005b. NFPA 99, *Standard for Health Care Facilities.* Quincy, MA: National Fire Protection Association.

————. 2006. NFPA 101, *Life Safety Code.* Quincy, MA: National Fire Protection Association.

Nicolle, L. E. 2001. "Preventing Infections in Non-hospital Settings: Long-term Care." *Emerg.Infect.Dis.* 7:205–207.

Occupational Safety and Health Administration (OSHA). 2006. 29 CFR 1910.1030, *Bloodborne Pathogen Standard* (retrieved September 2, 2008) (http://www.osha.gov/pls/oshaweb/owadisp.show_document?p_table=STANDARDS&p_id=10051).

————. 2003. *Guidelines for Nursing Homes: Ergonomics for the Prevention Musculoskeletal Disorders* (Rep. No. OSHA 3182).Washington, D.C.: Occupational Safety and Health Administration.

Plumbing-Heating-Cooling Contractors Association (PHCC). 2006. *National Standard Plumbing Code.* Falls Church, VA: Plumbing-Heating-Cooling Contractors Association.

Smith, P. W. and P. G. Rusnak. 1997. "Infection Prevention and Control in the Long-term-care Facility." *Am.J.Infect.Control.* 25:488–512.

Standaert, S. M., R. H. Hutcheson, and W. Schaffner. 1994. Nosocomial Transmission of Salmonella Gastroenteritis to Laundry Workers in a Nursing Home." *Infect.Control Hosp.Epidemiol.* 15:22–26.

Stone, S. P., C. C. Kibbler, C. Bowman, and D. Stott. 2001. "Controlling Infection in British Nursing Homes. It is Time for a National Strategy." *BMJ*. 322:506.

Trinkoff, A. M., M. Johantgen, C. Muntaner, and R. Le. 2005. "Staffing and Worker Injury in Nursing Homes." *Am.J.Public Health*. 95: 1220–1225.

CHAPTER 15

Environmental Health and Safety Concerns in Colleges and Universities

Timothy Ryan

Learning Objectives

1. Describe the types of facilities and operations found in colleges and universities.

2. Discuss environmental health and safety hazards in these facilities.

3. Describe the role of environmental health and safety professionals in these facilities.

4. Highlight regulatory elements and strategies affecting these facilities.

5. Discuss special problems in research and other unique areas in colleges and universities.

Because of the large number of specific differences among campuses, the one commonality all colleges and universities share is their diversity of operations, physical plant, people, and specialties. For that reason, the approach taken in this chapter will be to combine the various issues, concerns, and compliance matters into a unifying set of objectives. These four aspects will be discussed simultaneously with the specific campus element at hand so as to provide the reader a succinct yet meaningful overview of the exact issues associated with each topic.

There are few occupational settings in the U.S., or the Western world for that matter, which are as diverse and changeable as the typical college or university campus. From swimming pool hazards to linear accelerators, from day-care center hepatitis outbreaks to laboratories researching Mad Cow Disease, from steam co-generation physical plants to student–run, sustainability project houses, the continuum of issues in such environments is truly exceptional. And with this wide range of possibilities come great challenges as well as opportunities for the institutional environmental health and safety (IEHS) professional. Challenges include working with an extraordinarily diverse group of people, with varying education levels, which come from many nations and so also vary in their English communication skills. The opportunities are equally wide. The IEHS practitioner may be teaching hazard communication to under-educated, mostly Spanish-speaking laundry workers in the morning and reviewing a Nobel laureate's research laboratory for biosafety compliance that afternoon. On another day, he or she might be heading up a review of local exhaust ventilation concerns in the morning, while serving as part of an inter-disciplinary committee on campus violence that afternoon. There is really no other occupational setting quite like that of the typical college or university when it comes to occupational health and safety matters.

TYPES OF FACILITIES FOUND IN A UNIVERSITY

It is not an exaggeration to state that some larger universities are capable of acting as a wholly separate municipality. Under the laws of most states, the police at a college function as a jurisdiction apart from, yet equal to, the community in which the college resides. In addition, the extensive agricultural resources of many land grant universities, in combination with a developing desire for sustainability and carbon-neutral campus operations, means that an organization should be capable of providing at least some of the food needs of its residents. On a campus with a large residential component, housing for students and visiting staff (including the college president in most locations) is clearly a part of this milieu. Finally, when the administrative interests of a school involve lobbying and input at the level of Congress, it is possible for universities to act as an almost self-governed territory of the U.S. Such is clearly the structure of most national laboratories (for example, Los Alamos National Laboratory, operated by the University of California system). In such a large and complex organizational structure, it comes as no surprise that almost any operation or human pursuit found in the "real world" is likely to be found on one or more college campuses.

In addition to some unique college-affiliated endeavors, such as correctional hospitals, pilot-plant chemical engineering setups, small nuclear reactors, airports, farms, to name a few, most universities operate most of the following functions. Unique problems or issues with each are briefly highlighted.

Classrooms. These may range in size from small graduate seminar conference rooms to large amphitheaters designed to hold 500 or 1000 undergraduates for certain introductory courses. Given the large number of these facilities, issues related to classrooms are refreshingly few. Most complaints tend to involve nuisance odors; since most schools ban smoking indoors, those issues are in decline.

Office Space. The president and attendant staff need an office suite, as do the university's chief academic officer, the provost, the chief financial officer, the plant and operations group, accounting, purchasing, human resources, police and safety functions, and so forth. In fact, most universities have more staff members than faculty, and the majority of these job functions require a traditional office environment. Ergonomic issues related to prolonged computer use, indoor air quality (IAQ) complaints, and temperature disputes are frequently associated with such occupancies.

Laboratories. This is one area that sets the college campus apart from many other space utilizations found in the private sector. The term *laboratory* has become an extremely inclusive term in the last few decades, including not only the expected chemistry, physics and biology settings, but also undertakings such as nuclear facilities, geology or geographic land study areas, as well as sociological study units, such as daycare centers, psychology testing areas, or experimental schools.

Large Residential Structures. Dormitories have long been a defining element of the stereotypical residential undergraduate college campus, and continue to be constructed or renovated at most schools. Following World War II, as many young men returned from the war and were able to attend college under the benefits of the GI Bill, there followed a boom in building dorms and residential student housing. However, that housing stock has since been either extensively renovated or converted into service for other needs. Such conversions can lead to mixed-use conflicts (e.g., student housing in conjunction with research efforts) or simple, building-related oversights (e.g., dorm room shower stalls used for long-term storage of materials, allowing sewer traps to dry out and generate IAQ complaints).

Large Institutional Food Operations. Often existing in a hand-in-glove arrangement with dormitories, campus food operations may also be stand-alone dining halls. Stadiums for football, track, baseball, and basketball may also include food operations, as can well-known franchise operations. Increasingly, there is a trend toward smaller niche facilities, such as coffee houses in student centers, fast food take-out islands, and even food cart or trailer vendors on busy sidewalks transecting the college grounds. Thankfully, the importance of safe food operations (or perhaps the stigma of bad press or public relations associated with even a single foodborne illness outbreak) is well understood by most university food service operators. Other than the usual food code compliance issues specific to a given facility, most problems with these units tend to be at startup and center around necessary, sometimes expensive, equipment, including three-compartment sinks, dedicated hand-washing sinks, toilets, and other plumbing issues.

Healthcare Facilities. The many health and safety matters associated with hospitals have been covered in depth in earlier chapters of this book. Nevertheless, almost all schools of any size operate a student health center to serve the non-life-threatening healthcare needs of a young adult population. Airborne and contact-spread communicable diseases are commonly dealt with at such locations, as are sexually transmitted infections, birth control, and a multitude of preventive and mental health matters.

Daycare Facilities. Even a mid-size university (5,000–10,000 students) is likely to have a daycare facility for the benefit of faculty, staff, and students with pre-school age children. These units are often more complex than might be appreciated at first pass, and can include environmental issues (indoor air, presence of cleaners and other possible toxic ingestion hazards, and toxicity of art materials), security, communicable diseases with a fecal-oral transmission route, biohazards related to insulin syringes, asthma inhalers or other child-specific health needs, and food service considerations (CPSC 1999).

Animal Care Operations. The care, feeding, and security of animals in the campus environment are growing areas of IEHS concern for a number of reasons. Animal rights groups have become a serious threat to both the animal care physical environment, as well as the intellectual aspects of the research conducted with animals. This is despite significant and conscientious adherence to federal guidelines in virtually all animal care jurisdictions (NIH 2002). Waste products and odors associated with research herds at some locations are another environmental aspect that is becoming part of the domain of the IEHS practitioner. Laboratory animals have long posed well-recognized hazards in need of scrutiny, such as chemically contaminated urine and feces, biohazards, and the physical safety of the care providers (ILAR 2003). The last of these is of particular concern where potentially dangerous primates such as apes, monkeys, and gorillas may be kept for study.

Shops and Maintenance Areas. Occupational safety and environmental concerns abound at all universities, especially in the plant and shop areas. The provision of heating and cooling capacity at mid- to large-size campuses will constitute a formidable investment in space, hardware, personnel, and facilities. Examples of required elements may include some or all of the following: a coal or natural gas-powered electrical or steam generating plant; a motor pool to service, fuel, and maintain diesel, gas and electric vehicles; the lawn and grounds function entailing pesticides, herbicides, sanding and salting, numerous noise-generating cutting decks and tractors; primary power provision to the campus, as well as telephone, microwave, and networking (often through asbestos-containing areas or materials); carpentry, painting and lead-based paint identification and control; and street and traffic operations, such as signal maintenance, signage, pedestrian safety and walking surfaces.

Recreational Spaces. As any college student knows, a four-year education is hardly all work and no play. To attract a finite number of students, many schools have increasingly poured money into amenities that enhance the lifestyle and attractiveness of the experience to new and continuing students (Recreation Management 2008). These include modern and very well-equipped student recreational facilities. Within such complexes can be found swimming pools, diving pools (competitive pools as well as sport, underwater, or diving), spas, juice bars, weight and exercise rooms, climbing walls, tracks, saunas, and therapy or first aid functions.

ROLE OF ENVIRONMENTAL HEALTH IN SCHOOLS AND UNIVERSITIES

The role of the IEHS professional in a college or university is, for the most part, identical to that of the private sector or governmental employee. With the exception of some notable special hazard operations, most of the responsibilities that are contingent upon the safety professional in a municipality, state enforcement bureau, or corporate health and safety function also exist at even the smaller schools. As such, a brief review of these functions and duties is in order. Such tasks fall into the categories of ethical obligations, compliance-driven mandates, and the recognition and control of new or emerging problems. Details of each of those areas will be followed by a thorough discussion of the many specialty concerns unique to a campus environment.

Ethics

Ethics has traditionally been listed last, if at all, in most texts concerning environmental health and safety. However, under most existing or emerging professional codes of practice (such as the Board of Certified Safety Professionals (BCSP) and the American Board of Industrial Hygiene (ABIH)), as well as outcome-based performance criteria for the accreditation of applied science study areas (ABET 2008), ethics or similar rubrics are taking on heightened importance. This is largely due to some well-publicized and, unfortunately, frequent lapses of ethics on the part of politicians, regulators, prominent athletes, corporate CEOs, and others in positions of responsibility to the public. Ethics is clearly of high importance in any profession charged with the protection of the health and well-being of people or the environments in which they must exist. But what are the ethical expectations imposed upon the IEHS practitioner?

Several model canons of ethical conduct exist as they relate to those charged with safeguarding the health of other human beings. The first of these is arguably attributed to Hippocrates (c. 400 B.C.) in what has become known as the Hippocratic Oath associated with physicians (NLM 2002). "To do no harm" is perhaps the best known element of that set of guiding principles, although there are others. Its applicability to IEHS matters can be illustrated by cautioning students to fully consider the implications of their recommendations or requirements to ensure they are not short-sighted or lead to secondary environmental problems. For example, prohibiting the sink disposal of volatile solvents in laboratories, but providing no safe alternative so that users ultimately simply evaporate their volatiles via the fume hood, might be one example of the application of this guiding principle. Additional ethical considerations germane to IEHS include: avoiding conflicts of interest; staying current and informed about developments and the state-of-the-art IEHS practices; conducting oneself in a professional manner; and adopting a personal and professional goal of serving humankind to provide a healthful environment for all (NEHA 2007).

General Compliance

Compliance is probably the most visible, frequent, and unpleasant aspect of any IEHS practitioner's duties. The simple truth of the matter is that this is the unpopular job element that many IEHS personnel are hired to perform. Regardless of the specifics of a particular issue, the compliance role at a university necessitates exacting command of sometimes lengthy, subtle and arcane code requirements, a high level of tact, resilience, and patience in dealing with people, and the ability to know when to escalate an issue to a higher authority. Compliance actions can take place on three general levels, and in the course of a typical day it is not unusual to participate in actions at all three, which are:

1. Prevention;
2. Inspection; and
3. Remediation or control.

Prevention

The best way to solve a problem is to avoid it in the first place, an approach best summed up as prevention. The oft-repeated statement, "An ounce of prevention is worth a pound of cure" is as true in environmental health and safety situations as it is in the home. The anticipation of hazards, presumably for their potential prevention, is in fact the first of four sequential steps characteristic of the industrial hygiene process (Nims 1999). Given the high cost of retroactive fixes to improper or unsafe work areas, and the ever-present threat of litigation following a workplace injury or illness, it is more important than ever to strive to implement prevention first in all IEHS actions. In certain organizational structures, safety prevention may involve areas impacting the security and police functions as well include all of the following discussed below.

Plan Review. Design of new facilities or the renovation of well-known problem areas presents a unique, once-in-a-career opportunity to avoid or correct well-recognized facility issues. Common examples include the relocation of poorly placed building fresh air intakes, addition of local exhaust ventilation to places, such as laboratories where odor complaints are frequent, and placing fire sprinklers into dormitories where they may have been lacking. A good preconstruction hazard analysis of laboratory space will involve workflow, operations, and safety equipment, integrating established safety considerations such as control and safety systems (e.g., alarms, interlocks, fire protection), fail-safe designs, reliability, redundancy, and implications of all of these (Palluzi 1994). Plan review and assistance in interpreting safety-related building codes is one area where a competent, available, and personable IEHS representative not only adds value to the university, but also establishes inroads and credibility with the engineers, architects, and principal investigators constituting the major change drivers at so many institutions.

Substitution. Substitution can be simple or involved, and may be applied to materials, equipment, or processes (Burton 2003). The usual examples of substitution involve chemical examples, like using xylene or toluene for leukemia-causing benzene, or replacing older, noisy machinery with newer, quieter models. Emerging opportunities exist, however, and include such actions as replacing manual material handling in places like the campus warehouse with robotic or mechanized conveyors, or using patient lifts in hospital environments to replace the often–ignored, two-person lifting rule.

Trend Analysis. Virtually all workplaces have a mechanism in place for reporting accidental injuries or illnesses, either to the safety function, the workers' compensation unit, or both (Brauer 2006, 79–92). Indeed, for privately held schools, compliance with federal Occupational Safety and Health Administration (OSHA) reporting requirements is legally required. Such information should be studied to identify campus jobs or areas where prospective safety actions might identify future accident numbers or severity reduction.

Violence Mitigation. Jeanne Clery was a 19-year-old Lehigh University freshman who was raped and murdered while sleeping in her campus residence hall in 1986 (e2Campus 2008). Upon the disclosure that more than 35 additional violent crimes had occurred in or around that campus in the preceding three years, community action resulted in the passage of The Jeanne Clery Disclosure of Campus Security Policy and Campus Crime Statistics Act of 1990 (or Clery Act) (Clery Act 1990). Sometimes also called the Crime Awareness and Campus Security Act, this federal statute requires virtually all colleges and universities to publish information about crime on and near their respective campuses, with the intention that a knowledgeable student population might better take steps to protect itself (Clery Act 1990). This law has resulted in the publishing of detailed campus violent crimes statistics.

Although first response is clearly the purview of the university's commissioned police or security force, the IEHS professional may be involved in secondary crime mitigation efforts. These include performing measurements and surveys to ascertain campus lighting levels for the purposes of compliance with published standards, such as those of the Illuminating Engineering Society of North America (Benya 2001; ANSI/IESNA 2000). Other instances of IEHS involvement include an advisory role in the emergency notification systems established for a variety of campus issues, such as severe weather and flooding, unsafe road conditions, campus closure notification, and most recently, active shooter alerts.

With respect to active shooter concerns, the IEHS practitioner might be involved in a number of ways. He or she may help determine the sound pressure levels and signal clarity of broadcast alert speaker systems and sirens, and will often participate in risk management committee work for the selection and deployment of cellular phone text-messaging software systems, as well as web-based warning systems on popular student sites. In many instances, the director of the health and safety function will act as part of a team with respect to campus emergency information collection and disclosure (CSU 1999; UW 2008).

Inspection

An often-seen safety poster admonishes the IEHS professional, "Inspect What You Expect!" Here, it is wise to remember that the IEHS professional has to function as the in-house expert on any number of rules, regulations, and code requirements. Fortunately in this age of electronic media, quick reference to specific, up-to-date regulations, as well as regulatory opinions or case law precedents on innumerable esoteric or arcane applications is relatively easy to access. Knowing the rules is only part of the work, as the safety poster implies. An effective IEHS program cannot be run from behind a desk. In academia as in industry, change is a normal part of the environment. The steam autoclave in the student health center one week might be replaced with a much more hazardous, highly regulated ethylene oxide gas unit just a week later. The research direction of a new investigator might shift from low-level, unregulated and naturally occurring nutriceuticals (naturally occurring substances that have a health benefit) in June to more toxic, highly regulated (but readily available) carcinogenic agents by September. The only way to fully and accurately appreciate what is taking place throughout the university environment is to be present and engaged in it on a regular basis.

Inspection need not be intimidating or confrontational. To be sure, the inspector should fully understand the nuances of various rules, and to be prepared to justify the inspection request. He or she may be asking others to expend large amounts of money or time on resolving what they might perceive as low-risk or low-probability safety matters. A helpful mindset, in addition to expert command of the regulatory requirements, may even allow the inspector to find ways to more cheaply or effectively safeguard a process. In such instances, the inspector has an opportunity to be perceived not as a harbinger of onerous and tedious regulation, but as a facilitator and resource to the regulated community.

Having said all this, sometimes inspections will result in differences of opinion, which can deteriorate into difficult interactions (Palluzi 1994). Most organizations excel at having written policies and procedures in place that cover the handling of these unfortunate occurrences (University of Houston 2006). If not, it may be the wisest course to deal immediately with those that are most imminently dangerous to life and health, leaving the remainder to be resolved on a higher management level. This will typically translate to a meeting between the college dean and the IEHS director or his superior.

Remediation and Control

The control of hazards that have been identified can be complicated by the regulatory environment in effect at the university. OSHA regulations are of federal origin and, as such, do not directly apply to state entities, including state-sponsored universities (OSHA 2002). Unless a specific state has elected to adopt OSHA standards as an "agreement state," and subsequently mandates those same standards to state campuses, OSHA code and regulations will not pertain directly to them. Even where state or university rules exist, enforcement is seldom simply a matter of education of the end user. To further complicate control efforts, most third-party contractors hired outside of the university are covered by state as well as federal safety and environmental regulations.

Under non-contentious conditions, all that would be required for the abatement of health or safety issues would be to advise the lab director or groundskeeper of their particular rule oversight or OSHA violation. While it might make perfect sense to wear hearing protection while operating a high-speed sonicator in a lab, or running a weed-trimmer in the field, user motivation, equipment costs, availability, and a host of other factors may lead to noncompliance.

Some exceptions to correcting deficiencies or implementing controls do exist. For example, where grant funding is involved, principal investigators are generally highly motivated to comply. This is a good example of a prospective opportunity to assist the regulated community through actions such as plan review of the affected space at the time of grant preparation, in an effort to avoid improper, unsafe, or even prohibited installations. Accreditation reviews or guidelines from accreditation bodies, for example, the Joint Commission in healthcare settings, or the Association for Assessment and Accreditation of Laboratory Animal Care (AAALAC) for animal care operations, are other documents that can serve to strongly motivate facility operators toward compliance (AAALAC 2008).

University Research Facilities

Where better than the research facilities of the modern university to come across the latest academic areas of interest and their associated hazards? Although some biological agents originate in the natural world and are then brought to the laboratory for further study (e.g., HIV, Mad Cow Disease, Hantavirus), a great many new technologies, materials, and applications arise in the basic research labs that populate so many college campuses. Examples include the fission reaction first investigated under the bleachers at the University of Chicago during World War II, recombinant DNA techniques, the development of superconductors, the evolution and improvement of electronic chips and circuit boards, and the emerging discipline of nanotechnology.

Whatever the focus, the generalist's role for the anticipation and recognition of hazards or threats to health from these new developments logically falls to the IEHS professional working in the campus environment. Where new chemicals are under development or synthesized, the added responsibility for the proper management and disposal of reaction by-products and wastes exists. Under all federal jurisdictions, and many state communities as well, the responsibilities for implementation of both community (EPA 2008a) and employee (OSHA 1996a) hazard communication and right-to-know requirements falls squarely on the shoulders of the IEHS practitioner. In an era of increasing use of generalists for an array of environmental health and safety issues, the control of radiation and source materials is still mostly the domain of the more specialized health physicist (HPS 2008). The skills of the IEHS generalist are adaptable to such issues, however. As in so many opportunities for career growth and development, transitions of personnel to the more specialized roles of health physicist, industrial hygienist, or biohazards safety specialist are common.

CHALLENGES OF ENVIRONMENTAL HEALTH AND SAFETY IN A UNIVERSITY SETTING

Meeting the ethical obligations, compliance mandates, and identification of new and emerging problems is not without its difficulties. The unique nature of the university setting brings with it a number of similarly distinctive problems in addressing the issues. In addition to some of the obstacles mentioned earlier (i.e., lack of health or safety regulations bearing on the campus community, and attitudes among administrators or faculty), other challenges exist, which are discussed below.

Lack of Enforcement Will or Desire. It is virtually impossible to expect compliance with any regulation if the will of senior management within the organization wavers when it comes to enforcing unpopular or expensive requirements. One source has noted that if every U.S. workplace were inspected by OSHA's limited agency staff (2200 employees), it could only do so every 80 years (Government Executive 1999). Given such a statistic, the fear of heavy-handed safety inspections has simply disappeared, leaving many entities subject to rules and regulations that may never be subjected to any external, third-party enforcement or review.

Poor Attitudes by Faculty or Staff. Accidents are relatively rare events and for this reason, rote compliance with all but the most important safety recommendations can easily be deemed of limited urgency by faculty. Since many safety standards are incomplete and lack any real explanation for their mandates, blind compliance by highly educated scientists trained to question can be at odds with the entire concept of rule adherence (Palluzi 1994). Most faculty receiving grants nowadays can best be characterized as entrepreneurs, largely in charge of their own destinies, laboratories, personnel, students, and environments. Given the paradigm of "publish or perish"(Gad-el-Hak 2004), and appreciating that laboratory data and results are of tantamount importance to publication acceptance, even well-advised safety hindrances toward that end can readily be perceived not as useful or necessary, but as obstacles and unreasonable constraints to academic freedom (Palluzi 1994). This mindset is especially prevalent for long time faculty members with an impressive record of external funding.

Decentralized Authority. A popular concept, although hardly a common reality, is that of faculty governance of the university. In the college environment, it can be difficult to elucidate who truly is in charge of certain operations, programs, facilities, or areas. In fact most schools are set up with both an administrative as well as an academic officer. This dichotomy does not mean that all matters pertaining to an academic enterprise (e.g., hazardous waste generation and disposal) are the exclusive purview of the provost. Conversely, not all seemingly administrative duties are restricted from academic participation (e.g., collection of waste food oils from campus dining halls for use in biodiesel research). In many instances, such cross pollination is considered a good thing, but it can make individual accountability an elusive target.

Students as Workers. Student employees are one of the key ways that universities accomplish all manner of work, from lofty research in physics, chemistry, and biology labs, to picking up the wastes that are generated in those places. Even full-time employees frequently miss the mark in terms of performance, but the fear of job loss is intended to keep such failures to a minimum. Student-employees are by definition students first, employees second; their focus on the job and dedication to it is, at best, split. Furthermore, students placed into positions with exposures to potentially hazardous materials or conditions may or may not receive essential training, contrary to any rules or policy guidelines. Added to this poorly regulated community is the reality that a fair number of student workers in the sciences may be non-native English speakers. In fact, college campuses have never been more demographically, economically, politically, spiritually, and philosophically diverse (Rund 2002). The success of complex chemical or biohazards safety training for such a population will be of dubious effectiveness if only performed in a perfunctory manner.

Lack of Maintenance. College benefactors enjoy giving to the school of their choice, knowing that one likely outcome is the naming of a building after them. For this reason, it is not particularly difficult for universities to locate successful alumni to donate toward new facility construction. The downside to this equation is that support staff are never included in the planning of a new facility. This can be a problem if too many buildings are added without any consideration to increasing building maintenance and operation (M&O) budgets. Short-sighted funding approaches can be outright dangerous in cases where highly specialized space is constructed that is beyond the existing intellectual or educational capabilities of the M&O staff (OUS 2000).

This is not to imply that the M&O personnel lack intelligence or ability, but rather, to highlight the complexity and sophistication of many modern building systems or laboratories. Examples that illustrate and typify such difficulties include: variable air volume flow management systems in science buildings utilizing numerous fume hoods; construction and operation of high containment laboratories, whether for highly toxic chemicals or human pathogens; design and installation of anatomy laboratories necessitating cadaver or other specimen ventilation; and shielding and beam stops for linear accelerators or test reactors.

HISTORICALLY SIGNIFICANT CONCERNS

This chapter concludes with an extensive review of those concerns that are historically significant to colleges and universities. As university lead research continues, and new materials, techniques and processes come to light, this listing will undoubtedly increase. Since the founding of the first American university—Harvard University in 1636—the academic environment has functioned as an incubator of new concepts, ideas, and materials. With this growth have come new, and sometimes very poorly recognized, hazards to both faculty and staff. With the passage of time, the development of new schools, and the commercialization of so many college-derived ideas, it is now possible to identify at least eight major categories of issue areas in the university environment. These are: general facility safety, chemical, biological, and radiation safety, fire or life safety, electrical safety, environmental protection, and miscellaneous.

General Facility Safety

General facility safety issues are difficult to precisely define, but are most easily thought of as those matters dealing with personal safety readily apparent to the layperson. Slippery surfaces, wet floors, missing pavers, blocked fire exits and many more such issues exist. The following categories attempt to organize such frequently occurring concerns.

Walking Surfaces

Campus risk and insurance claim managers can attest to the fact that simple trip hazards and other problematic walking surfaces can be a significant source of injury allegations and settlements by the university's insurance carrier. This is because of the high volume of foot traffic that exists at colleges, as evidenced by the patchwork network of *ad hoc* sidewalks, pedestrian crossings, bridges, bike lanes, and access ramps. Potentially hazardous walking conditions can be exacerbated by weather conditions, such as snow, ice, and water, and their effects on the wide variety of people that frequent campuses (OSHA 2007a). These include the expected working-age population, but also the very young from daycare centers, school-age children who are visiting for plays, productions, and special events, and the elderly, who often are patrons of the arts, who are visiting campus health facilities, or simply strolling the grounds for exercise.

OSHA has standards for walking and working surfaces in places of employment (OSHA 1984) but these take a back seat to issues more directly germane to simple property liability or even OSHA's own general duty clause (OSHA 1970). Engineering design standards can also be consulted for flat, ramped, and stepped walkways (Brauer 2006, 139–160).

Noise

Most people think of the university grounds as a quiet, bucolic environment. Groundskeepers know this is not always the case, as when they use chainsaws, snow blowers, lawn mowers, garden tractors, leaf blowers or vacuums, and chipper/shredders. All such equipment can easily exceed the 85 dB-A action level established by OSHA for hearing conservation (OSHA 2006a), thereby triggering the requirement for a hearing conservation program, including noise monitoring and the provision of hearing protection devices. The university steam and chilled water plant can frequently exceed the higher 90 dB-A permissible exposure limit (PEL), at which engineering or administrative controls of environmental noise are required. Other potentially injurious sound levels may be found in mechanical rooms housing compressors, pumps, and ventilation equipment. Band rooms, especially percussion practice areas, can exhibit high sound levels, as can percussive work performed by the physical plant employees (e.g., use of pneumatic nailers, scrapers, and other construction associated tools); even attendance at events in enclosed stadiums may cause exposure to such high levels (Royster and Royster 1994). Because of their highly cleanable surfaces, animal care cage cleaning areas can be highly reverberant and noisy also. Where they exist as part of the campus facilities, police firing ranges pose an obvious impact noise hazard (in addition to possible lead exposure concerns for police officers or students engaged in competitive shooting teams) (Friis 2007).

Ergonomics

Returning to the theme of the university as a small city, campus logistics and material handling operations can be anticipated to present ergonomic hazards in the form of back safety from excessive or improper lifting. The existence of specific units is highly variable, but possibilities include food-receiving docks at dormitory or warehouse locations; the university stores operation typically found servicing the plant shops; shipping and receiving functions, including the campus branch of the U.S. Postal Service; and surplus, moving, and storage functions.

Office ergonomic complaints are common in the university environment in both faculty and staff areas. Typical problems include old or non-adjustable chairs; computer screens facing bright windows, causing excessive glare; and heavy keyboarding (Hedge et al. 2007). The latter includes purchasing, accounts payable, human resources benefits and employment, and phone banks operated by the development or alumni affairs offices. Fortunately, the control of ergonomic issues in offices has been addressed quite extensively, and many such problems require only one or two changes to the user's work area to resolve complaints.

Indoor Air Quality

Any institution with employees is subject to IAQ complaints, and the prospects of such problems grow with increasing headcount. Many college buildings have mixed occupancies and uses, so it is typical to find administrative offices located in laboratory buildings or classrooms in basic science buildings. Where different populations with different expectations about air quality exist, conflict and issues are more likely to arise. Many universities have over 100 separate buildings to manage, each with multiple heating, ventilating, and air conditioning (HVAC) units installed. Simple routine quarterly maintenance on this large number of HVAC units can be daunting; when poor design or installation issues develop, they may be slow to garner attention or corrective actions. All mechanical systems eventually require repair; it is the nature of IAQ problems that HVAC failures may go undetected until signs or symptoms of poor air quality are already experienced in the facilities.

There are many causes of IAQ complaints, but in early work on such problems, NIOSH determined that proper maintenance of the building's HVAC is essential to good building air quality (NIOSH 2008); for additional information, see the "Additional Resources" section at the end of the chapter. In terms of all possible causes and their remedies, the following is a list of the top ten causes of indoor air pollution or complaints (Ryan 1999):

1. Dried out S- or P-traps in sewer lines;
2. Blocked or closed dampers on supply or return air grilles;
3. User processes that cause odors objectionable to adjacent users;
4. Rusted or disabled outside air dampers;
5. Re-entrainment of vehicle exhaust from loading docks situated too close to building fresh air intake louvers;
6. Construction activities that include drywall sanding, priming, painting, and specialty coatings;
7. Roofing activities involving hot tar and the odors from that material finding its way into the facility;
8. Smoking;
9. Imbalanced HVAC systems, allowing for cross-connections between categories of users; and
10. Energy-saving measures, such as reducing temperatures on cold days, increasing temperatures on hot days, shutting off air handlers entirely on nights and weekends, and reducing the volume of fresh air.

See Chapter 8 for additional information on IAQ.

Chemical Safety

Chemical safety is a major and significant undertaking at most universities owing to the diversity and extent of their operations. Since many institutions function like small cities, chemical usage associated with virtually any municipal operation are typical. Added to that are the specialty concerns more often thought of in colleges, such as hazardous wastes and chemistry labs.

Chemistry Laboratories

Many college graduates remember their chemistry laboratory classes for all the wrong reasons. Anecdotes are seemingly endless about accidental fires, small explosions, sickness from solvent odors, acid or base burns, and so on. Despite the existence of an OSHA standard applicable to hazard communication in laboratories (OSHA 2006b), these regulations seldom apply to the non-industrial setting. Safety is further compromised by sometimes poorly trained, non-English-speaking teaching assistants placed in charge of laboratory sections with large numbers of entry-level students. A variety of publications are available for addressing the many specific and recognized laboratory safety issues, including liquid nitrogen Dewar flasks, compressed gases, glassware hazards, centrifuge safety, inert gas cabinets, gauges, and so on (Palluzi 1994; OECD 1992; National Research Council 1989; National Research Council 1998; Steere 1967; NIOSH 2006).

In the research setting, chemical safety is by no means assured, despite lower numbers of more informed, closer supervised research assistants or graduate students. Problems such as alphabetical chemical storage, which can result in incompatible materials placed directly adjacent to each other, are not uncommon, along with storage of corrosive materials above eye level. Unless flammable solvent storage cabinets are utilized, the safe storage of moderate to large volumes of solvents is typically not in compliance with the National Fire Protection Agency (NFPA) standards, particularly the *Flammable and Combustible Liquids Code®* and *Standard on Fire Protection for Laboratories Using Chemicals®* (NFPA 2003; NFPA 2004). Despite its almost universal adoption, the *Flammable and Combustible Liquids Code®* is one of the most commonly violated standards (Palluzi 1994). Lack of understanding of organizational waste disposal procedures can lead to laboratory waste container reactions. Failure on the part of principal investigators to educate not only their staff but also themselves can lead to serious injuries or death from the use of inappropriate lab equipment (for example, nonexplosion-safe refrigerators for solvent storage) or inadequate personal protective equipment (Corrosion Doctors 2007). By the very nature of research (namely, the discovery of new things), the research operation may lack established safety practices based on experience, thereby producing a serious safety gap (Palluzi 1994).

Agricultural Uses
There is a bewildering array of chemicals intentionally applied around college campuses, comprising all categories of control agents (i.e., insecticides, herbicides, fungicides, nematocides, rodenticides, and fumigants) and a number of chemicals in the Agency for Toxic Substances and Disease Registry (ATSDR) listing of the "top 20" hazardous substances (Friis 2007). Staff issues with respect to chemicals can include legitimate agricultural uses of pesticides and fertilizers on large, test-plot farms and in greenhouses. Where rodent and insect vector control is performed in-house, only trained and certified pesticide applicators should be allowed to prepare, apply, and dispose of toxic mixtures. Many groundskeepers at universities have significant responsibilities for the health and survival of an extremely large variety of both native and exotic plant species. This is turn can require the application of specialty chemicals, the hazards and toxicity of which may be unfamiliar to the applicator. Ornamental pools, fountains, and ponds may require application of slimicides, molluskicides, or other chemicals directly to waters with which the public may later come in contact. For all these reasons, the IEHS practitioner must maintain an accurate accounting of personnel and chemical use areas, and be able to crosscheck this data with required chemical safety and proficiency of use training records.

Other Activities

The listing of other chemical use areas at universities is long and changeable. Areas or uses that should be considered for the presence of unusual hazards and closer scrutiny are as follows (possible issues in parentheses):

- Pools and spas (chlorine and bromine, strong acids, basic buffers)
- Custodial (floor strippers, waxes, vinyl asbestos tile exposures)
- Motor pools (gas, diesel, chlorinated degreasers, greases, glycols)
- Coal-burning boilers (chromates in cooling water, arsenic deposits on heat exchangers, coal-dust particulate exposures)
- Food service areas (sanitizers, pesticide control chemicals, corrosive cleaners)
- Computer and telephone networking (spray-applied asbestos in cabled or WiFi areas)
- Office or secretarial (liquid paper, screen cleaners, dry erase markers)

Biological Safety

Biological safety means different things, depending on the environment in which the term is used. On the college campus or in the university hospital, the term most often refers to two specific concerns: biosafety in the laboratory, and infectious diseases.

Infectious Diseases

Biological safety in a school environment falls into one of two disciplines: the highly specialized biosafety controls (discussed in a subsequent section), and the traditional infectious diseases concerns. Sometimes referred to as *herd immunity*, the most common form of infectious disease management in the college environment has to do with ensuring the student population is properly immunized or otherwise resistant to biological threats that might easily spread through the relatively confined, close quarters of dormitories. Well-known campus contagions include mononucleosis, cold and flu outbreaks, and meningitis, with current concerns focusing on severe acute respiratory syndrome (SARS), avian influenza, and West Nile virus (WNV) (UIUC 2007). Controls in this respect have traditionally fallen to the student health center medical director. Under the confidentiality requirements of HIPAA, the IEHS professional is largely constrained from working in this area unless directly involved by primary care providers.

One aspect of traditional biohazards management in which the IEHS professional is involved is in the area of blood-borne pathogens. In the wake of the then-emerging epidemic related to AIDS, the Centers for Disease Control and Prevention (CDC) and OSHA adapted what had been called universal precautions for handling blood and other patient samples into a rigorous new standard. The OSHA *Bloodborne Pathogens* standard applies to all campus workers who are exposed or even potentially exposed to blood, urine, feces, milk, semen and other human excretions or secretions (OSHA 2006c). This includes not only physicians, nurses, and health center laboratory staff, but also research personnel handling human-derived samples. First responders (firemen, medics, and police) are covered by the standard, as well as athletic trainers and custodians charged with disposing of biohazardous waste.

Biosafety and Laboratory-Acquired Infections

Through the decades, there has been a small but steady number of laboratory-acquired infections. Many have been serious and some have been fatal. The CDC, in conjunction with the National Institutes of Health (NIH), published guidelines to minimize the prospects of future occurrences (CDC and NIH 1999). This publication is *Biosafety in Microbiological and Biomedical Laboratories* (BMBL); other publications exist for more specialized pursuits, such as r-DNA, gene transfer, and associated biotechnology issues (OECD 1992), as well as guidelines for handling and disposal of biological agents (National Research Council 1998). Though the BMBL is considered as a set of guidelines for virtually all federal grant dollar recipients, the conditions spelled out by CDC-NIH have the effect of a mandate, and failure to abide by their stipulations can result in a loss of funding. The contents of the BMBL are founded on the scientific principles of good microbiological practice, and for these reasons their adoption and use has been relatively easy for campus safety officers.

The BMBL spells out four levels of safety precautions, each one building on the previous level. Thus, the standard practices expected at Biosafety Level 1 (BSL 1) are included in BSL 2, in addition to added safeguards at the BSL 2 level. BSL 1 agents are considered low-risk agents that have on occasion caused infections. BSL 2 precautions are directed at more serious agents, especially those transmitted by contact spread (including droplets as a special case of contact transmission), while airborne transmission is the major mode of spread of the yet more hazardous BSL 3 viruses, bacteria, and so on. BSL 4 is reserved for a small group of restricted human pathogens that are very likely to cause death or economic losses should they escape from the containment that is the hallmark of the BSL 4 laboratory.

Radiation Safety

The control of hazardous radiation on the college campus is usually done under the aegis of an individual designated by the organization as the radiation safety officer (RSO). In most jurisdictions, this is a codified title created by the U.S. Nuclear Regulatory Commission (NRC) under the terms of a "broad scope license" granted to the university (HPS 2008). Charged first and foremost with the safety and security of radioactive materials (RAM), the RSO is also frequently given responsibilities for applied and research uses of x-ray producing devices, non-ionizing radiation hazards including microwave antennas, RF hazards from radio and TV stations, and lasers. For a more detailed review of such hazards, the reader is referred to Friis' *Essentials of Environmental Health* (Friis 2007).

Sources of Radiation

Radioactive source materials are used in many life science laboratories as tracer materials, to follow the metabolism or other biochemical conversion of chemicals of interest in living systems. Usual isotopes include the low-energy beta emitters Tritium (3H) and ^{14}C, the higher energy and higher hazard beta emitter ^{32}P, and a wide variety of other nuclides purchased specifically for reactions of interest to the researcher (Martin and Harbson 1996). Under some more unusual circumstances, the highly hazardous gamma and X-ray emitters such as ^{60}Co are found on college campuses. Control of all RAM has always been strict, with mandates existing for the safe receipt and campus transport, inventorying, and disposal of such materials. The RSO usually includes source users in a dosimetry program employing thermoluminescent detector badges (TLDs) or film badges. Finally, the handling, sorting, storage, and ultimate shipment for incineration or compaction of campus low-level radioactive waste (LLRW) are overseen by the RSO. Under NRC rules, disposal sites for such LLRW are similarly strictly controlled and managed by their licensed operators (NRC 2005).

X-ray Machines

The majority of x-ray exposures in the academic environment result from diagnostic uses in medicine and dentistry performed for the student population, while most x-ray producing equipment resides in research settings. Research uses of x-rays include chemistry, where x-ray diffraction is a common technique for materials analysis, x-ray fluorescence and diffraction for lead determination, and x-ray generation in a variety of advanced physics study areas.

Special Facilities

Even mid-sized universities can house specialty laboratories with unusual radiation hazards. Examples include the National Superconducting Cyclotron at Michigan State University, the engineering test reactor located at Texas A&M University in College Station, and the linear accelerator located at Ohio University in Athens. The largest of universities operate well-known installations like the Lawrence Livermore and Los Alamos National labs operated for the U.S. Department of Energy by the University of California, and the Fermi National Lab operated by an alliance including the University of Chicago. Extraordinarily complex radiation hazards involving sub-atomic particle interactions and emissions can be found at all of these facilities, as well as chemical, physical, fire and general safety issues.

Fire and Life Safety

The prevention of fires and their associated potential for loss of life and property damage present significant and ongoing challenges in the university environment. This is largely due to the student population in dormitory settings, where smoking materials may exist, despite prohibitions to the contrary.

There are no wholly effective controls concerning what students bring into their dorm rooms; well-known, fire-causing appliances, including halogen torchiere lamps, hot plates, and space heaters are often found. This situation is made infinitely worse by the fact that many college dormitories have no installed fire prevention systems, such as sprinklers. Owing to the cost of installation and a lack of regulatory requirements for their presence, many dormitories have never had sprinkler systems. Smoke and fire detectors do exist, although it is not uncommon to find missing batteries or devices that have otherwise been tampered with to allow banned smoking or cooking activities in the dormitory rooms.

The college campus usually follows conditions of the NFPA *Life Safety Code®* (NFPA 2006). Life Safety Code interpretations in universities are complex, owing to the great many occupancy types (residential, assembly, educational, health, daycare, to name a few), building construction types (normal, fire resistive, heavy timber, and so on), and the content types (e.g., flammables in shops, motor pools, and laboratory settings). All three of these categories must be carefully and accurately evaluated by the IEHS professional to ensure the best possible fire safety for the campus. Typical duties for IEHS professionals in the realm of fire or life safety include: occupancy load calculations; burn or open flame permit programs for grills and welding activities; consultation on the use of holiday decorations; and ensuring access to building fire exits. Since many campuses fire calls are met by the local municipal fire department, credible attempts at code compliance for the authority having jurisdiction—either the local fire chief for private schools or the state fire marshal for most other universities—is important for political as well as liability issues.

Electrical Safety

Electrocution hazards are almost limitless at universities, existing in literally all areas and for all persons. Primary power considerations may exist for a minority of schools operating their own steam-electricity co-generation facilities. Such operations are subject to not only NFPA's *National Electrical Code®* (NFPA 2005) but also to OSHA regulations for the proper design and installation of equipment and the safe servicing, testing, and maintenance of same (OSHA 1996c). Even where primary power generation does not exist, staff may still be at risk of electrocution owing to the nature of electrical feeds to the campus, the necessity to work in confined spaces in electrical vaults and tunnels, and work involving high voltage switches, fuses, and transformers.

Environmental Health and Protection

In most U.S. cities and counties, environmental health issues are addressed by a sanitation professional suitably educated and experienced in such matters. Universities and colleges, because of the size of their student population and extent of their food handling operations, typically have a dedicated sanitarian.

This person most frequently must deal with issues related to domestic wastes, water safety, and food protection, which are discussed below.

Food Protection

The provision of safe and healthy food on the college campus is perhaps the most time-honored duty of the IEHS practitioner, and as such, continues to be no small undertaking. Many institutions are required to provide as many as 10,000 or more full meals every breakfast, lunch and dinner period. This takes place in dormitories primarily, although satellite food operations are equally as common nowadays. These exist in academically isolated areas (e.g., the medical school/hospital complex or the law school) as well as in high traffic mainstream facilities such as the library or the student center. Add to these permanent facilities, temporary food service establishments like "bagel carts," stadium event food stands, chili cook-offs, and even campus-sanctioned bake sales, and it is easy to appreciate the scope of work in this area.

Failures of the food safety system can lead to serious, even fatal, outcomes. Symptoms may range from a simple stomachache to gastroenteritis, diarrhea, vomiting, fever, dehydration and death. Outbreaks involving such agents as *Salmonella*, hepatitis A, *E. coli* enteritis, *Shigella*, cholera, botulism, *Staphylococcus aureus*, Norovirus, and others are routinely reported, though not exclusively or even extensively at college food establishments (FDA 2001).

For many years, food service inspections were compliance checklist-driven occurrences that facility operators either passed or failed. Emphasis was largely on basic hygiene processes and hazardous foods (i.e., those with a high protein or carbohydrate content, moist, pH neutral, and low in salt or sugar). Examples of hazardous foods include: eggs, milk, most meats, fish and other seafood (Grey Bruce Health Unit 2008). Fear of failing an inspection was considerable, as the food health inspector was empowered to shut the doors to any facility, thereby threatening its existence by cutting off cash flow and damaging its reputation. Concerns about closure are still legitimate and shutdowns are not infrequent, but the approach to facility inspections has taken a new turn in the last decade (Friis 2007). Presently, most inspections are conducted in the form of *hazard analysis and critical control points* (HACCP) inspections.

HACCP is a systematic approach to food safety, consisting of seven principles applied in a series of seven steps (FDA 2001), consisting of the following:

1. Conduct a hazard analysis and list of steps in the process where significant hazards can occur.
2. Identify the critical control points (CCPs) in the process.
3. Establish limits for preventive measures associated with each CCP.
4. Establish CCP monitoring requirements.
5. Write corrective actions to be taken when monitoring indicates that there is a deviation from an established critical limit.

6. Mandate effective record-keeping procedures that document the HACCP system.

7. Verify that the HACCP system is working correctly.

In contrast to earlier food safety inspection efforts in which food service operators were simply issued rules to follow, the outcomes assessment process that is inherent in the HACCP model requires each operator to write and integrate its own operational rules. Whether this leads to better food safety is arguable, but ignorance of good standard operating procedures is no longer a significant issue.

Water Quality

Modern public health and environmental health practice is heavily involved with water quality issues, but the same cannot be said for most campus IEHS personnel (Friis 2007). Aside from the occasional milky or brown drinking water complaint, the provision of potable water falls to the municipality providing water and sewer facilities to the campus. Even septic systems, an enormous responsibility for environmental health practitioners in local health departments, are mostly absent from the vast majority of universities. Permitted discharges of pollutants, including thermal releases, are similarly absent from colleges. This leaves water runoff issues related to storm water discharges, where an occasional compliance role may emerge but only when one or more acres are involved in construction activities (EPA 2008b). Issues related to Legionnaires' Disease, Pontiac Fever, and other cooling-tower, water-associated outbreaks caused by the bacterium *Legionella pneumophila* are most frequently addressed as IAQ or physical plant routine maintenance matters (Friis 2007).

Wastes

Even small colleges may be large generators of wastes. These take the form of gray and black water sewerage, as well as storm water discharges. Additionally, food operations on campus generate putrecible materials such as garbage and waste cooking oils. Shops can collect sizeable volumes of waste motor oils and recyclable degreasing agents, and reportable quantities of air pollution can be released on a continuing basis through coal-fired steam plants. All campus users generate refuse and rubbish, although the dormitories are especially responsible for such materials because dormitory waste accounts for virtually all life-associated activities from the residents (shopping and packaging wastes, food wrappers, old clothing, bedding, and so on) while other campus waste producers live elsewhere and therefore channel similar wastes through other avenues of collection and disposal. In addition, most campus producers of large volumes of paper and plastic refuse can economically collect these materials at the point of generation (for example, with a dedicated office or computer lab paper recycling bin).

Hazardous wastes represent a special waste stream for college and universities that necessitate programs and expertise for their proper, safe, and legal handling and dispensation. *Mixed wastes* (i.e., those with radioactive as well as hazardous chemical constituents) present a special problem due to differing requirements and methods of disposal. Technically, LLRW are not considered hazardous wastes by the EPA although they are very strictly managed, as described earlier in this chapter. High-level radioactive wastes are rarely encountered on the vast majority of college campuses. Most university employees handling hazardous wastes, either as generators or as wastes for disposal, are subject to stringent internal health and safety training and certification requirements.

At some universities, hazardous wastes are collected in satellite accumulation areas located in high generation buildings, such as the chemistry, life sciences, and physical plant facilities. Other schools operate internally staffed collection programs for the more user-friendly pickup of wastes directly from the generators' locations. Both approaches have their benefits and costs. Ultimately, specialist contractors are hired to properly package, label, and remove campus waste materials on a regular basis, usually in less than 90 days. Where LLRW materials are generated, they may be collected in a similar fashion. Because of half-life considerations, it is often to the college's benefit to store many of their LLRW waste streams until the specific activity of the material is below regulatory concern. Then the materials can be safely disposed of in an environmentally adequate manner as either industrial wastes or even normal domestic garbage at a greatly reduced expense. See Chapter 9 for additional information on waste management.

Sustainability

Sustainability was defined by the United Nations Brundtland Commission as any development that "meets the needs of the present without compromising the ability of future generations to meet their own needs" (UN 1987). College campuses are rapidly taking steps that will place them on the road to sustainable practices. Environmental health issues related to the rapidly emerging academic interest area of sustainability are at present hard to define. Nevertheless, it might logically be expected that such issues will represent an evolutionary process creating new hazards from existing practices, as opposed to revolutionary new issues or hazards arising *de novo* from such sustainability efforts.

Current campus activities and research that have a sustainability element include: recycling of paper, motor oil, and frying greases; composting and solar-assisted composting (Friis 2007); heightened energy efficiency by conversion to compact fluorescent bulbs, education efforts toward turning off computers and lights when not in use; reduced carbon emissions through the conversion of motor pool vehicles to electric or natural gas; and creation of model student housing (i.e., "ecohouses") to serve as incubators for new ideas and their rapid implementation on a pilot scale). Clearly, some of these items have long-standing IEHS inputs and considerations.

Miscellaneous Issues

The miscellaneous category includes all of the safety matters not clearly associated with the previous sections, such as theater and art hazards and unusual natural hazards.

Theaters and the Arts

There is no shortage of unusual and arcane IEHS impacts on a college campus, as best illustrated by various concerns that can be found in the performing and fine arts. The toxicity of certain paint pigments has long been known (OEHHA 2007), and many oil-based, fine-art paints are still made according to age-old formularies. Jewelry-making introduces the potential for exposure to heavy metal fumes, such as gold, platinum, silver and lead, while sculpture and metal-working classes routinely create welding fumes of various concentrations and compositions. Corrosive patinas are also frequently encountered in sculpture work. Glass-working has its own unique set of material hazards in addition to the physical issues of burns, conjunctivitis, and dry eye associated with constant work around infrared heating sources. The same can be stated for ceramics, where glazes and kilns (with wood, gas, or electric energy sources) are employed. Print-making, photography, and lithography all involve considerable exposures to chemicals, some of which are volatile and enter the students' and faculty members' airspace. Concentrations in such cases are usually low, falling orders of magnitude lower than industrial experiences (Ryan et al. 2002). For a relatively comprehensive review of art hazards, see many of the publications of the Arts, Crafts, and Theater Safety organization (ACTS 2004).

The college theater and its associated workshop is perhaps the most unusual of all work environments at most colleges. Physical safety issues related to staged swordplay can and do arise, for example. Guns and knives of various forms are also called for at times by the script. The construction of sets for production routinely involves power tools, which are regulated by OSHA (OSHA 2007b), and the application of various paints and coatings. The safety of light riggings, catwalks, theater stairs for stage use, stage effects such as flares, smoke, and mortars, and laser light shows are all aspects of the theatrical environment that may require prudent oversight by the IEHS safety representative. Finally, when performances are held, safety concerns may once again arise with respect to limiting facility occupant load to the stated capacity, and maintaining a fire watch where required as the result of onstage pyrotechnics.

Lions, and Tigers, and Killer Bees

The career of an IEHS practitioner on the college campus can be both fascinating and bewildering at times. When the campus houses a school of veterinary medicine, it is common for exotic—sometimes deadly—varieties of cats, snakes, or other animals to be brought to campus for study or treatment. Other times, the threat may arrive of its own accord, as illustrated by the advance of the killer bees from South America into South Texas in the early 90s. Bees know no political or municipal boundaries, and the expansive acreage, luxuriant foliage, and even the architecture of many campuses may provide an attractive haven for migrating bee colonies. High-rise buildings, in particular, afford swarming bees the relative safety of height even though the total distance above ground of their hive may only be 50–100 feet. When this vertical separation is directly adjacent to busy campus thoroughfares or sidewalks, the potential for issues is present. Given the aggressive nature of the insects, normal activities causing noise and other vibration can be perceived as threats and result in sometimes fatal attacks (NMNH 2003). While no such attacks are recorded on a college campus, migrations have occurred (Ryan, personal communication). Since killer bees are incompatible with such environments, they must be destroyed on the basis of prudence and prevention alone.

SUMMARY AND CONCLUSIONS

While there are specific differences among campuses, the one commonality they all share is their diversity of operations, physical plant, people, and specialties. There are few occupational settings that are as diverse and changeable as the typical college or university campus. Larger universities are capable of acting as wholly separate municipalities unto their own. Usual elements found on all campuses include classrooms, offices, laboratories, dormitories, institutional food operations, healthcare facilities, daycare facilities, animal care operations, shops and maintenance areas, and recreational spaces. The role of the IEHS professional in a college or university is for the most part identical to that of the private-sector or governmental practitioner, with the addition of a great many unique, sometimes technically advanced, hazards to consider.

Aside from ethical considerations and professional growth related to identifying new hazards, compliance is usually the most frequent aspect of the IEHS practitioner's duties on campus. Efforts that fall into this realm include prevention and all that it entails (plan review, substitution, and trend analysis, inspection, and remediation and control).

The unique nature of the university setting brings with it a number of similarly distinctive problems. Lack of enforcement will, desire or funding, poor attitudes by faculty and staff, decentralized decision making, student employees, and poor maintenance can all affect the IEHS practitioner's effectiveness. Problems manifest themselves in all areas, but have been especially prevalent in facility safety areas as fire and life safety code matters, electrical safety, walking surface hazards, noise, ergonomics and IAQ. Laboratories pose multiple chemical hazards, as do agricultural areas. Biological issues exist in both laboratory as well as patient care settings, as do many radiation concerns. Traditional environmental health areas such as food, wastes, and water safety can also exist in the university setting to a greater or lesser extent. Finally, art and theater areas are renowned for their unique and diverse health and safety characteristics.

Review

1. List five areas of a college campus with hazardous materials. Are student or staff exposures possible? If so, name the regulatory agency that regulates such conditions.

2. Is a contractor working at a state-supported university covered by any safety regulations, and if so, which? What is the basis for your determination?

3. Identify three potential trip, slip or fall hazards common on a university campus. Explain why the hazard might exist, despite its recognition as a hazard.

4. St. Olaf University in Minnesota is a privately funded school. Using internet search capabilities, determine who might investigate workplace safety at that school in the event of a staff fatality.

5. List three to five safety hazards found in a university art or fine art department.

Additional Resources

National Institute for Occupational Safety and Health (NIOSH). 2001. *Building Air Quality: A Guide for Building Owners and Facility Managers.* (Publication No. 91-114) (retrieved September 4, 2008) (http://www.cdc.gov/niosh/baqtoc.html).

Reference List

Accreditation Board for Engineering and Technology (ABET). 2008. *Applied Science Accreditation Criteria* (retrieved September 3, 2008) (http://www.abet.org/forms.shtml#Applicable_to_All_Programs)

American National Standards Institute/ Illuminating Engineering Society of North America (ANSI/IESNA). 2000. *Guide for Educational Facilities Lighting* (Rep. No. RP-3-00 (R2006)). New York, NY: Illuminating Engineering Society of North America.

Arts, Crafts & Theater Safety (ACTS). 2004. *Providing Safety & Hazard Information for the Arts - Worldwide!* (retrieved September 3, 2008) (http://www.artscraftstheatersafety.org/datasheets.html).

Association for Assessment and Accreditation of Laboratory Animal Care (AAALAC). 2008. *What is AAALAC?* (retrieved September 3, 2008) (http://www.aaalac.org/about/index.cfm).

Benya, J. R. 2001. *Lighting for Schools* Washington, D.C.: National Clearinghouse for Educational Facilities.

Brauer, R. L. 2006. *Safety and Health for Engineers.* 3d ed. New York: John Wiley & Sons, Inc.

Burton, J. D. 2003. "General Methods for the Control of Airborne Hazards." In S.R.DiNardi. Ed. *The Occupational Environment: Its Evaluation, Control, and Management*. 2d ed. Fairfax, V.A.: American Industrial Hygiene Association.

California State University (CSU). 1999. *California State University Risk Management Policy* (Executive Order 715) (retrieved September 3, 2008) (http://www.calstate.edu/EO/EO-715.pdf).

Centers for Disease Control and Prevention (CDC) and National Institutes of Health (NIH). 2007. *Biosafety in Microbiological and Biomedical Laboratories,* 5th ed. (retrieved September 3, 2008) (http://www.cdc.gov/od/ohs/biosfty/bmbl5/BMBL_5th_Edition.pdf)

Consumer Product Safety Commission (CPSC). 1999. *CPSC Staff Study of Safety Hazards in Child Care Settings* (retrieved September 3, 2008) (http://www.cpsc.gov/library/ccstudy.html).

Corrosion Doctors. 2008. *Methylmercury and Dimethylmercury.* (Retrieved September 3, 2008) (http://www.corrosion-doctors.org/Elements-Toxic/Mercury-methyl.htm).

e2Campus (2008). *Prevent another tragedy.* (retrieved September 2, 2008) (http://www.e2campus.com/jeanne_clery_act_story.htm).

Environmental Protection Agency (EPA). 2008a. *EPCRA Overview. Environmental Protection Agency.* (retrieved September 2, 2008) (http://www.epa.gov/emergencies/content/lawsregs/epcraover.htm).

———. 2008b. *National Pollutant Discharge Elimination System (NPDES).* (retrieved September 2, 2008) (http://cfpub.epa.gov/npdes/stormwater/application_coverage.cfm#coverage)

Food and Drug Administration (FDA). 2001. *HACCP: A State-of-the-Art Approach to Food Safety* (Rep. No. *BG 01-4*). Washington, D. C.: Food and Drug Administration.

Friis, R. H. 2007. *Essentials of Environmental Health.* Boston: Jones and Bartlett Publishers.

Gad-el-Hak, M. 2004. *Publish or Perish—An Ailing Enterprise?* (retrieved September 2, 2008) (http://www.people.vcu.edu/~gadelhak/Opinion.pdf).

Government Executive. 1999. *The Safety Challenge* (retrieved September 2, 2008) (http://www.govexec.com/story_page_pf.cfm?articleid=16216&printerfriendlyvers=1).

Grey Bruce Health Unit. 2008. *Hazardous Foods* (retrieved September 2, 2008) (http://www.publichealthgreybruce.on.ca/FoodSafety/Hazardous_Foods.htm).

Health Physics Society (HPS). 2008. *Radiation Safety Officer (RSO) Qualifications* (retrieved September 2, 2008) (http://hps.org/publicinformation/ate/faqs/rso.html)

Hedge, A., M. Barrero, and L. Maxwell. *Ergonomic Issues for Classroom Computing* (retrieved July 7, 2007) (http://cehd.umn.edu/kls/ecee/pdfs/iesclassroomcomputershedge.pdf).

Institute for Laboratory Animal Research (ILAR). 2003. *Occupational Health and Safety in the Care and Use of Nonhuman Primates* Washington, D.C.: The National Academies Press.

Jeanne Clery Disclosure of Campus Security Policy and Campus Crime Statistics Act (Clery Act). 1990. 20 U.S.C. §1092 (retrieved September 3, 2008) (http://www.securityoncampus.org/schools/cleryact/34cfr668.46.html).

Martin, A. and S. A. Harbson. 1996. *An Introduction to Radiation Protection.* 4th ed. London: A Hodder Arnold Publication.

National Environmental Health Association (NEHA). 2007. *Code of Ethics for Members* (retrieved September 2, 2008) (http://www.neha.org/pdf/member/Code%20of%20Ethics%20Oct%2001.pdf).

National Fire Protection Association (NFPA). 2003. NFPA 30, *Flammable and Combustible Liquids Code).* Quincy, MA: National Fire Protection Association.

————. 2006. NFPA 101, *Life Safety Code.* Quincy, MA: National Fire Protection Association.

————. 2005. NFPA 70, *National Electrical Code.* Quincy, MA: National Fire Protection Association.

————. 2004. NFPA 45, *Standard on Fire Protection for Laboratories Using Chemicals.* Quincy, MA: National Fire Protection Association.

National Institute for Occupational Safety and Health (NIOSH). 2008. *Indoor Environmental Quality (IEQ)* (retrieved September 2, 2008) (http://www.cdc.gov/niosh/topics/indoorenv/).

————. 2006. *School Chemistry Laboratory Guide* (DHHS (NIOSH) Publication No. 2007-107) (retrieved September 2, 2008) (http://www.cpsc.gov/CPSCPUB/PUBS/NIOSH2007107.pdf).

National Institutes of Health (NIH). 2002. *Public Health Service Policy on Humane Care and Use of Laboratory Animals* (retrieved September 2, 2008) (http://grants.nih.gov/grants/olaw/references/phspol.htm).

National Library of Medicine (NLM). 2002. *The Hippocratic Oath* (retrieved September 2, 2008) (http://www.nlm.nih.gov/hmd/greek/greek_oath.html).

National Museum of Natural History (NMNH). 2003. *Killer Bees.* (retrieved September 3, 2008) (http://www.si.edu/Encyclopedia_SI/nmnh/buginfo/killbee.htm).

National Research Council. 1989. *Committee on Hazardous Biological Substances in the Laboratory Biosafety in the Laboratory: Prudent Practices for Handling and Disposal of Infectious Materials* Washington, D.C.: National Academies Press.

National Research Council. 1998. *Prudent Practices in the Laboratory Handling and Disposal of Chemicals* Washington, D.C.: National Academies Press.

Nims, D. K. (1999). *Basics of Industrial Hygiene.* New York: John Wiley & Sons, Inc.

Nuclear Regulatory Commission (NRC). 2005. 10 CFR 20, *Standards for Protection Against Radiation* (retrieved September 4, 2008) (http://www.nrc.gov/reading-rm/doc-collections/cfr/part20/full-text.html).

Occupational Safety and Health Act. 1970. 29 U.S.C. 654, Section 5(a), *General Duty Clause* (retrieved September 5, 2008) (http://www.osha.gov/pls/oshaweb/owadisp.show_document?p_table=OSHACT&p_id=3359).

Occupational Safety and Health Administration (OSHA). 2006c. 29 CFR
        1910.1030, *Bloodborne Pathogens* (retrieved September 3, 2008)
        (http://www.osha.gov/pls/oshaweb/owadisp.show_document?p_tabl
        e=STANDARDS&p_id=10051).

———. 1996c. 29 CFR 1910.147, *The Control of Hazardous Energy
        (Lockout/Tagout)* (retrieved September 5, 2008) (http://www.osha.
        gov/pls/oshaweb/owadisp.show_document?p_table=STANDARDS&
        p_id=9804).

———. 2007b. 29 CFR 1910.241-244, *Hand and Portable Powered Tools and
        Other Hand-Held Equipment* (retrieved September 5, 2008)
        (http://www.osha.gov/pls/oshaweb/owadisp.show_document?p_table=
        STANDARDS&p_id=9848-9851).

———. 1996a. 29 CFR 1910.1200, *Hazard Communication* (retrieved September 3,
        2008) (http://www.osha.gov/pls/oshaweb/owadisp.show_document?
        p_table=standards&p_id=10099).

———. 2006a. 29 CFR 1910.95, *Occupational Noise Exposure* (retrieved
        September , 2008) (http://www.osha.gov/pls/oshaweb/owadisp.show_
        document?p_table=standards&p_id=9735).

———. 2007a. *Safety and Health Topics: Walking/Working Surfaces* (retrieved
        September 3, 2008) (http://www.osha.gov/SLTC/walkingworking
        surfaces/index.html).

———. 2002. 29 CFR 1902, *State Plans for the Development and Enforcement of
        Standards* retrieved September 3, 2008) (http://www.osha.gov/pls/
        oshaweb/owadisp.show_document?p_table=standards&p_id=10099).

———. 2006b. 29 CFR 1910.1450, *Toxic and Hazardous Substances* (retrieved
        September 4, 2008) (http://www.ohsa.gov/oshaweb/owadisp.show_
        document?p_table=STANDARDS&p_id=10106).

———. 1984. 29 CFR 1910.21-1910.28, *Walking-working Surfaces* retrieved
        September 5, 2008) (http://www.osha.gov/pls/oshaweb/owadisp.
        show_document?p_table=standards&p_id=9713-9720).

Office of Environmental Health Hazard Assessment, State of California
        (OEHHA). 2007. *Education—Art Hazards* (retrieved September 3,
        2008) (http://www.oehha.ca.gov/education/art/index.html).

Oregon University System (OUS). 2000. *Deferred Maintenance Problems on State
        Campuses Reach "Critical" Condition.* (retrieved June 28, 2007)
        (http://www.ous.edu/news_and_information/news/022703.htm).

Organisation for Economic Co-Operation and Development (OECD). 1992.
        Safety Considerations for Biotechnology (retrieved September 2, 2008)
        (http://www.oecd.org/dataoecd/8/3/2375496.pdf).

Palluzi, R. P. 1994. *Pilot Plant and Laboratory Safety.* New York: McGraw-Hill, Inc.

Recreation Management. 2008. *The Main Street Vision: University of Cincinnati
        Campus Recreation Center* (retrieved September 3, 2008) (http://www.
        recmanagement.com/200705aw1j.php).

Royster, L. H. and J. D. Royster. 1994. "Nonoccupational Noise Exposures and
        Estimated Daily L_{eq} Values for Attendance at College Basketball Games
        and Shopping Centers." *Journal of the Acoustical Society of America*, 96:3273.

Rund, J. A. 2002. "The Changing Context of Campus Safety." In C. K. Wilkinson and J. A. Rund, eds., *Addressing Contemporary Campus Safety Issues: New Directions for Student Services, No. 99*. New York: John Wiley & Sons, Inc.

Ryan, T. J., E. M. Hart, and L. L. Kappler. 2002. "VOC Exposures in a Mixed-use University Art Building." *AIHA.J.* 63:703–708.

Steere, N. V. 1967. *CRC Handbook of Laboratory Safety*. New York: Taylor and Francis Group.

United Nations (UN). 1987. *Report of the World Commission on Environment and Development* (Rep. No. 42/187) (retrieved September 3, 2008) (http://www.un.org/documents/ga/res/42/ares42-187.htm)

University of Houston (UH). 2006. *General Laboratory Safety Manual* (retrieved September 3, 2008) (http://www.uh.edu/plantops/emanual/forms/ehrm/manuals_Lab_Saf.pdf)

University of Illinois at Urbana-Champaign (UIUC). 2007. *Avian Flu* (retrieved July 7, 2008) (http://www.ocep.uiuc.edu/avianflu.htm).

University of Wisconsin (UW). 2008. *Safety & Loss Prevention* (retrieved September 3, 2008) http://www.uwsa.edu/oslp/)

CLASSROOM ACTIVITY

Safety Procedures at Colleges and Universities

Using a Smart Classroom, visit three university Web sites selected at random. At each school, determine or locate the following:

A. Forms for reporting accidents

B. Laboratory safety manual

C. Staff structure of listing of health and safety department

D. Level at which the chief safety officer reports within the organization

E. Hazardous waste disposal procedures

F. List of health and safety office responsibilities/services offered

Appendix: Institutional Environmental Health and Safety Matrix

	General Environmental Health	Radiation Protection	Infection Control
	▪ Air ▪ Water ▪ Food ▪ Sanitation ▪ Environmental Protection	▪ Non-ionizing ▪ Ionizing ▪ Nuclear Medicine	▪ Patient Care Procedures ▪ Biohazard Control ▪ Applied Epidemiology
Anticipation Surveys Communication Literature Review	General data gathering Pollution prevention activities	Awareness of new technology	Awareness of new technology & emerging pathogens
Recognition Surveillance Surveys Monitoring Reporting	Air, water, food samples or surveys Environmental assessments	Surveys of lasers, UV, x-ray, radioisotopes, shielding Dosimetry	Nosocomial surveillance Review of patient care procedures Spore testing Employee screening
Evaluation Data Acquisition Analysis Interpretation	Survey forms, tabulation Special studies Investigation of air, water, waste, food outbreaks	Equipment performance & quality assurance evaluation Comparison to FDA standard	Infection referrals, summary reports Focused studies & risk assessment Trends analysis Epidemiology studies
Intervention Engineering Administration PPE	Plan review Disinfection of water Air cleaning Policy/guidance development Training	Shielding design Worker rotation Radiology & dental staff training Radiation safety policy Lead aprons, gloves, eye ware	Barriers/isolation, devices & design Training on asepsis, decontamination, & patient care practices Policy development

		Safety Management	Industrial Hygiene
		▪ Patient, Visitor, Employee Safety ▪ Plant & Technology Safety ▪ Emergency Preparedness	▪ Biological, Chemical, & Physical Hazards ▪ Ventilation ▪ Hazard Communication
Surveys Communication Literature Review	Anticipation	General data gathering Awareness of new technology	General data gathering Awareness of new technology
Surveillance Surveys Monitoring Reporting	Recognition	Hazard surveys, measurements, samples Injury reports Internal & external disaster drills	General or focused hazard survey Personal full shift or grab samples Ambient samples Biological monitoring Incident reports
Data Acquisition Analysis Interpretation	Evaluation	Surveillance & injury summaries Trends analysis Equipment evaluation & job safety analysis Other special studies	Sample or disease summary reports Trends analysis Equipment & exposure evaluation or other special studies
Engineering Administration PPE	Intervention	Design or process change Training on fire, electrical, disaster response & ergonomics Policy development Consultations/meetings Many types of PPE	Design or process change, e.g., Isolation, ventilation Hazard Communication, respiratory protection, & hearing training Policy development Many types of PPE

Glossary

ACGIH: American Conference of Governmental Industrial Hygienists

Action Level: The level at which certain regulations take effect. For OSHA, this is commonly one-half the PEL.

Airborne transmission: Certain microorganisms survive the drying process when released as droplets in air and remain infectious as droplet nuclei. These particles are typically smaller than ≤5 microns and may be infectious at distances greater than 3 feet.

Antineoplastic agents: Chemicals or other methods used for the treatment of cancer.

Antiseptics: Antimicrobial agents used on living tissue and regulated by the FDA. There are three categories of antiseptics:

> *Patient preoperative skin preparation.* A fast-acting, broadspectrum, and persistent antiseptic-containing preparation that substantially reduces the number of microorganisms on intact skin.
>
> *Antiseptic handwash or HCW handwash.* An antiseptic containing preparation designed for frequent use; it reduces the number of microorganisms on intact skin to an initial baseline level after adequate washing, rinsing, and drying; it is broad-spectrum, fast-acting, and if possible, persistent.
>
> *Surgical hand scrub.* An antiseptic-containing preparation that substantially reduces the number of microorganisms on intact skin; it is broad-spectrum, fast-acting, and persistent.

Attribution Theory: Theory which states there is a natural human tendency to search for patterns in order to understand why things happen and to predict future outcomes.

Bacteremia: The presence of bacteria in the bloodstream.

Bactericidal: An agent capable of killing bacteria.

Bacteriostatic: An agent that interferes with bacterial growth or reproduction without killing them.

Biological Safety Cabinet (BSC): Three classes of cabinets used for the safe storage of biological agents in laboratories.

Body Mass Index (BMI): BMI is calculated as the subject's weight in kg divided by his/her height in m2. BMI is classified as: Normal <25, Overweight 25–29.9, and Obese ≥30

Body Substance Isolation: Older term for *Standard Precautions.*

Building Commissioning: The final step before an organization accepts a new building that verifies the design requirements have been met.

Building Related Illness (BRI): BRI means that the problem with air quality can be directly attributed to the building

Building Related Symptom (BRS): BRS means that a group of building occupants share similar complaints about air quality.

CAA: Clean Air Act

Carrier: A person with an infectious agent without obvious disease who may serve as a source of infection. It is also important to remember that there are stages and degrees of clinical disease. Often a person is most infectious prior to the onset of clinical symptoms, or an infected person may have such mild symptoms that they are ignored or missed.

Ceiling Level: This is the maximum exposure level to a chemical. This level should never be exceeded at any time.

CERCLA: Comprehensive Environmental Response, Compensation and Liability Act

Chemotherapy: A general term for the use of chemicals to treat disease. The term is usually applied to cancer treatment. See also antineoplastic agents,

Cleaning: The removal of all visible dust, soil, & any other foreign material

Cognitive Dissonance Theory: Theory which states that humans need to rationalize behaviors that cause psychological discomfort.

Colonization: The presence of microorganisms without tissue invasion or damage.

CWA: Clean Water Act

Decontaminate: The removal of disease-producing microorganisms & rendering the object safe for handling

Disinfect: A chemical or process that destroys most disease producing microorganisms (rarely kills all spores). Disinfectants are regulated by the EPA.

Droplet transmission: Certain microorganisms do not survive the drying process when released as droplets in the air. These particles are typically larger than 5 microns and are not infectious at distances greater than 3 feet.

EPCRA: Emergency Planning and Community Right-to-Know Act

Ethylene Oxide (ETO): Compound used in the healthcare industry as a sterilization agent.

Excursion level: A maximum exposure limit for a short term, usually 15 to 30 minutes' minimum. See also *STEL*.

Fume hood: A type of hood with an adjustable glass front shield (called a sash) that is designed to protect the worker from airborne toxic chemicals. By lowering the sash, the air entering the hood (called face velocity) can be maintained in the optimal range of 75 to 200 feet per minute. A similar device called a biological safety cabinet is used to prevent occupational exposure to infectious agents.

Germicide: A chemical or process that will destroy microbes.

Globally Harmonized System of Classification and Labeling of Chemicals (GHS): GHS is an international system for standardizing and harmonizing the classification and labeling of chemicals.

FEMA: Federal Emergency Management Agency

FIFRA: Federal Insecticide, Fungicide and Rodenticide Act

Haddon's Matrix: Model developed by William Haddon to assist in identifying appropriate control measures.

HAI: Healthcare Associated Infection

Halide Compound: Germicides that include chlorine and iodine.

Hazard Analysis and Critical Control Points (HACCP): Systematic approach to food safety consisting of 7 principles applied in a series of 7 steps.

Hazard Communication: A comprehensive program as described in 21 CFR 1910.1200 designed to inform workers of hazards in the workplace. The program is also known as *Workers' Right to Know*. See also The Globally Harmonized System of Classification and Labeling of Chemicals (GHS).

Hazardous Waste: Hazardous waste as defined by Resource Conservation and Recovery Act (RCRA), is determined by the degree of ignitibility, corrosivity, reactivity or toxicity of the material.

Healthcare-associated infection: An infection occurring in any type of health care setting. See also *iatrogenic* and *nosocomial* infections below.

HEPA: High efficiency particulate air filters are capable of removing 99.97% of all particles 0.3 microns in size.

Hepatotoxin: A chemical that is toxic to the liver.

HBV: Hepatitis B Virus

Histopathology: A section of the laboratory that receives, examines, sections, and stains tissue for eventual microscopic examination by a medical pathologist. There are a number of infection and chemical exposure risks that place histopathology technologists at risk.

Iatrogenic infection: A word that means physician induced infection (*iatros* means healer in Greek). See also healthcare associated and nosocomial infections.

IEHS: Institutional Environmental Health and Safety

Incident Command System (ICS): Chain of command structure utilized in disaster and emergency response.

Incubation period: The period of time from exposure to an infectious agent to the onset of symptoms.

Infection: The invasion and reproduction of an infectious agent in a susceptible host.

Infection Control Risk Assessment (ICRA): Process by which a healthcare facility identifies the potential for exposures of susceptible patients to dust and moisture and determines the need for dust and moisture containment measures

Interim Life Safety Measures (ILSMs): These are temporary measures to be applied when construction or other activities have compromised the institution's life safety systems. Examples of temporary measures might include additional training and drills for personnel in the affected areas.

Ionizing radiation: Includes alpha rays, beta rays, gamma rays, X-rays, neutrons, high-speed electrons, high-speed protons, and other atomic particles

JCAHO: Joint Commission on Accreditation of Healthcare Organizations

Legionella pneumophila bacteria: Bacteria responsible for Legionella infection resulting in Pontiac Fever and Legionnaires Disease.

Life Safety Code: National Fire Protection Association's NFPA 101 codes for the design and maintenance of facilities which preserve lives in the event of a fire or other emergency.

Local Emergency Planning Committee (LEPC): A local committee appointed by the state emergency response commission, as required by SARA Title III, to formulate a comprehensive emergency plan for its jurisdiction.

Material Safety Data Sheet (MSDS): Informational document for hazardous chemicals used in the workplace.

Mitigation: Taking actions that prevent an event or reduce the consequences of an event. Mitigation activities take place before and after emergencies.

Mixed Waste: A combination of medical, chemical, radioactive, or general refuse.

MRSA: Methicillin Resistant *Staphylococcus aureus*

National Priorities List: EPA's list of the most serious hazardous waste sites in the US

NFPA: National Fire Protection Association

NIOSH: National Institute for Occupational Safety and Health

Non-ionizing radiation: Radiation sources which include ultraviolet light, visible light, infrared light, microwaves, radio frequencies, and extremely low frequencies.

Non-preventable infection: An infection that will occur despite all possible precautions

Nosocomial infection: Healthcare associated infections that were acquired in a hospital that were not present or incubating prior to admission or subsequent to care.

NRC: Nuclear Regulatory Commission

NRCP: National Council on Radiation Protection

OPA: Oil Pollution Act

ORSA: Oxacillin Resistant *Staphylococcus aureus*. Oxacillin is the current name for methicillin.

Ortho-phthaladehyde (OPA): A high level germicide used as an instrument disinfectant.

OSHA: Occupational Safety and Health Administration

Pathogenic: These are microorganisms which are capable of causing disease.

PEL: The Permissible Exposure Limit (PEL) is the time-weighted average (TWA) or absolute value of the maximum permitted exposure to a hazardous chemical.

Phenolic Compound: General purpose surface disinfectant

Plan-Do-Check-Act (PDCA): Steps in a continuous improvement process.

Phase I Environmental Site Assessment: A visual inspection of materials and processes at a site to identify potential violations of environmental rules. Phase II audits focus on special concerns such as the presence of undisclosed sources of asbestos or lead-based paint.

Potable: Water that is suitable for drinking.

Presbycusis: This form of hearing loss is due to old age.

Quaternary ammonium compound: General purpose surface disinfectant

Rad: Radiation absorbed dose is a measurement of the energy absorbed in tissues. Rad is being replaced with Grays (Gy). One Gy = 100 rad.

RCRA: Resource Conservation and Recovery Act

Rem: Radiation equivalent man is a measurement of biological effects of a certain dose of radiation. For example, 1 rem of gamma ray exposure is equivalent to 0.05 rem of exposure to alpha radiation because alpha radiation is more damaging if taken inside the human body. Rem is being replaced with the international unit the *sievert* (Sv). One Sv = 100 rem.

Resource Conservation and Recovery Act (1976, 1984) (RCRA): This is the EPA law that regulates the management of hazardous wastes currently generated, treated, stored, disposed of, or distributed.

Risk Communication: An interactive process of exchange of information and opinion among individuals, groups, and institutions.

Sanitize: A chemical or process to reduce the microbial population on an inanimate object to a safe level.

SARS: Sudden Acute Respiratory Syndrome

SDWA: Safe Drinking Water Act

Sensitize: After repeated exposure to an allergen (usually a biological or chemical agent), some individuals may develop an allergic reaction. These individuals may have severe health problems when exposed to levels far below what is considered to be normal or acceptable.

Septicemia: A bacterial infection of the blood. A similar term *bacteremia* simply means the presence of bacteria in the blood.

Social Judgment Theory: Theory which states that before one attempts to change a person's behavior, it is important to understand this person's beliefs and biases.

Social Marketing: An approach that uses business marketing techniques to change ideas, attitudes, and behaviors. It differs from business marketing in that the goal is not to increase sales but to increase the target audience's acceptance a public health concept.

Special Waste: waste streams that require special handling and may pose some risks, but are not considered hazardous waste.

Standard Precautions: This is the basic approach used in the prevention of bloodborne pathogens. The concept of *Standard Precautions* assumes that all individuals may be infected and that steps must be taken to prevent contact with blood or body fluids. The older terms used for this approach are *Universal Precautions* or *Body Substance Isolation*.

State Emergency Response Commission (SERC): A commission appointed by each state governor according to the requirements of SARA Title III. The SERCs designate emergency planning districts, appoint local emergency planning committees, and supervise and coordinate their activities.

STEL: A short term exposure limit is the maximum allowable chemical exposure for a worker over a short period of time, usually 15 minutes.

Sterilize: A chemical or process capable of destroying all forms of microbial life, including bacteria, viruses, spores, and fungi.

Superfund Act: the Comprehensive Environmental Response, Compensation, and Liability Act of 1980 (CERCLA) is the EPA law that concerns the removal or cleanup of hazardous waste sites.

Superfund Amendments and Reauthorization Act (SARA) Title III: This law is also known as the "Community Right to Know Act," requires health care organizations and other industries to develop an inventory of hazardous chemicals and to share this information with the community's emergency preparedness organization.

Surveillance: The systematic collection, evaluation, and prompt dissemination of pertinent data to those who need it.

Threshold Limit Value (TLV): The concentration of an airborne substance that is considered to be safe even after repeated exposures to all but the most sensitive individuals.

TSCA: Toxic Substance Control Act

TWA: The time weighted average is the average concentration of a exposure to a worker over a period of time, typically 8 hours.

Universal precautions (UP): Older term for precautions developed by the Centers for Disease Control and Prevention to prevent personnel from blood borne infections. See also *Standard Precautions*.

Index

Note: An italicized page number indicates a figure, table or illustration.

D

Databases, 23

Data gathering and uses, 91–93, 98, 131. *See also* Baseline measurements; Reporting; Surveillance; Surveys; Under-reporting
  environment, about, 148
  molds, 231–232
  national, 93
  nursing home, 327

Daycare, *15*, 33, 268–270, 338

DBA scales, 56

Deaths. *See also* Morgues
  biosafety level and laboratory-acquired infections, of, 351
  causes of, 279, 304
  chemical agents and, 32, 115
  CJD and, 119
  evacuation issues, 328
  food, 354
  insects, from, 358
  mold and, 44
  nosocomial infections, from, 77–78
  radiation and, 55
  worker, 130, 163
  WPV caused, 291

Debridement, wound, 119

Debris, 312

Decibels, 56

Declination statements, 41

Decontamination. *See also* Contamination; *specific activities, contaminants, objects, sites and substances*
  areas, 58, 83–84, 124
  emergency, 203, 204, 209–210
  overviews, 109
  standards, 56, 248, 251

Decubitus ulcers, 324

Deemed status, 142

Degreasing, 175

De Looze, M.P., 51

Demand-control model, 62

Dementia, 294, 324

De minimus violations, 135

Demolition, 304, 306–309, 312

Dentistry
  AIDS/HIV rates, *39*
  building design, 306
  chemical agents, 37, 116, 121
  gases, 16, 37
  mercury, 33, 34
  noise, 58
  radiation, 59
  vehicles and, 82
  water and, 44

Departmental concerns, 83–90, 150, 155

Department of Transportation (DOT), 12, 136, 248

Department of Veterans Affairs environmental management and, 173

Dermal issues. *See* Skin issues

Dermatitis, 32, 34, 59

Desflurane, 37

Design. *See also* Construction standards, 308

Detectors, 56, 228, 297, 352, 353

Detergents, laundry, 324

Devices, 109–110, 115. *See also* Instruments; *specific devices*

Dewar flasks, 349

Diabetes, 44

Dialysis, 82

Diarrhea, 19, 29, 33, 96, 354

Diethylene glycol, 35

Diffusers, 227, 305

Digital technologies, 34, 253

Dilution, chemical, 209

Dilution ventilation, 222, 227

Dioxins, 249, 253

Direct transmission, 80, 81, 86

Dirty areas, 84, 89, 90, 305, 311

Disabilities, persons with, 165

Disability income, 163

Disasters, 194, 222. *See also* Emergencies; Emergency planning/preparedness

Discharges, 176, 210

Disease triangle, 8–16

Notes

Notes

Notes